D0902967

The Theatrical World of Osaka Prints

嵐橘三郎
西花亭
西光亭芦国画
全五冊

THE THEATRICAL WORLD OF OSAKA PRINTS

A Collection of Eighteenth and Nineteenth Century Japanese Woodblock Prints in the Philadelphia Museum of Art

By Roger S. Keyes *and* Keiko Mizushima

PHILADELPHIA MUSEUM OF ART · 1973

FRONTISPIECE:

Arashi Kitsusaburō I as Gofukuya Jūbei, by Shibakuni (Plate 19, Cat. 298)

LIBRARY OF CONGRESS CATALOG CARD NUMBER: 75-178869

PRINTED IN THE UNITED STATES OF AMERICA

Contents

Foreword

THE ENTHUSIASM with which the great Japanese printmakers of Edo were suddenly discovered in Europe during the third quarter of the nineteenth century did not extend to their contemporaries in Osaka. In some ways this is strange, for the prints created in this coastal city portrayed subjects drawn from the theater, while in Europe theatrical prints were enjoying immense popularity in a vogue that had been nurtured by the Romantic fascination with personality and emotions. Yet even with this parallel focus on the dramatic moment, Osaka's achievement was ignored in the first flush of Europe's discovery of Japan.

As the stature of the Edo masters came to be recognized in the West, the Osaka school continued to attract little attention; instead, its flamboyance was dismissed with notable condescension. The Museum of Fine Arts in Boston did acquire a considerable representation of the school during its years of voracious collecting, but otherwise these prints have been disregarded and, until now, little studied. This catalogue proves that Osaka's achievement deserves serious consideration; the work is as dramatically handsome as it is absorbing.

The acquisition of this remarkable collection by the Philadelphia Museum of Art is entirely the result of the enthusiasm and persuasive conviction of Kneeland McNulty, the Museum's Staunton B. Peck Curator of Prints, Drawings, and Photographs. A characteristic frequently evident in his career has been the imagination with which he has delved into little-appreciated aspects of the history of the graphic arts and, as a result of his studies and his acquisitions, introduced new perceptions into the life of even the most learned connoisseur. His respect for the learning of Roger Keyes and Keiko Mizushima has been rewarded by the publication of this catalogue, which studies the Osaka school with a method and a clarity too rarely found in Western publications on the East.

That the collection and the scholarship should be published with such thoroughness and style is the result of a most deeply appreciated grant from the Ford Foundation.

Evan H. Turner, Director

Curator's Preface

THIS CATALOGUE represents a collection of almost 900 separate woodcuts and drawings by artists of the Osaka school. The bulk of the collection, comprising some 850 items, was acquired in 1969 with the generous support of certain members of the Museum's Prints, Drawings, and Photographs Committee, supplemented by the Lola Downin Peck Fund. Those contributors whom we especially wish to thank are: Lessing J. Rosenwald; Robert A. Hauslohner; the Trustees of the Robert L. McNeil, Jr., Trust; Dr. Emanuel Wolff; David M. Gwinn; Mrs. Bernard Behrend; Mrs. Edward G. Budd; Mrs. Meyer P. Potamkin; Dr. Ralph B. Little; Mr. and Mrs. Sidney Lipschutz; Mrs. N. William Winkelman, Jr.; the Howard A. and Martha R. Wolf Fund; and Mrs. William Wolgin.

Additional items were later added to the collection through purchase funds and gifts. Acknowledgment of this further encouragement is gratefully made to: Dr. Luther W. Brady, Benjamin D. Bernstein, R. E. Lewis, Inc., and Mr. and Mrs. Roderick Seidenberg.

To Roger Keyes and his wife, Keiko Mizushima, are owed the thanks and gratitude of all who read and use this book. Without their scholarship and agreeable response to the chore of editing, the information in this book would simply not be available.

To the Ford Foundation Program for Catalogues of American Fine Arts Collections, the Museum and the reader are equally in debt, for without the foresight and financial support of the Foundation, it would have been most difficult to produce such a comprehensive survey.

Among the persons whose aid and involvement made this book possible are Evan H. Turner, Director, who wholeheartedly supported the original acquisition of the collection and its publication; Judy Spear and George Marcus, who undertook, with keen interest, the responsibility for a difficult editorial and publishing assignment; Raymond E. Lewis, who aided in assembling the collection; William H. Helfand, who assisted with certain negotiations in Paris; Alfred J. Wyatt, Staff Photographer, who produced much of the documentary photography; and Susan London, who valiantly coped with all manner of difficult typing problems.

The Department of Prints, Drawings, and Photographs wishes to thank these as well as the many other persons whose concern for the outcome of this project has sustained it to completion.

THE PRINT CONNOISSEUR knows that Japanese color prints are produced entirely by hand, from cutting the woodblocks (a separate one for every color), to applying and grading the pigment on each block, and then to the final printing in perfect register onto paper. Japanese prints of the Edo school have long been admired for the beauty and refinement of their color printing, yet the opulence of color and intricacies of composition that are to be found among some of the Osaka prints are probably unequaled in any other school of printmaking, whether in Eastern or Western art. The subtly shaded rich darks, the myriad colors that sparkle in complex designs, the exquisite deep blue (unique to Osaka), the fine embossing and metallic pigments frequently unnoticed unless cross-lighted—these qualities, when combined, often raise Osaka prints to the pinnacle of color-print technique. Their craftsmanship is rivaled only by that special class of Japanese prints known as surimono, which were prints commissioned for special occasions, and were usually more elaborately and delicately printed than those published commercially.

The present book is an attempt to increase knowledge and appreciation of a little-known and undeservedly neglected aspect of Japanese prints. The research represents nearly a decade of work. It began when the authors and their colleague, Raymond E. Lewis, were first presented with the problem of informing themselves about Osaka prints only to discover how difficult that was. In many books on Japanese prints one can find no mention at all of Osaka printmaking, let alone a serious study of the work. This may be due to the fact that few collections of Osaka prints exist, or because past authors have simply accepted the verdict of their better-known predecessors.

Almost fifty years ago Louise Norton Brown wrote in her *Block Printing & Book Illustration in Japan* that Osaka "vied with Kyōto and Yedo [Tokyo] as a publishing centre, and its printing-houses were noted for the beauty and technical excellence of their work . . ."; whereas Arthur Davison Ficke, in his *Chats on Japanese Prints* commented in 1915: "Most of the work of these men is crude"—a more generally held opinion that has affected the proper study of Osaka prints.

The reader is asked to form his own judgment from the evidence given in this book, since no similar presentation has been available previously to the public. The authors searched the collections and libraries of three continents, examined literally thousands of prints, and checked all available original source material. The result of that intense research is published herewith. Perhaps it is not too much to hope that Osaka prints will receive more regard in future histories of Japanese prints.

Kneeland McNulty

Authors' Preface

To Ray Lewis, this book; to those who use it, our gratitude.

THIS BOOK is the record of several years spent studying and collecting the prints of a little-known school that the authors find both interesting and beautiful. The essay discusses in a general way the differences between printmaking in Osaka and Edo, gives a brief history of the Osaka style, and touches briefly on kabuki theater, the constant subject of Osaka prints.

The eighty plates recapitulate the history of the school and should give the reader an idea of the particular excellence of the Osaka style. Most technical material has been relegated to lists at the back of the book. This section, for all its shortcomings, should provide a usable résumé of what is presently known about Osaka prints and printmaking.

The authors would like to thank the many scholars, dealers, collectors, and interested friends who have given good advice, patient encouragement, and great comfort for most of a decade. We owe special thanks to the following:

(*in America*) Mr. and Mrs. Raymond E. Lewis; Kneeland McNulty and the staff of the print room and the editorial staff of the Philadelphia Museum of Art; Emily Biederman, Money Hickman, and the staff of the Department of Asiatic Art at the Museum of Fine Arts in Boston;

(*in Europe*) Dr. Lubor Hajek; Mr. and Mrs. Jack Hillier; Chantal Kozyreff and M. Bouchat of the Musées Royaux d'Art et d'Histoire, Brussels; Richard Kruml; Susumu Matsudaira; R. G. Sawers; Lawrence Smith and the staff of the Oriental Study Room of the British Museum; the staff of the Victoria and Albert Museum print room; Fernando Zobel and our friends in Cuenca;

(*in Japan*) Toyohisa Adachi; Iwao Anzako; Shirō Hattori of the National Theater; Yoshikazu Hayashi; Kōzō Hida of the Osaka Prefectural Library; Hiroshi Higuchi; Shiyō Makimura; Hideo Matsuo, Kanji Inoue, and the staff of the Ikeda Library; C. H. Mitchell; Dr. and Mrs. Usaburō Mizushima; Dr. Muneshige Narazaki; Mr. Sōma and the staff of Tōhoku University Library; Tadashi Sugase; Jūzō Suzuki of the National Diet Library; Professor Shin'ichi Tani; Mr. and Mrs. Tadasu Watanabe; Professor Tetsuji Yūda and the staff of Tenri University Library; with a special debt of gratitude to the late Teruji Yoshida.

The Ford Foundation deserves particular acknowledgment for the grant that made this catalogue possible.

R. K. and K. M.

Celebration of the Tenman Shrine Festival, by Yashima Gakutei. Mid-1830s.
Authors' Collection.

The summer festival honoring Sugawara Michizane, the patron deity of scholarship, was held on the twenty-fifth day of the seventh month of the lunar year. The celebrations culminated in a barge procession along the Yodo River illumined by torchlight and fireworks. We are watching the barges row west under Tenjin Bridge. Naniwa Bridge rises at the left and, in the center, at the entrance to the Horikawa Canal we see Taihei Bridge. The barges carry officials and relics of the Shrine, and rowboats alongside are filled with dancers and musicians. A vast crowd peers down from the great bridge in the shadow of lanterns emblazoned with the plum-blossom crest of the deity.

Introduction

The Social Setting of the Japanese Woodblock Print

Whether Osaka pictures
Are worthwhile or not
Is hard to determine.
—Okumura Masanobu, Edo artist, c. 1740s

If you were to pause for a moment and imagine a Japanese print perhaps you would see Hokusai's towering wave before you, or Hiroshige's porters running through the rain; one of Sharaku's menacing portraits, or a gentle beauty by Harunobu or Utamaro. Whatever the gulfs of time and sensibility between these men they shared one common bond as print designers: they all lived and worked in Edo, modern Tokyo, and were part of the mainstream of Japanese print design. By the middle of the eighteenth century, color prints had become so closely associated with the nation's capital that guidebooks regularly spoke of them as "famous products of Edo," adding that "visitors to the city buy these 'brocade prints' and carry them back to their villages as souvenirs." Since the overwhelming majority of single-sheet Japanese woodblock prints were designed, published, and sold in Edo, the art form itself has long been considered as properly "belonging" to the capital. This has had two unfortunate consequences.

The first is historical. Edo was undoubtedly the center of the production and sale of single-sheet Japanese prints from the end of the seventeenth century to modern times, but many of the styles that ring their changes through two centuries of print design were brought in fully formed by artists trained in the Kyoto-Osaka area and elsewhere. These artists were attracted to Edo, much as Western artists were drawn to Paris, Rome, London and New York. The career of Suzuki Harunobu, an important and influential Edo print designer of the 1760s, illustrates this point. After a few years of designing conventional actor portraits, Harunobu was commissioned to design a number of calendar prints for 1765. These mark the first flowering of full-color prints in Japan and were drawn in a gentle, elegant style, the grace of which had scarcely been seen in the rough Eastern capital. Harunobu's style was affected by every print designer of his generation and although he is usually credited as an innovator, he was an eclectic, transforming designs by earlier Edo artists like Masanobu, Toyonobu, and Kiyohiro to his own mold. The wellspring of his special grace was the work of the Kyoto painter and book illustrator Nishikawa Sukenobu, who forty years earlier had elaborated and refined the style that Harunobu translated so effectively into color prints; and recent discoveries indicate that Harunobu, whose birthplace is unknown and whose career before around 1760 is uncertain, indeed studied with Sukenobu in Kyoto. This is one example and there are many more, of the neglected truth that "Edo" styles were often created by artists who were trained in different regional traditions.

The second unfortunate consequence of the notion that Japanese prints are an Edo art form has been the neglect of other schools. From the 1720s until the middle of the nineteenth century, local artists in Nagasaki designed prints of foreign merchant seamen and their families that are often charming and beautiful. Provincial centers like Toyama and Aizu had local print designers, and larger cities like Nagoya and Kyoto, with a flourishing trade in illustrated books, had their own schools of printmaking that seem to have satisfied their public at least as much as they have puzzled historians.

The only regional prints to seriously rival those of Edo on their own ground of quality in design, engraving, and printing, were those produced in Osaka. But in a century of the study and collecting of Japanese prints, those of the Osaka school have been virtually ignored. There are several reasons for this neglect: the first being their scarcity. Between the 1790s and the late 1800s some two hundred Osaka artists produced between ten and fifteen thousand single-sheet print designs. This does not seem to argue rarity, but in mid-nineteenth century Edo three popular artists, Kunisada, Kuniyoshi, and Hiroshige each designed well over ten thousand single-sheet prints, and Kunisada, who was active for sixty years, may have designed over twice this number, not to mention book illustrations. Each of these prodigious artists had pupils, many of whom designed hundreds and even thousands of prints in their own right. Yoshikazu, for example, an otherwise unremarkable disciple of Kuniyoshi, designed nearly a hundred prints of Yokohama subjects alone in the early 1860s; and Yoshitoyo, a little-known contemporary who may also have worked in Osaka, designed perhaps a score of portraits of the elephant that was exhibited at Ryōgoku Bridge in 1863. Even earlier Edo artists were prolific. Utamaro designed a good two thousand prints over a period of two decades, and nearly all of Harunobu's eight or nine hundred surviving color prints appeared in one brief interval between 1765 and 1770. By contrast, no Osaka artists before the appearance of Hirosada in the late 1840s are known to have designed over two hundred compositions, although their careers spanned ten, twenty, and in the case of Kunihiro, nearly thirty years. And the Osaka artists before 1850 who designed even a tenth of that number can be counted on the fingers of both hands.

The second reason for the neglect of Osaka prints is accidental: they were simply unavailable to students and collectors. The first Western collectors and their dealers in the closing decades of the nineteenth century bought prints almost exclusively in the nation's capital. The taste and casual discrimination of these early collectors were bequeathed to their successors. Scholars naturally studied what they could see and tended to disparage what fell outside the classic canon, with the result that most nineteenth-century figure and actor prints, Edo and otherwise, suffered the same prejudicial neglect. Osaka prints, especially *outré,* were relegated to the miscellaneous box, a catchall chapter or a footnote, if they were collected or mentioned at all.

A third reason for the neglect of Osaka prints is a curious restriction on subject matter. The nineteenth century Edo artist could design landscapes, heroic battles, portraits of beauties, parodies, documents, genre, erotica, or scenes from the theater as his fancy, public, and publisher moved him; the Osaka print artist almost always portrayed actors in current theatrical performances. There are exceptions to this general rule: from the 1820s on, many privately commissioned, privately printed, non-theatrical surimono were printed, and late in the nineteenth century, their attention swayed by the currents of modernity, many print artists turned away from the theaters to portray and memorialize their city. But for practical purposes, certainly to the Osaka publishers and their public, Osaka prints were portraits of actors on stage. This limitation affected the style of the Osaka school and contributed to its later neglect. Two explanations for it, one economic, one social, seem probable.

The economic explanation lies in the different patterns of print publishing in Edo and Osaka. Between the 1790s and 1816, the first flowering of print publication in Osaka, color prints were the monopoly of one publisher, Shioya Chōbei. In 1816 four well-established publishers of theatrical programs and illustrated books, Tenmaya Kihei (Tenki), Wataya Kihei (Wataki), Honya Seibei (Honsei), and Tokuraya Shinbei (Toshin), were apparently granted franchises, and within a year or two Shioya retired from further activity in this field. Throughout the remaining first half of the nineteenth century, whether by restrictive government licensing, or by a careful self-imposed program of subsidy and cooperation, the remaining firms managed to exclude competition. By contrast, shortly after 1800, the number of regular commercial Edo publishers, who had always been fairly numerous, suddenly and drastically increased until, during the 1850s, hundreds of them were in competition with one another.

The rapid increase of publishers in Edo created a necessity for wider markets and Osaka, then as now the second largest city in Japan, would have been a natural outlet. There was good communication between Osaka and the capital three hundred miles to the east. A miscellany of the 1840s mentions a shop in Osaka, the Edoya, where Edo products including color prints were sold, and there are albums of prints in the Victoria and Albert Museum with Edo and Osaka prints bound haphazardly, an occurrence so otherwise uncommon that we suspect they may have been assembled in Osaka.

If Edo prints were easily available in Osaka, the publishers, whose historical ties were to the theater in any case, may have preferred to monopolize a proven market rather than risk loss in competition with the popular products of the capital. But whether or not Edo prints were commercially available, it is clear that until the second half of the nineteenth century experiments in non-theatrical subject matter were rather unsuccessful. When Gochōtei Sadahiro returned to Osaka from a trip to Edo in the 1830s and talked the publisher Tenki into beginning a series of Hiroshige-like views of Osaka, the idea was a failure and no more than two or three of his designs ever saw the light of day.

The economic cause of the subject restrictions of Osaka prints may have lain in publishing practice and competition from Edo; the social cause certainly lay with their audience: the man who commissioned or bought an Osaka print wanted an Osaka actor's portrait. In the early days of the kabuki theater, when Edo audiences were demanding fire and brimstone, Osaka crowds craved intricate, heartrending plots. Chikamatsu Monzaemon, their great playwright, contrived a puppet theater to convey the poetic complexity of his tragedies without the confused bathos of inept human actors. His greatest success, *The Battles of Coxinga,* rested less on the script, however, than on the ingenuity of his collaborator and producer, Takeda Izumo, who combined the most sensational devices of the popular *karakuri,* or mechanical theater, with Chikamatsu's lifelike puppets to create an unprecedented spectacle. Nature imitated art: forthwith, the struggling human theater of kabuki adopted plots, machinery, and even acting styles from the puppets, and by the second half of the eighteenth century, kabuki was not only the *primus inter pares* of Osaka entertainment, it was the center of a good part of the literary and intellectual life of the city as well.

The twin sources of support for the kabuki theater in Osaka were paid admissions and patronage. Paid admissions kept the theaters open, rebuilt them when they burned, paid the salaries that attracted stars from Edo and Kyoto, and kept the backers solvent. Patronage helped provide the sumptuous wardrobes of the leading actors, and gave a steady stream of gifts, encouragement, and support. The taste and connoisseurship of the patronage organizations, combined with their economic support, were responsible for the consistently high level of theatrical performances in the late eighteenth and nineteenth century.

Although less documented, the same system of patronage and public sales seems to have supported the production of Osaka prints. During its early years, Osaka printmaking was a vigorous public art; but in the mid-1810s, a group of theater enthusiasts began commissioning prints from the painter Ashikuni. Some of these prints eventually acquired publisher's marks and found their way into the hands of the general public, and gradually the skillful engraving and elaborate printing of the private surimono became the hallmark of the Osaka school. Although most prints seem to have been designed for direct public sale, publishers apparently reserved the right to print commercial editions of privately commissioned prints and the practice continued until the mid-1830s, when patronage was curtailed by nationwide famines, food riots, economic depression, and general urban disorder. This dialectic between public and private publication had precedents in Edo as early as the 1760s when a coterie of cultivated literati, who were enthusiastic patrons of fine printing, commissioned calendar prints that were often reissued commercially on cheaper paper with less expensive pigments. This fruitful concourse lasted in Edo at least until the long surimono format was introduced for private prints in the 1790s.

Another influence on Osaka prints was the presence of an unusually large number of "amateur" artists. *Kyōka* poetry, an ironical, unconventional, often satirical verse, cast in the straitlaced thirty-one-syllable classical mold, was the cheerful literary art that suited the taste and experience of the urban intelligentsia, and certain groups of *kyōka* poets like the Jukōdō Circle had particularly close ties to the theater. Yoshikuni, the head of the Jukōdō Circle, was a poet and print designer, and many pupils whose poems appear on his prints tried their own hand at print design. It is unclear whether these "amateur" prints were subsidized by the poetry circles, or whether the publishers' monopoly was sure enough that they could risk publishing prints by unknown artists and presenting them directly to the public.

In some cases it seems that far fewer artists designed prints than signed them. In the 1820s when Onoe Tamizō, a young Osaka actor, returned from training in Edo, a rash of prints appeared, signed by a bevy of artists named Shunshi, Shunsei, Shunsho, and so on. Since the style of these prints is identical and some of the artists are known by no other print, it is probably fair to imagine that one artist designed all of them to give an impression of numerous pupils, as the nineteenth-century Edo novelist Takizawa Bakin attempted at the beginning of his career, or to suggest that an entire school of artists supported the young actor.

Before giving a brief history of printmaking in Osaka, it may be worthwhile to describe briefly the process of woodblock printmaking in Japan and quickly review the history of the art form in Edo. In the early years of this century Kanae Yamamoto, Kōshirō Onchi, and other committed artists of the *sōsaku hanga* or "creative print" movement began engraving and printing their own woodblocks. To them and their contemporaries this was a radical departure and they justified themselves on the ground that the unity of conception and workmanship made up for any technical shortcomings.

For centuries before this, according to most descriptions of Japanese printmaking, there was a threefold division of labor among the artist who conceived and drew the design, the engraver and his assistants who transferred it to woodblocks, and the printer and his assistants who applied the engraving to the paper, producing a finished print. One other person, the publisher, often acted as a coordinator among the craftsmen, and occasionally as a guiding sensibility, commissioning designs and maintaining standards of quality. In the second half of the nineteenth century, according to one Osaka artist, print designers corrected the engravers' proofs, submitted color separations to the engravers for making the color blocks, advised the printers on color balance, and chose the "bon à tirer" or model impression for an edition. It is uncertain, and probably unlikely, that this can be taken as a model for earlier practice. Some artists, Hokusai for example, who was trained as an engraver, took a special interest in engraving technique; other artists like Sharaku used an unconventional palette, and may have had some contact with their printers; but there is no clear evidence that artists before the 1860s closely supervised the transformation of their sketches into prints.

It has usually been assumed that print designers drew *hanshita-e,* the finished or "block copies," which the engraver pasted down on his blocks, and which were directly responsible for the drawing and overall proportions of the design. However, an Osaka document, the *Naniwa Shoryū Gajin Meika Annai* ("A Guide to the Famous Painters of Osaka," *see* Appendix XI), naming print artists of the 1830s, distinguishes between a class of artists who designed actor portraits and another class who drew *hanshita-e* for cutting. The names of the "portraitists" appear continually on Osaka prints of this period; the names of the "copyists" rarely, if at all. Two artists are named who combined both skills: the Kyoto designer Nagahide, and Shigeharu, a native of Nagasaki, whom a contemporary source names as the only Osaka print designer who earned his living as an artist. It is unclear whether this untrumpeted practice of "block-copying" was current in Edo as well, but in early nineteenth century Osaka at least, the copyist was another frequent intermediary between the designer's conception and the final print.

The story of Edo printmaking is briefly told. Ignoring an age-old tradition of Buddhist prints and an early seventeenth century style of conventional book illustration, Edo artists of the second half of the seventeenth century began translating the current Osaka-Kyoto style of book design into their own terms and by the 1680s had arrived at a mature, unmistakable style of their own. It was not long before artists bypassed their texts, and albums and large single-sheet prints began to appear, mostly unsigned but many related to paintings and books by Moronobu and Sugimura Jihei. The early prints were usually uncolored but were occasionally daubed with white lead, yellow, and red lead or *tan,* a color that became so popular by 1700 when the Torii, an Osaka family of artists, began dominating the print world, that hand-colored prints were called *tan-e.*

Around 1720 elaborate hand-coloring with a wider palette and touches of lacquer and brass dust replaced the earlier daubs; the *urushi-e* or "lacquer print" held sway for two decades until the invention of a register mark, or *kentō,* in the early 1740s made commercial color printing possible, with two colors at first, three in the late 1750s, and full-color printing from the spring of 1764, if we can accept a group of Shunshō actor prints as preceding the many calendar prints of 1765.

The late 1760s saw more than the first enthusiastic and energetic experiments with color printing and the gathering of a repertoire of printing techniques that remained current for over a century. During this period when naturalism and the notion of drawing "things as they are" were being propagated by the painter Maruyama Ōkyo and his pupils in Kyoto, Katsukawa Shunshō and his colleague Ippitsusai Bunchō designed the first true likenesses of actors and introduced a new note of realism into the conventions of Edo design, striking a chord as clear and fruitful as the Kyoto-inspired innovations of Harunobu. Color printing went commercial in the 1770s. Paper sizes and pigments were standardized and the 1780s became a period of recapitulation.

After the sumptuary edicts of 1790 were relaxed, a host of new artists and publishers appeared on the Edo scene; this was the decade of Sharaku and Utamaro, of the mica-ground bust portrait, of the beauties against yellow ground, and actors full-length against gray; the decade of Shun'ei with his quiet engaging pathos, of Toyokuni's taut brilliance, of Eishi and his elegant followers, and early Hokusai. For many this was the heyday of the Japanese print, and certainly with the proliferation of publishers and increasing print production in the early 1800s, standards began to fall. A new range of brighter pinks and redder purples replaced the elegant colors of the eighteenth century and a new generation of engravers exchanged a harsh precision for the supple graces of an earlier day. The artists who survived this turning point, notably Toyokuni I, were at first at a loss to cope with these changes. Gradually, around 1810, Toyokuni began altering his style, adding backgrounds, broadening his figures, creating a model for actor-print design that affected Osaka as much as Edo style.

Print connoisseurs remained, but they turned their attention to the past and to the private world of the surimono, appreciating design and craftsmanship for their own sake since they no longer so directly served the embracing, ideal, human vision of the eighteenth century. In the1820s Edo surimono artists traveled to Osaka to work with that city's incomparable engravers and printers. Shigenobu, Hokusai's son-in-law, stayed only a few years. Others, like Gakutei, settled down and produced much of their finest work there.

Sometime in the 1820s, it is supposed, a mineral blue, often called ultramarine, was introduced into Japanese prints and transformed Edo printmaking. Within a few years, Hokusai, Hiroshige, Kunisada, Kuniyoshi, all the major and a host of lesser Edo masters experimented with landscape prints and established a new, peculiarly Edo, genre.

Like the edicts of the 1790s, the sumptuary laws of 1842 reimposed censorship of Japanese prints, restricting subject matter and printing techniques. The Edo trade survived handsomely and in the years that followed there was a revival of design and an outbreak of innovation. In this period the upright format was introduced for landscape, and printers rivaled one another in introducing new pigments and achieving new effects.

Around 1864 aniline dyes were introduced into printmaking. While they were new and expensive they were used with considerable tact, but by the late 1870s they cost less and in the 1880s were cheap enough to oust natural pigments in coarse reprints, with disastrous effect.

Western-influenced perspective appeared in Japanese prints from the second quarter of the eighteenth century and throughout the late eighteenth and early nineteenth century, there was an undercurrent of interest in Westernizing touches. Kuniyoshi was especially taken with the grotesqueries of Western art, but the first print artist to study Western painting with a view to adapting it to

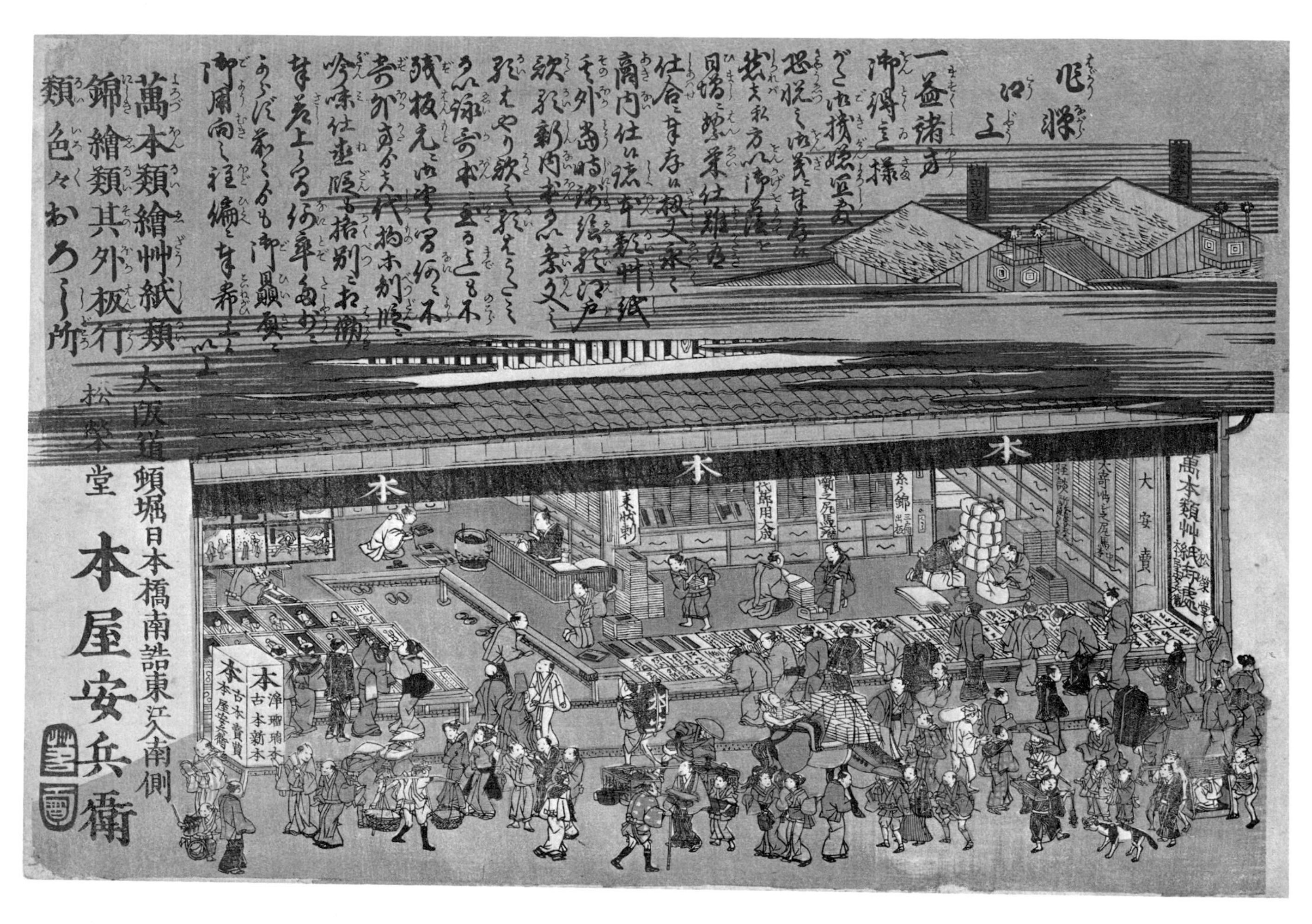

View of the Shopfront of Honya Yasubei, or Shōeidō, Book and Print Publishers at Dōtonbori in Osaka, by Yoshiyuki. c. 1860. Authors' Collection.

Customers inspect woodblock prints, set out in trays at the left, and printed books at the right. Shipments are loaded on horseback and lugged by men through the crowd outside. Employees cater to clients inside the shop while a printer or engraver plies his trade behind the print display. The picture was issued as an advertisement and the inscription above begs the public to continue their kind patronage of "our books of every sort, illustrated novels, color prints, and other publications." Two neighboring theaters, the Takeda and the Wakadayū, appear behind.

landscape prints was the late nineteenth century artist Kiyochika, whose career culminated in a series of heroic triptychs for the Wars of 1894 and 1904 that were conceived in colors and shapes as evocative and abstract as the "creative" prints of the next generation. Collaborative printmaking survived the transition to modern times and enjoyed a revival in the 1920s and 1930s, then suffered eclipse until the present vogue for transfer- and photo-lithography.

There is good reason to think that a few of the vigorous single-sheet prints by the Kanbun masters, a group of anonymous but extremely capable designers of book illustrations in the 1660s and 1670s, may have been done in Osaka. Certainly the subject and style of several of these prints are related to the *Kinpira-bon,* small illustrated chapbooks published in Osaka and Kyoto depicting the exploits of Sakata Kinpira, a Herculean Japanese hero, who was a regular denizen of the popular puppet theater. And there is every reason to believe that single-sheet prints were produced in Osaka in the closing decades of the seventeenth century as they certainly were in the neighboring city of Kyoto, but no clearly identifiable Osaka prints of this period survive.

By 1700 Edo was clearly the center of woodblock printing in Japan and maintained her virtual monopoly on print production until the 1770s. Aside from a hand-colored *hosoban* portrait of two actors in the roles of warrior and servant, which was designed by a Kyoto artist named Baisetsudō Sadamichi for a kabuki performance in 1743, and a few unsigned actor prints of the 1740s and 1750s, very few single-sheet prints from the Kyoto-Osaka area datable before the 1770s seem to have survived. It is worth asking why there was no woodblock print tradition in this area of affluence and urban prosperity in the first three quarters of the eighteenth century. Edo prints may have been available, and certain subjects like the triptychs of beauties of the three cities, Edo, Kyoto, and Osaka, may even have been popular; on the other hand, the Osaka and Kyoto public may have been visually satisfied with their local traditions of book illustrations, and had no need for modern prints to fill their scrapbooks, paste on their screens, or hang in the alcoves of their sober homes. Of course, there may have been a tradition of printmaking in either or both cities that has simply failed to survive. Looking through this catalogue or through most collections of Osaka prints, one would hardly imagine that most of the major artists of the first half of the nineteenth century regularly designed stencil prints usually printed in *hosoban* format on rather poor paper for cheap sale and wide circulation. In our travels we have not seen more than a handful of these prints, but others have been described and it is clear that they were abundant in their day.

In 1768 the Osaka actor Nakamura Utaemon I traveled to Edo and performed the rôle of the degenerate renegade priest Seigen with great acclaim. Katsukawa Shunshō portrayed this performance in a print that was popular enough to be printed in two editions, one with a blue ground, one with black simulating a night sky. An impression of this print may have found its way to Osaka, because the first surviving Osaka actor print, a stenciled *hosoban* by Okamoto Sekkeisai Masafusa, shows Utaemon as the same priest with a similar pose and expression looming over the figure of Mimasu Daigorō as the servant Yodohei in a play that was performed in Osaka in the third month of 1771. One impression of this historically important and rather wonderful print had the fortune to be pasted in a scrapbook by the novelist Bakin as an example of "Kyoto-Osaka pictures of the 1770s," and is the only one that is known to have survived.

Masafusa, a professional illustrator of books and theater programs in the 1770s and 1780s, deserves credit as the grandfather of actor portraiture in Osaka. His early portrait of Utaemon may have been inspired by Shunshō, but his other portraits, including color-printed *hosoban* of 1775 and 1777, and an album of the roles played by Nakayama Bunshichi published on that actor's retirement in 1782, are recognizable likenesses in a fluent, unmistakable style. Masafusa also designed a few *hosoban* prints of young women in the style of Tsukioka Settei, with whom he may have studied. Neither he nor his successor, Terasawa Masatsugu, who designed a few actor prints in the late 1780s, influenced the later course of Osaka actor portraiture, but the public became accustomed to single-sheet prints through their work and in this way they prepared the ground for the portraits by Ryūkōsai and Shōkōsai that were published by Shioya Chōbei in the 1790s.

The *Suifutei Gigafu* ("The Suifutei Album of Light Sketches"), a book of thirty-six harsh and often brilliant half-length portraits of actors by an unknown artist, published privately in 1782, is fully described and discussed in Cat. 357 (Plate 2). Suikyōrō, the author of the Japanese postface, describes how the book came about:

> Master Suifutei went up to Kyoto and was dazzled by the fantastic sight of the big theaters there. He drew pictures of the famous actors there so truly that they seemed to be alive. He wondered if he should keep them all to himself, but thought that, no, he would like to show them to some other people, so he brought them home with him as a souvenir. When we saw them they looked so real we thought they would answer if we spoke to them. Anyone would have been delighted! To preserve them for posterity, Suifutei was asked if it would be all right, and this was printed.

Aside from the suggestion that Suifutei was a provincial painter (an Osaka playgoer would hardly be dazzled by the stage in Kyoto), Suikyōrō's account says that Suifutei drew portraits of the actors he saw, and it was only afterward, "to preserve them for posterity," that they were engraved and printed in book form. Suikyōrō praises Suifutei for his "lifelike" portraits in the same vocabulary that his contemporaries talked about the achievements of Maruyama-Shijō painting; and actor portraiture, which found its way into woodblock prints in the 1760s, was one reflection of this new-found interest in the immediate and well observed. This extraordinary book is often described as the fountainhead of the Osaka school of actor portraiture, but since there is a flicker of realism in Masafusa's actor portraits of the 1770s, and Ryūkōsai was painting his portraits by 1782 at least, the Suifutei artist cannot be said to have invented the Osaka style.

Taga Ryūkōsai Jokei, or Ryūkōsai as he signed his prints, was the direct pupil of an academically-inclined Osaka painter named Shitomi Kangetsu, the eldest son of Tsukioka Settei. Sometime in the 1770s, Ryūkōsai apostatized and set up on his own as a painter of actor portraits. The author of *Ōsaka Dachin'uma* (*see* Appendix I) writes that he was well known as a fan painter by 1782 at the latest, and pages of his first illustrated book, *Yakusha Mono Iwai,* published in 1784, illustrate performances as early as 1776, although most of Ryūkōsai's dated paintings are from the 1780s. In 1792 and 1793, on the heels of another illustrated book, *Ehon Niwatazumi,* he designed a series of perhaps twenty *hosoban* triptychs. These are the first full-color single-sheet Osaka woodblock prints. Technically, they were very simple, seldom using more than four or five color blocks, with no particular refinements of printing. The triptychs were normally signed on one panel only, and since none of them, to our knowledge, has survived intact, many of Ryūkōsai's unsigned prints have been mistakenly attributed to his pupil Shōkōsai, who succeeded him as a print designer for the publisher Shioya Chōbei. The beauty of Ryūkōsai's prints is the contrast between the harsh accurate likenesses of his actors and the large, quiet patches of color that figure their costumes. If Ryūkōsai's portraits recall Sharaku, the enigmatic artist who worked in Edo in 1794 and 1795, his colors and sense of design remind one of Katsukawa Shun'ei. And since recent discoveries indicate that Sharaku was from Osaka, and Shun'ei had connections with Osaka of his own, it is possible that Ryūkōsai, whose work in this style predates them both, may have influenced them both.

During the decade following the appearance of the triptychs, Ryūkōsai designed illustrated books, and in 1804 painted a portrait of the Osaka actor Segawa Rokō as the fox-lady Kuzunoha. An inscription above the portrait exclaims about the pleasure of being in one's seventies. Since Rokō was fifty-four at the time, the inscription probably refers to Ryūkōsai himself. If this were so, the artist would have been well into his forties when he left Kangetsu's studio, and this may explain why his name still appeared on a nineteenth-century genealogy of the Settei clan as a pupil of Kangetsu "who unfortunately took up popular painting and drew portraits of actors" (*see* Fujikake, p. 58).

Although he illustrated another book titled *Geppyō Kien* in 1805, Ryūkōsai's name does not appear in *Ehon Masukagami,* a volume of poetry and portraits by his pupil Shōkōsai that was published in 1806. Ryūkōsai was a poet of some note, and as the book is a virtual anthology of Osaka *kyōka* verse, his absence may suggest that he had died, and that his last recorded work, a portrait in the memorial volume published for the actor Ichikawa Danzō IV in 1809, may have been a posthumous copy of an earlier drawing. In any case, a book of poems published in 1810 illustrated by Ryūkōsai's son was signed Ryūkōsai Taga Shiken, and we can assume from the signature that by then his father had passed away. One of Ryūkōsai's last books, an album of poetry and landscapes titled *Shibai Gashi* (1803) had a curious later history. The blocks passed to a Nagoya publisher and a new edition was published in the late 1810s with larger figures added in the landscapes by Hokusai and a portrait of Ryūkōsai in priest's robes facing Hokusai over a writing table. The book, one of the rare cases of the work of an Osaka and an Edo ukiyoe artist appearing side by side, was popular and went through several editions. Written with different characters, Ryūkō means "popularity," and Ryūkōsai achieved a reputation in his own day that lasted, with respect, well into the nineteenth century. Although he wrote an illustrated manuscript on the drawing of actor portraits and may well have been interested in teaching, he had only one Osaka pupil of any note, the young author, illustrator, and print designer named Shōkōsai.

Shōkōsai Hanbei, or Shōkō, as he often signed his prints, took up where Ryūkōsai left off. Ryūkōsai's last *hosoban* date from the eleventh month of 1793 and Shōkōsai's first signed prints seem to have appeared in mid-1795, although the unsigned portrait of Arashi Sangorō as Kan Shōjō entered in the *Kyota Kyakushoku Jō* for 4/1794 may also be his work. Very few of Shōkōsai's single-sheet prints have survived, but some of them were advertised in 1798 in the colophon of *Ehon Futaba Aoi,* his first illustrated book, as a "selection of single-sheet color prints with half-length likenesses of actors." No printed half-length portraits of this date seem to have survived.

Following the success of *Futaba Aoi,* Shōkōsai wrote and illustrated *Shibai Gakuya Zue* (1800), an account of the kabuki and puppet theaters in Osaka that proved so popular that Shikitei Samba wrote a rival version for the kabuki theater in Edo, illustrated by Toyokuni I and Shun'ei. Shōkōsai's book is an invaluable document and the hard, physiognomically accurate half-length portraits of actors he included are a link between the tradition of Suifutei and Shunshō's *Ehon Butai Ōgi* and later Osaka bust portraits by his pupil Hokushū and others. A sequel published in 1802 includes one of the first portraits of a foreigner ever published in Osaka, a Dutch "Kapitan" who came to see a kabuki performance and is shown sketching with a feather pen.

At his own word, Shōkōsai was a painter of theater billboards in Osaka, but most of his surviving paintings and drawings are small bust portraits of actors, and his finest book, the *Ehon Masukagami* (1806), is a collection of fifty of these portrait heads printed in color on yellow ground. Shōkōsai wrote several of the poems in the book himself, but three of them were composed by a young pupil named Shunkō, or Hokushū as he is better known. Shōkōsai's last dated book, *Ken Mawashi Chikara Zue* was published in 1809 and around that time he and Hokushū collaborated on a book titled *Ume no Miyako Butai no Omokage* ("Memories of the Stage in the Plum Blossom Capital"). Shōkōsai must have died shortly afterward because in 1810 Hokushū's first single-sheet print appeared, a double-bust portrait, and the following year he designed a print that he signed "Shunkō *aratame* Shōkōsai" ("Shunkō changing his name to Shōkōsai II"), a signature he could have used only if Shōkōsai had passed away.

We know less about Hokushū than about any other major Osaka printmaker. In 1817 he met Hokusai in Osaka and apparently worked for him as a copyist on an illustrated book, changing his name from Shunkō to Shunkōsai Hokushū.

In the early 1830s he was living east of Ishiya Bridge and appeared first on the list of actor portraitists published at that date (*see* Appendix XI). According to E. F. Strange, his real name was Shima Jinsen, and he was a bookseller in 1810, but we have found no proof of this. In the spring of 1813, right after the return of the actor Nakamura Utaemon III from a tour in Edo, Osaka prints began appearing in the large multi-panel format that we associate with the school and Hokushū was in the vanguard of print design. In the late 1810s when rival publishers broke Shioya Chōbei's monopoly on print production and began competing for the public with innovations in style and technique, Hokushū began his fruitful collaboration with the great Osaka engraver Kasuke, "the block master" [*hangi-shi*]. Working together throughout the 1820s, Hokushū and Kasuke produced a series of masterpieces that in strength of design and brilliance of execution became models for their contemporaries and touchstones of the Osaka style. Hokushū's last prints date from 1832 and he probably died shortly thereafter.

Shōkōsai had a host of pupils and imitators besides Hokushū, including Baikō, Jukō, Rankōsai, and other artists whose names end in "kō" or "kōsai." These artists designed occasional prints and it is possible that they were literary pupils of Shōkōsai's as well. Another artist who should be mentioned as a pupil of Shōkōsai's is Yūrakusai Nagahide, whose first stencil prints, published in Kyoto around 1806, were large bust portraits. At least one of these (Plate 8) seems to copy a Shōkōsai book illustration. Nagahide outlived his debt to Shōkōsai, and continued to work eclectically both as a portraitist and block-copyist in Osaka and Kyoto well into the 1830s.

Asayama Ashikuni was born in Osaka in the mid-1770s and died there in 1818. His common name was Nunoya Chūzaburō, and he may have been related to the playwright Hamamatsu Utakuni, with whom he worked on occasion and who was commonly called Nunoya as well. At the beginning of his career he studied with the painter Suga Ranrinsai Shoboku, taking the name Ran'ei. In his youth, Shōboku had studied with the self-taught Kanō painter Ōoka Shunboku, who designed a book of stencil-colored reproductions of Chinese paintings published in 1746, the first recorded use of a technique that later became closely linked to the Kyoto area. He died at the age of seventy-six in 1806. Two years before his master's death Ashikuni's attention had already drifted to popular art and in 1804 he designed his first theatrical book, *Shibai Ehon Kiku no Tawamure*. From that date until his death in 1818 he was the most important and prolific of the Osaka theatrical illustrators. We have traced the titles of twenty-five books that he designed during this period, and he undoubtedly produced many more.

Ashikuni's earliest illustrations strike one as Hokusai figures with Osaka faces in Hokusai landscapes. Hokusai was then in his fifties, at the height of his career as an illustrator, and the two artists may have had a personal acquaintance. Hokusai's first recorded visit to Osaka was in 1812, but a pamphlet he designed for a play inspired by Bakin was published in Osaka in 1808 and Ashikuni's *gō* Kyōgadō may be a reversal of Hokusai's *gō* Gakyōjin ("Mad About Painting"), which the elder artist gave up that year. This may be coincidence, but among the nine frontispieces of *Saten Suminoe Zōshi,* a nine-volume book illustrated by Ashikuni and others, published in 1810, first place is given to Hokusai, followed by ranking illustrators of Osaka and Kyoto, brought up at the end by another Edo artist, Utagawa Toyokuni I. The book is of special interest because a printed inscription on the title page next to Ashikuni's signature says that the book was published by the bookseller Kyōgadō Shōhikaku. Since Kyōgadō was Ashikuni's *gō,* it seems that in 1810, at least, he was involved in publishing, a fact that would support a rather vague contemporary account that says he achieved a name in portraiture, but didn't earn his living at it. As the two albums (Cat. 2 and 3; Plate 9) in the Museum collection show, Ashikuni was an excellent and well-regarded painter. He designed very few single-sheet prints, most if not all of them for private circulation. But many other artists whose signatures begin with "Ashi" designed actor prints, and he is credited as being an influential teacher.

The figure of Hokushū overshadowed the band of Osaka artists who designed actor prints in the 1820s, but three of his contemporaries are worth separate mention. Gigadō Ashiyuki, who was perhaps the eldest of the three, was the most volatile and uneven of the early Osaka artists and seems to have introduced several technical innovations into the Osaka style. He produced no illustrated books that we know of, but between 1814 and 1830 designed nearly two hundred prints, most of them published by Honsei and Wataki, two of the three leading Osaka publishers of the day. Aside from his prints, his only biography and memorial is a list of Osaka artists (*see* Appendix XI), where he and his address are placed right after Hokushū among the "artists who specialize in portraits."

Ganjōsai Kunihiro was a less remarkable artist than Ashiyuki but the circumstances of his career are more tantalizing. He began designing prints for Wataki in the spring of 1816 when that publisher, Tenki, and Honsei successfully broke Shioya Chōbei's monopoly on full-color actor prints. The next year his prints were issued by Hirooka, an otherwise unrecorded publisher, and in 1818 he began an association with the major print publishing firm Tenki, which lasted the rest of his active life. Several of Kunihiro's prints, including a memorial portrait based on an early Ashikuni drawing (Plate 20), a reissue with an altered portrait of an Ashikuni print, and a set of *ōban* prints related to a privately published print by Ashikuni (Plate 41) all indicate that Kunihiro had some special relation to the earlier artist. Further, there is virtually certain evidence that Kunihiro was the artist-proprietor of Tenki for nearly twenty years. In Edo, the publisher Tsutaya Jūzaburō contributed poems to prints, and Hiroshige's contemporary Eijudō designed a few landscapes, but no Edo publisher since the days of Okumura Masanobu is remembered as an artist. A tradition of artist-proprietorship for at least one of the three major Osaka publishers would help explain the high standards of Osaka printmaking, and deserves further study.

We are on surer ground discussing the Nagasaki-born artist Shigeharu. Born in 1802, the son of a money-changer named Yamaguchi Zen'emon, Shigeharu arrived in Osaka and was already designing prints under the name of Kunishige by 1821. He apparently studied with Yanagawa Shigenobu after the Edo artist arrived in Osaka the next year, and changed his name to Shigeharu in 1826. Nishizawa Ippō, a contemporary playwright and grudging chronicler, speaks quite approvingly of him as the one professional artist of the entire lot. His last Osaka print dates from 1838, although his books appeared on into the 1840s, and it is often assumed that Shigeharu returned to Nagasaki either in the late 1830s as a result of the general depression in Osaka after the famines of the early 1830s and the Ōshio Heihachirō rebellion in 1837, or after the Tenpō Reforms and the ban on actor prints in 1842. If so, he may have returned briefly in the late 1840s to design a group of bust portraits signed Kunishige, his earlier name. He died in Nagasaki in 1853 and was succeeded by a daughter Yonejo, who painted pictures of beautiful women that were popular among foreigners and often taken abroad (*see* Appendix XVII).

In 1800 a young Osaka artist named Gyokuensai Jukō designed illustrations and wrote the colophon of a book of poetry called *Naniwa no Ume* ("Plum Blossoms of Naniwa"), which was published by his father, the eighteenth-century *kyōka* poet, Baikō. Thirteen years later Shioya Chōbei published an actor portrait signed Jukō. In 1814 a few portraits appeared signed Ashimaro, an artist who changed his name first to Ashimaru, and finally to Jukōdō Yoshikuni in 1817. Besides being a print designer, Yoshikuni was a poet of some distinction in the 1820s, and it is tempting to identify him with the young artist of the book and the 1813 portrait mentioned above. In any case, he was the head of the poetry group called the Jukōsha and many of the pupils whose poems appeared on his prints also designed actor prints during the 1820s in their own right. Yoshikuni's last prints appeared around 1830 and he is probably the "Ashimaru" listed toward the end of the portraitist section of Appendix XI.

One line of direct descent was maintained among Osaka print designers from the 1790s through the 1830s. Ryūkōsai's pupil Shōkōsai worked until 1809 and his pupil Shunkō, or Hokushū, from 1810 to around 1832. Hokushū's main pupil was an artist named Hokuei who worked briefly from the late 1820s to the mid-1830s. Virtually nothing is known of his life beyond his name and address (in Appendix XI) and a surimono-style portrait of the actor Nakamura Utaemon IV, which was published posthumously in the spring of 1837 as a memorial to the artist with a eulogy from his publisher (translated in Appendix XIV). Hokuei was worthy of his lineage and produced, often in collaboration with the engraver Kasuke, some of the masterpieces of the Osaka surimono style. Originating with the first use of gold, copper, and silver pigments in the late 1810s, the style was advanced by Shunkōsai Hokushū and Gigadō Ashiyuki in the 1820s. Both artists used embossing, metallic pigments, and color without outline; and Ashiyuki introduced the startling visual contrast between meticulously engraved and brilliantly printed ukiyoe-style figures against pale, painterly Shijō-style grounds. Around 1830 a new range of luminous, saturated colors began to appear in the prints of Hokuei and Shigeharu, which combined with the earlier techniques to lift the surimono style to its apogee. The style ceased abruptly in 1837 in the face of the city's political and economic disturbances. The technique but not the scale of these sumptuous and probably privately printed surimono *ōban* was revived successfully in the late 1840s.

After Hokuei's death, Osaka print publication languished. In the late 1830s very few prints of any kind appeared, and in 1842, at the moment that a new generation of artists led by Sadamasu, Sadahiro, and Sadanobu was beginning to prove itself, the shogun's government enacted the sweeping, repressive legislation known as the Tenpō Reforms. These ill-conceived, unwieldy regulatory edicts that touched nearly every form of civil life were intended to stabilize the nation's economy, and were enforced vengefully. Entertainments like the theater, and luxuries like color prints, were particularly hard hit. The publication and sale of actor portraits were forbidden, and violators were severely fined. All woodblocks in the city were recalled for inspection and censorship, and all proposed publications required government approval. In Edo, an elaborate apparatus of censorship was established, and print production continued, but in Osaka it came to a virtual halt.

For five full years after the Tenpō Reform edicts were promulgated, no actor prints were published in Osaka. Around the middle of 1847 an artist named Hirokuni designed a test sheet of four small quarter-block portraits of actors with titles suggesting they were idealized likenesses of legendary heroes. The government overlooked the sheet, or turned a blind eye, and nearly immediately another sheet of quarter-block portraits appeared announcing that Hirokuni was changing his name to Hirosada. When it was clear that the government was not going to interfere, there was a tremendous rush to publish, and from the late 1840s through the 1860s Osaka saw a renascence of printmaking that recovered and often exceeded the achievements of the generation past. The bust portrait that had been treated so skillfully by Shōkōsai and Hokushū was revived as a major genre, the diminishing figures of the surimono *ōban* of the 1830s were accommodated to the half-block or *chūban* size. A new style of engraving suited to the clear precision of portraiture and an entirely new range of intense mineral pigments lent the prints of this period a brilliance unique in the history of Japanese printmaking. The market for prints may have widened as well and the bewildering variety of stamps in the margins of prints in this period seems to indicate a vast increase in the number of print publishers or print sellers, or both. The man most responsible for this rebirth was the man who had the courage to defy the government bans, Hirosada. In the next few years, Hirosada designed several hundred actor portraits, brilliantly exploiting the *chūban* format and the technical achievements of the Osaka print. In many ways his career seems to resemble that of Suzuki Harunobu, the Edo artist of the 1760s. Both appeared suddenly, were active for a short time, restricted themselves to designing one type of color print that they perfected, and both completely dominated their own and the succeeding generation of print designers.

Until recently, all that has been known about Hirosada is that he used the *gō* Gosōtei. Recently, however, evidence has accumulated that suggests that

Hirosada was active as a poet and as a print designer both in Osaka and Edo since the early 1820s, using the names Tomikuni, Tamikuni, and Sadahiro; and from the mid-1830s until the early 1850s may have been the succcessor of Kunihiro as the proprietor of the publishing house Tenki (*see* biography preceding Cat. 32). After the death of the actor Nakamura Utaemon IV in the spring of 1852, Hirosada traveled to Edo with his teacher and colleague Kunimasu and joined him and other pupils of Kunisada in designing the backgrounds for a series of half-length portraits by the senior Edo artist that was published in the eighth month of that year, by which time Hirosada had already returned to Osaka. His career tapered off sharply at this time, and for the next decade very few prints appear with his signature. A memorial portrait for Arashi Rikan III was published in 1863, and he died shortly afterward, bequeathing the name Sadahiro to his pupil Hirokane.

After Hirosada's virtual retirement in the mid-1850s, Osaka actor prints lost their inspiration. The public preferred caricatures to likenesses, and under the pressure of deadlines and conflicting obligations, the Osaka artists, like their early nineteenth century Edo predecessors, drifted into convention and mannerism. The working methods of the leading actor portraitist of this last period, Nakai Yoshitaki, a precocious teenager, but a trite designer, and the general circumstances of print production in the latter half of the nineteenth century are engagingly described by Kyosen Kawasaki, his son, in an article that is translated in Appendix XXIII.

Although the late nineteenth century saw a general diminishing of actor portraiture in Osaka, other genres of print design appeared, mostly based on Edo prototypes. Hasegawa Sadanobu, a contemporary of Hirosada, who was trained as a Shijō painter and who was a proven, albeit brief, scion of the house of Tenki in the 1840s, continued working well on into the Meiji period, designing landscapes, views, historical prints, and news sheets for a newly awakened Osaka audience. His descendants succeeded him in this work and the elderly artist Sadanobu V, Sadanobu's great-great-grandson is still alive in Osaka today.

The Kabuki Theater

> I doubt that there is another country in the entire world as rich as Japan in material for the study of its theater. If someone were to open his eyes afresh, arrange this material systematically, and use it critically, we cannot even guess at the wonderful and unparalleled accumulation of materials for theatrical history he would discover.
>
> Shōyō Tsubouchi, *Memories of Plays Seen in Childhood*

ON THE TWELFTH OF JUNE, 1826, the young German doctor P. F. von Siebold visited the Kado Theater in Osaka on his way back from Edo to Nagasaki with the Dutch consul. He described what he saw in his diary (*see* Bibliography):

> Today we visited a famous theater in Osaka. At the entrance there were large paintings of scenes from the plays. A dark passageway led toward the stage which was fairly large, and more or less similar to those in Europe, but bare, without much care or decoration. . . . As in our country, there are orchestra seats and upper and lower boxes. The gallery, which in Europe opens on a corridor, is left open to let in light, since plays are performed during the day in Japan, not at night with artificial lighting. Two high, bridgelike passages leading from the back of the theater to the stage allow actors to enter, exit, and act in the midst of the audience. . . .
>
> We sat down in the orchestra. For about fifteen minutes simple Chinese-style drum and flute music played. Then an actor appeared to deliver a short speech, and the performance followed. . . . Many first-class artists performed, who would have been acclaimed even in Europe. Their gestures and style of delivery deserve the highest praise, and the impression they created, heightened by their luxurious costumes, was enough to make us forget the poor appearance of the theater itself.
>
> Although the structure of the stage is quite similar to those in Europe, the curtain is drawn to the center from both sides instead of falling from above. . . . The stage sets were appropriate to the action of the play. Instead of movable flats, they change scenery very quickly with a revolving stage. There is a stand covered with bamboo mats on either side of the stage. A narrator sits on one and describes the details of the plot which are left out in the performance, in the manner of a Greek chorus, and *samisen* players sit on the other.

A more detailed description of the Osaka stage is given in *Gakuya Zue* (*Pictures of the Green Room*), which was written and illustrated by the print designer Shōkōsai Hanbei and published in 1800. From Shōkōsai's illustrations we see that the four main theaters in Osaka were on one side of a narrow street that ran parallel to the south bank of the Dōtonbori Canal (*see also* map on page 37). The facades of the theaters were lined with placards inscribed with the names of actors and scenes from the plays. Sets of costumed dolls were arranged in tableaux and suspended at eye level of the passing crowds. Ticket sellers sat to the left of the "great door" where customers entered for standing room or single scenes. For thirty *mon,* the price of two haircuts, a playgoer could enter the low "rat door," further to the right, and take a seat in the "coop," a wooden platform in the back of the theater next to the entrance of the raised gangway to the stage called the *hanamichi.* The "coop" was jammed with noisy enthusiasts who greeted each actor's appearance with loud shouts and cries. At the end of the passage leading in from the "rat door" another ticket seller sold seats in the floor boxes on eye level with the stage for an additional twenty-four *mon.* In the Meiji period, and possibly earlier, publishers reserved floor boxes for opening performances and attended with their artists, but generally the floor section was filled with a rowdy hoi polloi. Two tiers of balconies were ranged on either side of the theater with boxes that cost up to 2,200 *mon* and could seat six people. Tickets for these boxes were sold by the teahouses that lined the street opposite the theaters. The teahouses provided catering and toilet facilities for their guests and were allotted a number of boxes, which could be identified by curtains bearing their crests. The balcony boxes provided a certain amount of privacy, and merchants, courtesans, and samurai would usually sit there. "Front boxes," midway between the floor seats and balconies in price, were located on either side of the theater just below the balconies at ground level. Connoisseurs especially prized the front boxes and lower balconies on the east side of the theaters because the actors threaded their way along the passageway behind on their way to the *hanamichi* and they could practically reach out and touch them as they passed. Meals were sent in from the teahouses, but a refreshment stand sold tea, programs, and souvenir prints—reduced versions of posters outside.

The stage door opened on an alley behind the theater and special guards kept a close watch to prevent unpaid entries. There was a bathhouse down the alley for the staff and most of the actors, but the female impersonators bathed separately in a special tub set up for them just inside the back door. Backstage was a warren of rooms for props, effects, stagehands, actors, and musicians. Ladders led down to the stage machinery with its trapdoors, revolving stage, and other devices. Rehearsal rooms were upstairs. Lead actors were allowed to return to their own homes to rest for an act or two when they were not appearing on stage and a messenger was sent to call them before they went on again. At the theater these actors had large, private, six- or seven-mat rooms upstairs. The actors of male roles had rooms "like rented suites," and those of the female impersonators were "like the quarters of the concubine of some great lord." The leading actors were the soul of kabuki, and it was natural that they should have been given princely accommodations. Besides their profession, they were often men of great learning and literary accomplishment. Nakamura Utaemon III, for example, was a painter, playwright, and poet as well as an actor, and it is difficult to imagine today what storms of controversy he aroused and the degree to which he was an arbiter of taste and fashion.

Born in 1778, Utaemon was forbidden by his father, the great actor Nakamura Utaemon I, to even consider acting as a career. At the age of seven he somehow managed to get a part in a children's play and was so applauded that his father was won over and gave him his blessing. In five years' time he became the head of the children's troupe and shortly afterward entered the major theaters, attaining the rank of lead actor by 1801.

Up until this time, actors had specialized in type roles. Utaemon performed them all: "young heroes, villains, women, dancing even—he does it all, a preposterous trickster" was a contemporary comment. As a dancer he was incomparable and was particularly fond of sets of seven to twelve quick changes known as *hengemono*. Theater fans in the nineteenth century were extremely partisan. A suit to the Osaka city government by a rival actor, Arashi Kichisaburō, to ban one of these dance performances in 1817 because they were "unbecoming to an actor" and encroaching on his popularity, turned out to have been a hoax by a group of Utaemon's supporters.

Whenever Utaemon appeared on tour, fighting was likely to break out between his fans and those of some jealous rival actor. During the rioting that followed his first visit to Edo in 1808, which saw banners flying by the thousand, a fireman who supported Bandō Mitsugorō struck him on the forehead with a fan and drew blood. Utaemon appeared the next morning with a violet patch on his forehead and distributed a surimono he had commissioned overnight with a poem he had composed reading: "The Edo iris is a hit in purple." In the following disturbances, two of Utaemon's fans were imprisoned, but his popularity reached such heights that a performance of *Chūshingura* at the neighboring Ichimura Theater had to be canceled seven days after opening.

On the same visit, shortly before he returned to Osaka, Utaemon took on the entire Edo literary establishment in a poetry contest. Shokusanjin, an excellent writer and a classical scholar, who considered Utaemon "an upstart jack-of-all-trades," wrote a poem comparing the actor to oblivion, which Utaemon answered in kind, saying that leaving Edo was like "leaving darkness for the light of day." Shokusanjin's enmity was bitter while it lasted, but the two were later reconciled.

Utaemon acted with Arashi Kichisaburō in Osaka in 1802 and they remained on good terms despite intense rivalry. In the summer of 1821, representatives of both camps proposed a formal reconciliation and a gala joint performance at the face-showing ceremonies that fall. Both actors agreed, and a banquet was held that June aboard boats on the Ōkawa River. A date was set, programs agreed upon, broadsides published, and popular songs comparing the actors were heard all over Osaka. Two months before the performance, Kichisaburō fell ill and suddenly died. In their grief and disappointment, the fans could not bring themselves to attend the plays, and the ceremonies were cut short for lack of audience.

Utaemon rewrote seven plays. Nishizawa Ippō, a professional playwright who was occasionally asked to look over the manuscripts and correct them thought they were "horrible—illogical plots, discrepancies beginning and end, and needing uncounted corrections." We can be sure that Utaemon's plays were written to suit his own style of acting and reflected his genius for stagecraft. Preparing for the revenge soliloquy outside the palace gates in act four of *Chūshingura,* a perennial chestnut, he scattered fish scraps on the roof of the theater. When the scene began late in the morning, crows and gulls were wheeling over the theater, giving a poignant, desolate counterpoint to his speech with their cries.

Actors were non-persons to official eyes and were forbidden to associate publicly with samurai and townsmen. Their movements were strictly watched and regulated and they were hemmed in by laws and restrictions. These were rarely enforced, but occasionally an actor found himself on the wrong side of the law and had to be forced to comply. Utaemon's second tour of Edo began in 1814 on a three-year contract. By the middle of the following year he decided he had had enough of the Eastern capital and returned to Osaka. He probably had a premonition of trouble brewing because not long after his return he announced a retirement performance. In 1817, prodded by the theaters, the Edo city government issued an indictment accusing Utaemon of violating the sumptuary laws by accepting two lavish curtains from a fan club, and ordered him to appear immediately to pay a fine and submit to questioning. Once he was back in Edo, the theaters had no trouble obtaining orders to make Utaemon perform, and posters with his name were published and hung for the New Year's performances at the Nakamura Theater. Utaemon refused to act until the very last minute, insisting that they all knew that Utaemon had retired and that his name was Shikan and they had gotten the wrong man. The theater owner pleaded with him, and just before the curtain went up Utaemon finally agreed to bill himself as "Utaemon's twin brother, Shikan," and beg the audience's indulgence. He stayed out the term of the contract, but refused to return to Edo for the rest of his life.

Bad health always threatened actors and Utaemon staged a second retirement performance in 1825 after a disturbing bout of illness. The plays were impressively received, his health revived, and he went on playing without interruption until his death in 1838. Over two thousand admirers attended his funeral, the same number that had seen him off on his first departure to Edo a generation earlier. Memorial prints were published and a booklet of his sketches and poems was published posthumously by his admirers.

When the Edo government graciously proposed as part of the Tenpō Reforms in 1842 that any actor who so chose would be allowed to renounce his calling and assume full town-citizenship with the privilege of paying taxes and so on, not a single actor accepted and an indignant open letter was returned. But few actors led as varied a life as Utaemon's. Performing month in and month out and going on tour was a great strain on most actors and many set up private businesses and looked forward to the day they could retire. Onoe Kikugorō III finally

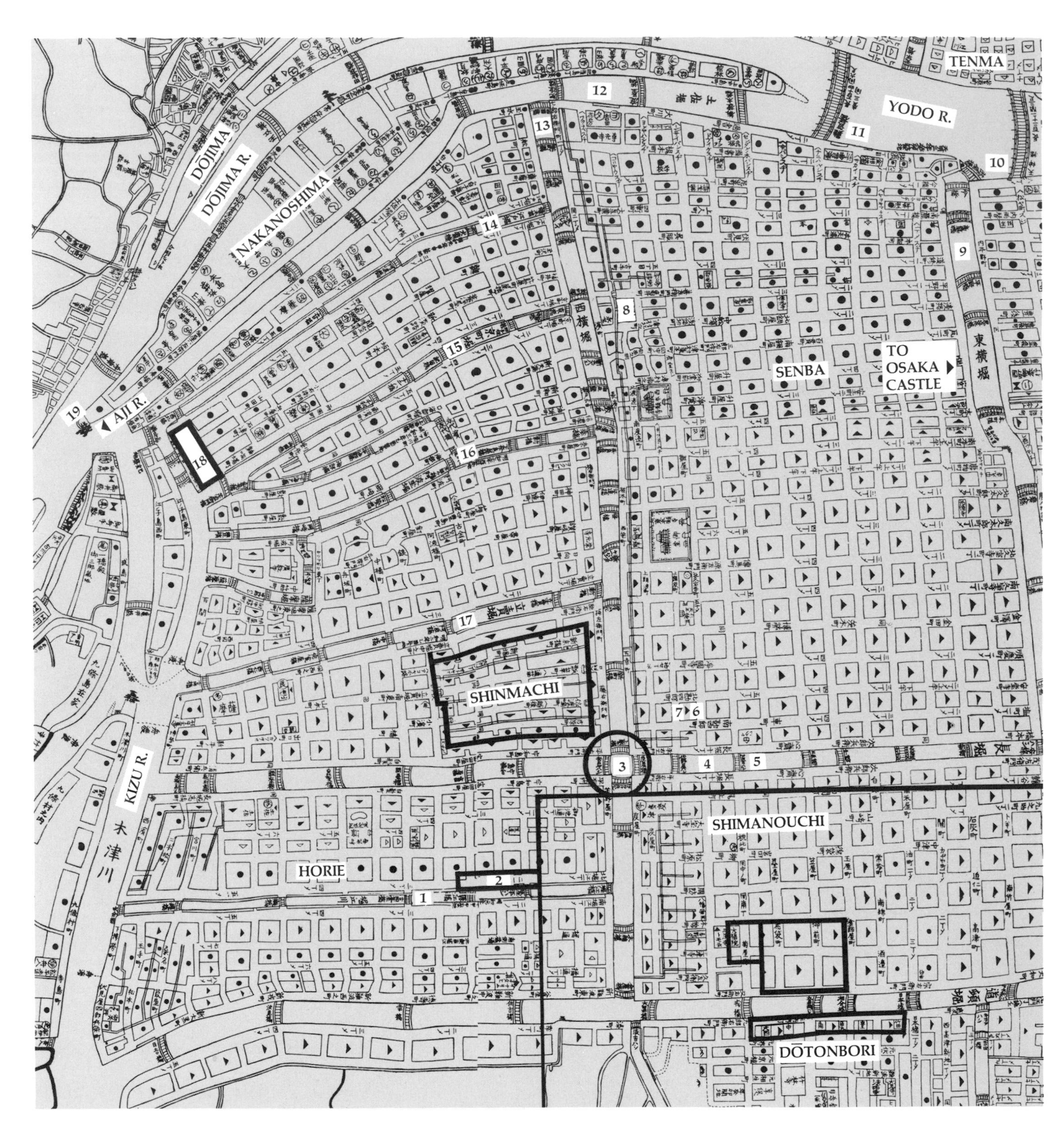

1. Horie River
2. Horie Ichinogawa District Location of the Horie Ichinogawa Theater and the publisher Wataki about 1841
3. Four Bridges
4. Nagabori Canal
5. Shinsaibashi Bridge
6. Location of the publisher Honsei before about 1835
7. Location of the publisher Wataki about 1852
8. Goryō Shrine, location of Goryō Theater
9. East Yokobori Canal
10. Tenjinbashi Bridge
11. Naniwabashi Bridge
12. Tosabori Canal
13. West Yokobori Canal
14. Edobori Canal
15. Kyōmachibori Canal
16. Awazabori Canal
17. Itachibori Canal
18. Zakoba District
19. Matsugahana Pine

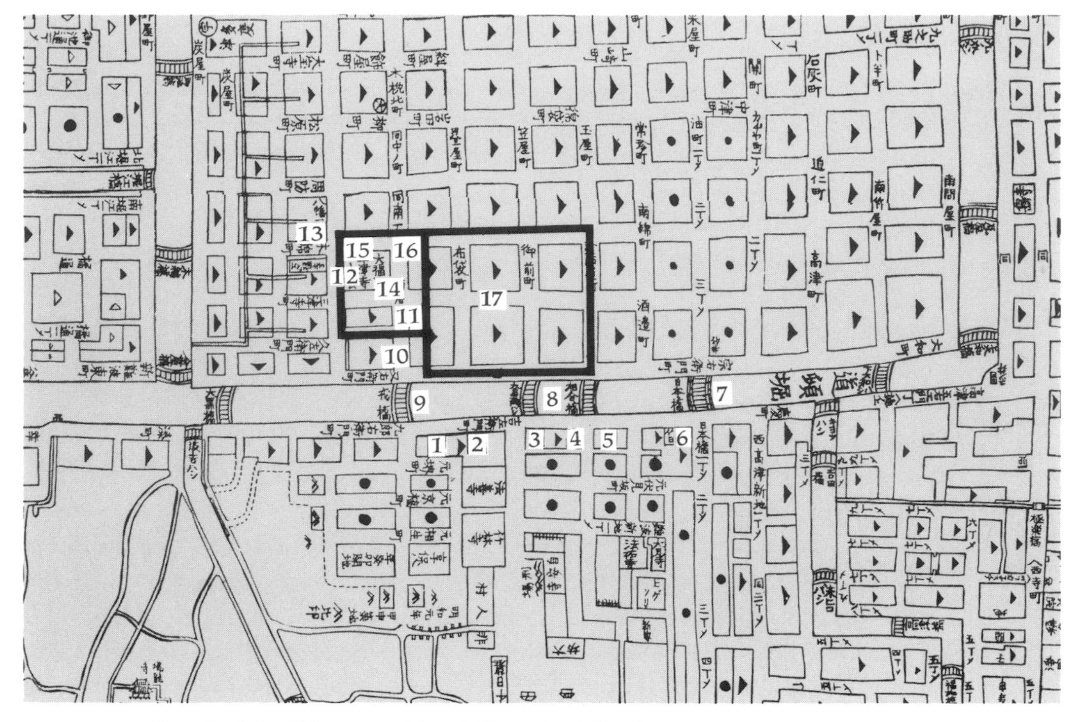

Detail of the Shimanouchi and Dōtonbori districts

1. Ōnishi Theater, later the Chikugo Theater
2. Naka Theater
3. Kado Theater
4. Kadomaru Theater
5. Wakadayū Theater
6. Takeda Theater
7. Dōtonbori Canal
8. Tazaemonbashi Bridge
9. Ebisubashi Bridge
10. Shinsaibashisuji Street
11. Kikuyamachi District
12. Mitsudera Temple
13. Hachiman Shrine
14. Location of the publisher Tenki to about 1834
15. Location of the publisher Tenki after about 1834
16. Location of the publisher Honsei around 1835
17. Shimanouchi Entertainment District

Zōshū Kaisei Sesshū Ōsaka Chizu (an enlarged and revised map of Osaka in Settsu Province), begun by Okada Gyokuzan and other artists in 1789 and published in this form by Akamatsu Kyūbei in 1806. The complete map, which extends from Osaka Castle in the east to various suburbs, on a scale close to the detail of the theater district above, measures 60¼ x 50¾″.

fulfilled his dream of retiring in 1847 and opened a tea-and-cake shop in Saruwaka-chō, the theater district of Edo. He called himself Kikuya Manpei, and while his customers nibbled their cakes, and clockwork dolls in Chinese costumes served the tea, he busied himself in the garden, raking leaves and looking after his famous collection of miniature trees. Before the year was out Kikugorō was already restless. One day after two guests left he exclaimed, "A tour of the garden, cakes, and sweet talk from me—all for a measly sixty-four *mon*—how ridiculous!" Shortly afterward he returned to the stage and appeared in Osaka. But as fate would have it, he fell ill on the return to Edo and died.

Theaters were destroyed by fire, closed by epidemics, and emptied by civil and economic disorder, but kabuki survived and prospered. Government interference was a more serious and unpredictable threat, since city governments had sweeping powers, but no set policy toward the theaters. When the three major Edo theaters burned down in 1841, Mizuno Tadakuni, the shogun's adviser, petitioned the city government to abolish them altogether as fire hazards and threats to public morals. Tōyama Saemonnojō, a council member, and from the days of his libertine youth a champion of the people, argued that the theaters supplied entertainment and distraction for a potentially unruly populace, and suggested that abolition would create more new problems than it solved. His argument carried, and the theater district was merely moved to the outskirts of Edo, but the following year actors and theaters were singled out for particularly severe censure and control under the edicts of the Tenpō Reforms.

The government had some reason for concern. In 1838, in the wake of the Ōshio Heihachirō rebellion in Osaka, Ichikawa Ebizō VII toured the dissident provinces in the far west, performing a dramatization of the revolt to large audiences. These performances were probably in the government's mind when they singled out Ebizō for arrest, trial, and banishment for violation of the new sumptuary laws in the summer of 1842. After citing previous warnings against ostentatious luxury that the actor had refused to heed, the indictment continued:

> Against our orders, he built his house in Nageshi style, with lacquered frames and engraved copper nail covers. He placed granite lanterns and large stones in the garden and a statue of Fudō in his warehouse, and coffered his ceiling with gold powder for "solemnity." His cabinets are decorated with copper and he commissioned sword ornaments and other extravagant metal work. He bought Chinese chests, picture frames, and a set of painted Nara dolls of fine paulownia wood which are sprinkled with gold and have crests painted with lime and foreign blue. The dolls were arranged on a stand covered with scarlet foreign wool. Besides, to curry favor with his audience and increase his popularity, he used real armor on stage, made of leather and metal, and carried an inlaid inro with a coral netsuke. He has a silver wine kettle, which he inherited and still possesses, although it has been pawned, sold, and left as pledges. When the sumptuary laws were promulgated, he expressed repentance of his luxurious ways and razed part of his mansion, but he insolently and outrageously refuses to know his place. He even tried to get rid of a seventeen-foot

stone lantern on the pretext of donating it to the public! We therefore order confiscation of all items illegally possessed, demolition of his quarters and banishment from a thirty-mile radius of Edo. (Translated from *Sanbutsujō*, by Nishizawa Ippō [*see* Bibliography under *Shin Gunsho Ruiju*, vol. 2].)

Ebizō left Edo and lived for a while under a pseudonym at Shinshōji temple in Narita. Afterward he made his way to Osaka, insolently defying a new government ban on provincial performances by acting in small towns and post stations along the way. When the political climate in Edo eased in 1850, he was recalled. Nakamura Tomijurō, an Osaka actor, was not so lucky. In 1843, in his fifties and on the verge of retirement, he was banished from Osaka for life and never allowed to return.

What part did the woodblock prints play in this kaleidoscopic theatrical world? *Shūkaku Nikki*, a diary kept by the Edo actor Nakamura Nakazō I during a performing tour to Osaka in 1787, makes it clear that the actors and their patrons were very conscious of commemorative prints. In the fourth month of 1787, some time after his arrival in Osaka, Nakazō received a parcel from two members of an Edo poetry circle. The parcel contained one hundred impressions of a print showing Nakazō and the Osaka actor Ichikawa Danzō IV in the formal costumes they wore for the delayed *kaomise* ceremonies held during the first month of the year. One of the poets enclosed a verse hoping that the prints would "strengthen the pull of the bows of your fans down there," probably a suggestion that Nakazō should distribute the prints to increase his popularity. This was not the type of advertisement that Toyokuni had in mind when he designed his portrait of Utaemon III in advance of the Osaka performance (*see* Catalogue 362); the print of Nakazō was designed for the Edo audience who wanted to follow their idol on tour, rather than for the Osaka playgoers. The same month, the playwright Kawatake Shinshichi, an old and intimate friend, mentioned in a letter to Nakazō that two prints had appeared in Edo showing the actor in the role of Tadanobu, a role he had just finished when the letter arrived. Shinshichi added a poem saying that thanks to them he could see what Nakazō was up to in Osaka. One of the prints was by Katsukawa Shunkō. The other, by Shundō, may have been especially popular in Edo because the following month another Edo friend sent Nakazō one hundred impressions to give away, and two months after that the playwright Kasanui Sensuke brought him what sounds like yet another impression as a present from Edo.

In the middle of the summer, Nakazō received a letter from the young Edo actor Ōtani Haruji. Haruji explains that he has just appeared in a print for the first time, in the role of Sadakurō in the play *Chūshingura*. Since he had modeled his costume and performance on Nakazō, he respectfully encloses two impressions of the print. This was the beginning of a long friendship between the two men that ended with the younger actor succeeding to the older actor's name. About this time, the Osaka actor Nakamura Noshio invited Nakazō to come and look at part of his private collection of pictures.

After showing his guest some scrolls, Noshio produced a calendar print for 1744 depicting his foster father, Nakamura Tomijūrō I, performing the dance of the fox-woman Kuzunoha during a visit to Edo. Looking at the print, Nakazō was overcome with nostalgia. His foster father had sung for that performance. He had been a child of nine, watching from backstage.

To imagine what actor prints meant to the people who bought them, we must first imagine the intensity of their preoccupation with the kabuki theater. People not only attended plays faithfully, and cheered their favorite actors with abandon; they did their best to imitate them. The Edo artist Shunshō wrote and illustrated a book instructing would-be Danjūrōs how to strike their favorite actors' favorite poses. In Osaka, Ryūkōsai designed a do-it-yourself manual for drawing actors' portraits. Famous passages from plays were printed in leaflets called *Ōmuseki* ("Parrot Rocks") and, so equipped, an enthusiast could put on an authentic performance of his own, from opening curtain to commemorative print.

The imitation of actors and the theater carried over into daily life and had reached such a pitch by 1770 that the author of *Taiheikoku Onridan* could write that "some of the young samurai dress and behave exactly like Sōjūrō and Hikosaburō on stage. Maids in samurai and merchant households imitate Segawa Kikunojō. Preachers affect the voices of Ebizō and Koshirō. Wherever you go, barbershop or bathhouse, whatever people are discussing, whether loyalty, chastity, or filial devotion, every example is kabuki." (Quoted in *Nihon no Rekishi,* by Tatsuya Naramoto, Tokyo, 1966.) In the early nineteenth century, this state of affairs had proceeded even further. The grouchy author of *Seji Kenmonroku,* a miscellany completed in 1816, writes: "Theaters these days do not imitate the world, theaters are the model the world imitates. People praise men of rank and birth by comparing them to actors. Strict magistrates, government officers, even the august person of the Shogun himself, are mentioned with reference to the stage. Courtesans' costumes are just like kabuki, and the designs and colors of the stage costumes are the fashion of the town." (Quoted in *Shibai Fūzoku,* by Engyo Mitamura, Tokyo, 1928.)

After two centuries of peace, the citizens of Osaka found little inspiration in the heroism of their ancestors on the ancient battlefield. They needed a new, living model for their lives and found it in the kabuki theater. The actors, the "riverbed beggars," sub-citizens and outcasts in the official eye, became cultural heroes to the townsmen, their behavior on stage a lifestyle. The woodblock portraits served them both as mirror and reminder. Nature imitated art.

Plates

The order of the panels within a single entry is the order as viewed from right to left.

Bracketed names identify actors not indicated on prints.

Terms relating to the format of prints are defined in the Glossary.

References to published works are to be found in the Bibliography.

1 Anonymous

Sawamura Sōjūrō I as Mino no Shōkurō and Nakamura Tomijūrō I as Toyamano in *Ōmonguchi Yoroi Gasane* 12/1743
Catalogue 432c

The plot of this complicated drama involves three men engaged in a search for the lost treasures of their respective houses: Shumenosuke seeks a precious jewel; Mino no Shōkurō, a famous kettle named Cicada; and Ise no Shinkurō, a treasured sword. Their paths lead to a brothel district where two of them fall in love with a courtesan, Toyamano, who is momentarily unaware that she is the daughter of Shumenosuke's lord. Vendetta enters the story when Shōkurō realizes that Shinkurō was the man who killed his lord, and Shinkurō discovers that Shōkurō was responsible for his father's suicide. The appearance of Gantetsu, an outcast who blames them both for his family's ruin, averts a duel, and the two are reconciled by the discovery that Gantetsu has murdered Shumenosuke's lord. They join in killing him, exchange treasures, and see that Shumenosuke and Toyamano are united.

The play described here is an extensively revised version of the original scenario as performed in 1823. It was revived again in 1862 and is the subject of a series of prints by Yoshitaki in the collection (Cat. 403-407). The illustration of the first performance of the play does not clearly match the later script. Mino no Shōkurō is disguised as an oil seller writing a poem in oil with a message for Toyamano, who is tied to the tree at the right. The man kneeling under the porch is Ise no Shinkurō, played by Nakamura Jūzō, the troupe leader, while the sleeve pulling the courtesan's sash belongs to Iwai Hanshirō III in the role of Katsuie, which may have been the original name of Shumenosuke.

This is the frontispiece of an *ehon banzuke,* a type of illustrated theater program that evolved out of the theater booklets [*kyōgen-bon*] of the late seventeenth century. The earliest known example was published in Edo in 1734; they began appearing in Osaka shortly afterward. These programs were carelessly engraved and frequently reprinted with new crests and actors' names plugged into the blocks. Rarely attractive as prints, they have historical value in preserving the casts and stagecraft of plays that are often lost or fragmentary. *Banzuke* were designed by a special class of artists who rarely signed their names. Their conservative style is often very difficult to date, particularly during the nineteenth century.

Six double sheets, including this frontispiece and ten unnumbered pages of scenes from the play, are here bound together with three other *ehon banzuke* for performances in 1765, 1766, and 1767. The upper half of the frontispiece bears the title of the play; the lower half, the words *Zen* ("Complete"), *Nakamura Jūzō Za* (the troupe name), *Ni no kawari* ("Second change-of-program"), and *Ezukushi* ("Illustrated"). Actors in the scenes that follow are identified by costume crests and role names written alongside, interspersed with other comments, like *ō-atari* ("great hit") and *ō-deki* ("well-done"). All four *ehon banzuke* are printed without color.

Ni no kawari is a word associated with kabuki in the Kyoto-Osaka area. The theater year began in the eleventh month of each calendar year with *kaomise,* or "face-showing" performances, when young actors were introduced and the public learned the membership of the various troupes for the following year. The next program, the second in the theater year, was the *ni no kawari.* This usually fell around New Year's, but no date was set during the eighteenth century and occasionally the new program began during the last month of the year, as in this case.

Many mechanical devices were introduced into kabuki staging from the puppet and *karakuri,* or automated, theaters in the early eighteenth century. Namiki Shōzō, the Osaka playwright who wrote this version of *Ōmonguchi,* and devised the first revolving stage, invented a mechanical lift that raised an entire two-storied building during this performance. Trap doors with lifts had been used before to raise single actors, but Namiki's rising house was treated as an innovation and was enthusiastically received.

大門口
鎧襲
二の

2 Suifutei

Yamamoto Giemon and Nakayama Raisuke
Suifutei Gigafu 3/1782
Catalogue 357 (1b and 2a)

Over two thirds of the thirty-six portraits in this album are of actors performing in Kyoto in the spring of 1782 when the book was published. The theater facade in the frontispiece has sprays of cherry blossom above, and a sign saying that Nakamura Tomijūrō is performing inside. Tomijūrō I went up to Kyoto for the *kaomise* performances at the end of 1781 and, although he fell suddenly ill, was scheduled to appear at the Nakayama Theater that spring. Most of the roles are unidentified, but two Kyoto theaters and one in Osaka were playing *Tenga Jaya* concurrently, and since broadsides were published comparing actors in the same roles, it is possible that many of the portraits reflect these performances. The actors' names appear in different scripts and are assumed to be facsimiles of their calligraphy. The seals on each portrait, which usually bear the actors' *haigō,* are hand-stamped.

Actor portraits were published in Japan from the seventeenth century on, but few recognizable likenesses appeared before the mid-1760s when the artist Katsukawa Shunshō began his career in Edo. In 1770 he and a colleague named Ippitsusai Bunchō designed a three-volume book of half-length actor portraits that was destined to become a touchstone for later portraitists. The *Ehon Butai Ōgi,* as it was called, was republished in Kyoto in 1778 as an album of Kyoto-Osaka actors, with alterations and additions by a certain Takahashi Kikei; and as late as 1794 this "revised" edition was still appearing in advertisements of the Osaka print and book publisher Shioya Chōbei. The Suifutei artist chose the half-length format to parallel the *Ehon Butai Ōgi*; and the author of the Chinese preface says that he meant his work "to be in no way inferior" to the earlier book.

The Suifutei artist is usually credited with being the founder of actor portraiture in the Kyoto-Osaka area. But recognizable portraits by Okamoto Masafusa and others had been published in Osaka during the 1770s; Ryūkōsai Jokei, whose first illustrated book was published in 1784, two years after *Gigafu,* was well known as a painter of actor portraits at least as early as 1782; Shunshō himself may have come from the Osaka area. And until more is known about painted portraits in this period the *Gigafu* designer should not be given undue credit.

To this day the identity of the artist who designed the illustrations of this thoroughly remarkable publication is uncertain. The album's elaborate paraphernalia, deliberate mystery, and Chinese feel is typical of the Chinese-influenced Nanga school, and we wonder if the Suifutei artist was a Nanga painter who digressed briefly into portraiture for his own amusement. The Japanese afterword mentions that "Suifutei went up to the capital and was dazzled by the sight of the big theaters there." He took drawings back home with him to show to friends as souvenirs, and the drawings were published in book form "to preserve them for posterity." If we can take Suikyōrō, the author of the afterword, seriously, then the Suifutei artist may have been a provincial painter, and the album a provincial production, accounting for some of the bold directness of the style. A recently published painting of peacocks and cherry trees dated 1785 is signed "Koretaka, at Suifutei (the Suifu Studio)," but there is nothing more known about Koretaka, and no other record of any artist named Suifutei.

The album is extremely rare. Three genuine copies are recorded in the *Kokusho Sōmokuroku.* One other recorded copy outside Japan is in the New York Public Library (Sorimachi 144). A facsimile was published by the Association for the Reproduction of Rare Books [*Kisho Fukusei Kai, dai 9 ki*]; the original is reproduced complete in an article by Teruji Yoshida in *Ukiyoe,* no. 39.

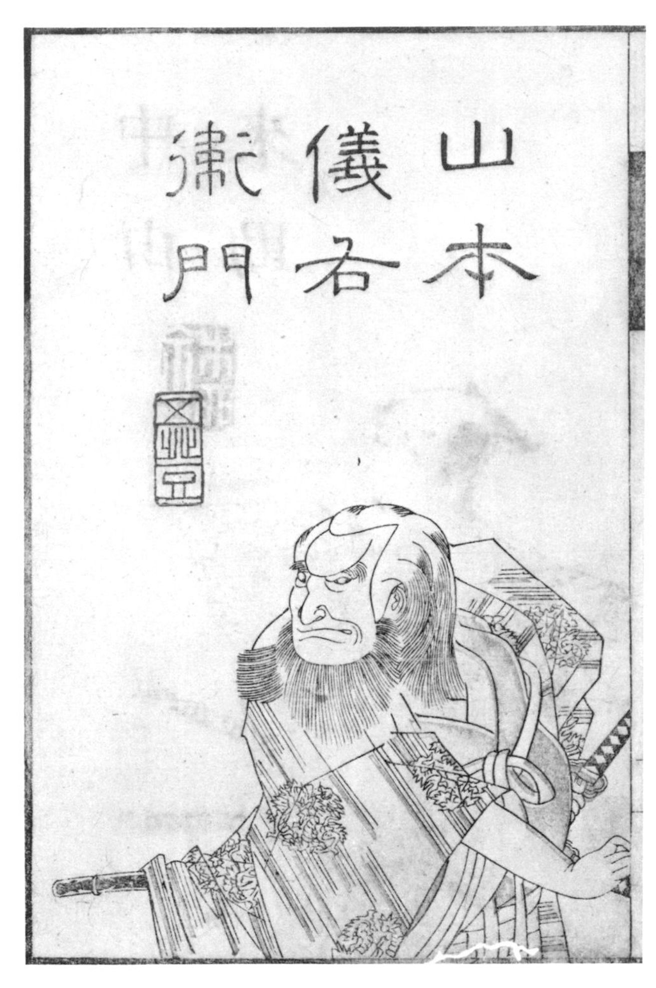
山本
儀右衛門

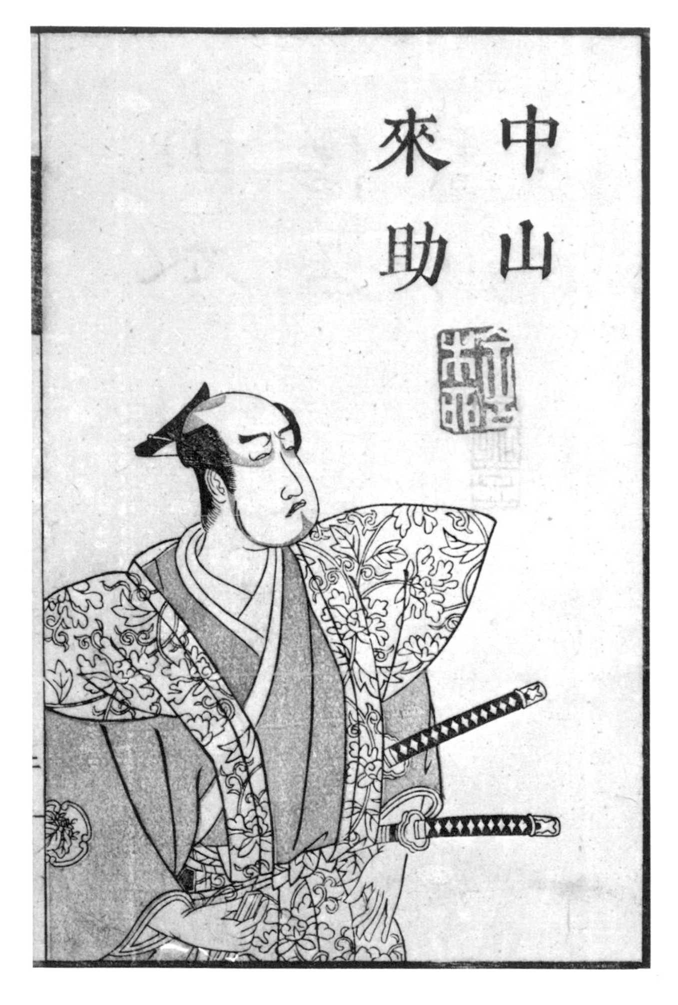
中山
來助

3 Ryūkōsai

Onoe Shinshichi I (Fujaku)
[as Isshiki Yūkinokami]
in *Keisei Yanagi Sakura* 1/1793
Catalogue 273

The Ashikaga shogunate, endangered by a scheming *tairō,* head of the shogun's advisory council, is preserved through the skillful intervention of Isshiki Yūkinokami and his followers, who unravel the intrigue and defeat the conspirators. In this scene from the first performance of the play, Isshiki is standing in a snowy garden holding a fragment of a handscroll he has just been discovered reading.

In Edo, a play on the revenge of the Soga brothers was invariably performed for the New Year. Not so in Osaka, although it was a convention to preface the title of every New Year's play with "*Keisei*" ("courtesan") whether or not a courtesan was involved in the plot.

This is the unsigned left panel of a *hosoban* triptych. Okada's impression, attributed to Shōkōsai in his manuscript catalogue, is reproduced in Kuroda, *Kamigatae Ichiran* (pl. 55). Another impression in the *Kyota Kyakushoku Jō* is trimmed around the figure, as usual, mis-identified as Nanpō Jūjibei, and mis-entered for a performance of *Futatsu Chōchō* at the Kado Theater in 1/1797.

Two other prints by Ryūkōsai illustrating different scenes of the same performance have survived: a signed portrait of Yoshizawa Iroha as a salt-water carrier, and a signed portrait of Yamamura Giemon as Sakai Hidakanokami printed with the title of the play. Both panels bear the publishers' marks *Shio* and *Rin* and do not match the present subject. Two other snow scenes by Ryūkōsai, a signed portrait of Nakayama Raisuke and a signed portrait of Ichikawa Danzō IV, probably belong together; neither is related here.

尾上彩七
芙雀

4 Shōkōsai

Arashi Sangorō II [as Kosobe no Tomoharu]
in *Aigo no Waka Meika no Kachidoki* 5/1795
Catalogue 348

The story of Aigo no Waka is the tragedy that befalls a young man who refuses to make love to his stepmother. Prince Nijō, the courtier who appears in the right panel of this diptych, is Aigo no Waka's gullible father. Believing his wife's slanders, he disinherits his son, but just as impetuously kills her when his despairing son plunges into an icy torrent, protesting his innocence. The role of Kosobe no Tomoharu does not appear in the usual synopses of the play, and there is no way to judge his relation to Prince Nijō. In spite of his nobleman's name, he is disguised as a lower-class street hawker, wearing the flat cap and sleeveless jacket that were typical of the profession and carrying a whirligig, which was swung round in the air to accompany a song.

This is the left panel of a *hosoban* diptych, the right panel of which shows Arashi Koroku II standing in court dress [*kamishimo*] and facing right. The diptych is complete in volume 14 of the *Kyota Kyakushoku Jō,* with manuscript notes identifying the roles as Kosobe no Tomoharu and Nijō no Kurando. The prints pasted into the *Kyota* albums to illustrate performances are often misplaced and mis-identified and there is no way to decide whether the roles are correct in this case. If they are, this print and its companion are Shōkōsai's earliest dated prints, preceding his first illustrated book (1798) by three years, and his portrait of Nakayama Bunshichi I as Ogurusu Jūbei by over a year. The *kakihan* (device) of pine needles after Shōkōsai's signature, is derived from the "Shō" in his name, which means "pine."

嵐三五郎
春好
塩長

5 Rankōsai

Kataoka Nizaemon VII as Karaki Masaemon and
Arashi Isaburō I as Ishidome Busuke
in *Igagoe Dōchū Sugoroku* 8/1805
Catalogue 272ab

The tale of how young Shizuma tracked down Kawai Matagorō, his father's murderer, with the help of his indomitable and persevering uncle-in-law, Masaemon, finally exacting revenge on him at Iga Pass, was one of the perennial favorites of the Osaka stage. In the present prints, Karaki Masaemon and his lieutenant, Busuke, have finally cornered Matagorō. Masaemon unfurls a drawing of their enemy as proof of his identity, and Busuke poses threateningly.

Certain plays were performed year in and year out, and it naturally occurred to publishers that they could alter the key blocks of prints they published and reissue them for later performances of the same play. In some cases the entire background of a print was removed; more often only the head of the actor and perhaps his crest were re-engraved. Often the reissue bore the name of the original designer, but frequently the name of the artist who designed the new portrait or altered the picture replaced that of the earlier artist. Altered republication was common in Edo in the late eighteenth century; in Osaka there are a few cases in the early 1800s and again around 1820, but it was never a common practice.

The illustration is of two left panels of a triptych originally designed by Ryūkōsai for a performance of *Igagoe* at the Kado Theater in the eleventh month of 1793. An impression of Ryūkōsai's unsigned left panel showing Anegawa Shinshichi III as Ishidome Busuke is reproduced in Kuroda, *Kamigatae Ichiran* (pl. 56) and elsewhere, and a cutout impression of the center panel of Arashi Hinasuke I as Masaemon, included in the *Kyota Kyakushoku Jō,* is reproduced in Haruyama's article on Ryūkōsai. The signed right panel of Ryūkōsai's triptych showed Asao Tamejūrō I as the villain Kawai Matagorō, standing under a pine tree in the same pose as Masaemon's drawing. An impression of this panel from the Okada collection is reproduced in color in *Kabukie Taisei* 11 (pl. 8), and again in black and white in *Ukiyoe Zenshū* 5 (fig. 161).

Rather than commission an entirely new triptych for the 1805 performance, the publisher Shioya Chōbei had Rankōsai, an otherwise unknown artist, alter the portrait heads on the two unsigned Ryūkōsai panels whose blocks had survived. Instead of changing Ryūkōsai's portrait of Tamejūrō I, Rankōsai designed an ill-matching portrait of Asao Kuzaemon I standing in an unkempt black kimono, sword drawn, by a haystack. The three prints were apparently issued together and the complete triptych is reproduced in Ishiwari, "Kamigatae" (pl. 5).

6 Shōkōsai

Nakamura Utaemon III as Hanazono Michitsune in *Keisei Nazuna no Sekku* 1/1806
Catalogue 349

Several plays were based on the Christian revolt of 1637-38 against the newly established Tokugawa shogunate. In a version by Chikamatsu Monzaemon, Amakusa Shirō, the Christian leader of the revolt, is adept in frog magic. In the course of the play, Shirō transforms himself into the courtesan Sarashina in order to lure her father into the plot. The father sees through the disguise and commits suicide by way of a sincere refusal. Shirō retreats to his castle in Kyūshū and is defeated only by the miraculous intervention of the golden snake of the rope of the Benten Shrine at Enoshima. In the present play, Shirō appears as the lord Hanazono. According to the inscription on the print, he magically assumes the form of Princess Itsu, in a variation of the plot mentioned above.

Shōkōsai lived in an entertainment district along the Horie Canal, south of the Yodo River, and the word "*Kōnan*" before his signature on this print means simply "south of the river." Although he illustrated books through 1809, this may be his last dated print.

Practically all of Ryūkōsai's actor portraits are full length, and Shōkōsai's early prints and illustrations continued this tradition. In *Gakuya Zue,* the theater guide that Shōkōsai wrote and illustrated around 1800, he designed a series of half-length portraits, and found the form congenial. This is one of a series of bust portraits in *hosoban* format, published by Shioya Chōbei between 1804 and 1806, which are related to *Ehon Masukagami,* a book of bust portraits printed in color and issued by the same publisher in 1806. Another plate from the set by Shōkōsai is reproduced in Kuroda, *Kamigatae Ichiran,* and a bust portrait of Morita Kanya in a Shibaraku role from the same group, signed Baikō, is illustrated in *Ukiyoe Geijutsu* 12, no. 4 (pl. 6).

中村歌右衛門

7 NAGAHIDE

Sawamura Tanosuke II [as Oryū]
in *Kyōhabutae Kawari Hinagata* 10/1806
Catalogue 265

Tsutsumi Takubei and Ishioka Sazen, rival archers, engage in a contest at the Sanjūsangendō in Kyoto. Takubei wins the match, but the more virtuous Sazen gains the prize. The rest of the play is devoted to Takubei's attempt to disgrace the legal heir of Sazen's ward, the lord of Kameyama, and control the clan's succession. Oryū, the daughter of a swordmaker, is in love with Sazen, and the two are eventually united.

The print is one of the finest of a group of single- and double-bust portraits of actors in octagonal fan-shaped formats designed by Nagahide and printed with stencils in Kyoto around 1805–1806. These are among the artist's earliest prints and are clearly related to Shōkōsai portraits of the same date. A nearly identical portrait of Tanosuke as Oryū is contained in a manuscript copy (Cat. 350) of an illustrated book by Shōkōsai dated 1806. An impression of this print and six other octagonal prints for fans are described, and six illustrated, in Keyes, "Japanese Fan Prints," nos. 7-13.

Stencils were first used in Kyoto in 1746 to color the pages of *Minchō Seidō Gaen,* an album of reproductions of Chinese paintings by Ōoka Shunboku. By the 1760s they were commonly used for illustrated books and the frontispieces of theater programs. At the beginning of the nineteenth century single-sheet prints colored by stencils appeared, with a distinctive range of bright, transparent colors that became a hallmark of the medium. Shortly afterward, stencil printing spread to nearby Osaka where it was used as a cheap substitute for full-color woodblock printing. The vogue lasted well into the century, but seems to have been cut off by the Tenpō Reforms of the early 1840s.

澤村田之助
長秀画

8 NAGAHIDE

Arashi Kichisaburō II [as Yojirō]
in *Sarumawashi Kadode no Hitofushi* 4/1807
Catalogue 266

The main plot of *The Monkey Leader: A Song at Parting* is the story of the love between Denbei, a samurai in search of an heirloom scroll, and Oshun, a geisha, the sister of the monkey leader Yojirō. Denbei locates what he takes to be the scroll, but kills the possessor in a rage when it is torn in a scuffle. Unable to live as a murderer, Denbei plans a joint suicide with Oshun, and the couple agree to meet at Yojirō's home. Oshun arrives first and Yojirō greets her warmly, but refuses to let Denbei enter when he learns their plans for suicide. As he realizes their love for one another, he unites and marries them, letting his monkey dance for them as a parting present for their journey. Denbei is finally vindicated on the way to their death and the play ends happily. The present print shows Kichisaburō carrying his monkey on his shoulder.

This stencil print of an Osaka performance was published in Kyoto. This impression, the only one recorded, was illustrated in Kuroda, *Kamigatae Ichiran* (pl. 28), and reproduced on the cover of the book in color facsimile. It is one of the masterpieces of stencil printing.

嵐吉三郎
長秀
柏宗板

9 Ashikuni

Nakamura Utaemon III as Adachi Tōzaburō c. 1815
Nakamura Utaemon III as Kakinoki Kinsuke in *Keisei Shigeshige Yawa* 1/1813
Nakamura Utaemon III as Ono no Komachi
Nakamura Utaemon III as a lion dancer in *Sono Kokonoe Saishiki Zakura* 3/1816
Catalogue 3 (23a, 10b), 2 (24a, 28a)

Utaemon III returned to Osaka from a five-year stay in Edo for the New Year's performances of 1813. As a finale he performed a dance of seven changes that he had devised in Edo the year before. In the spring of 1816, he returned from Edo once again and performed a dance of nine changes, two of which, a lion dancer and the poetess Ono no Komachi praying for rain, are shown here. Both dances were widely acclaimed, and the 1816 performance became the subject of a set of eight prints by students of Ashikuni, modeled on a set of prints designed by Toyokuni I for a performance of the same dance in Edo the year before. Six of the eight Osaka prints are reproduced in Speiser (pp. 66-69).

The collection contains two albums with thirty-four drawings in color on silk of actors in role by Asayama Ashikuni, two drawings in color by Gyodai Masayuki, and other drawings, inscrip-

tions, and poems by Osaka artists, actors, and writers. Volume 2 contains a preface by Naotari dated 10/1818, the month after Ashikuni's death. Both albums are composed like scrapbooks; the pages have ruled borders, and most of the pictures and calligraphy have been pasted in.

The only other extant drawings by Ashikuni seem to be the twelve unsigned colored sketches in the *Kyota Kyakushoku Jō*. Of these, two are bust portraits of Arashi Kichisaburō II as Konoshita Tōkichi and Nagai Genzaburō pasted into volume 21 (1811); the latter used by Kunihiro for the well-known memorial portrait of Kichisaburō II, which is reproduced on plate 21. The remaining ten drawings appear in volume 23 (1813) and include a complete set of the seven changes Utaemon III danced in the first month of that year. Nine of these ten drawings are duplicated in the Museum albums; the tenth, a portrait of Utaemon III as a praying maiden, has been lost.

Of the four representative Ashikuni drawings illustrated here, one of the bust portraits is in a style derived from Shōkōsai; the other is closer to Shijō style. The drawing of the lion dancer may have been used by Kunihiro for the *ōban* reproduced on Plate 41.

10 Toyokuni I

Nakamura Utaemon III as Akugenta Yoshihira
in *Hirugaesu Nishiki no Tamoto* 11/1812
Catalogue 362

The script of the present play has not survived, but Akugenta Yoshihira, a member of the Heike clan, killed Yoshikata, a Genji warrior, and tried unsuccessfully to kill his son as well. The present picture probably shows Yoshihira posing triumphantly with Yoshikata's kidnapped son, Komawakamaru, clutched to his bosom. The baby is later rescued and grows up to be Kiso no Yoshinaka, a great warrior on the Genji side.

This print was designed by an Edo artist and published in Edo, for sale or distribution in Osaka. It was printed before Utaemon's return to Osaka late in 1812, and in the actual performance of the play he did not appear in this role. The inscription before the actor's name and role says "New Face-showing Performance at the Kado Theater in Osaka." Toyokuni signs his name as an Edo artist; Kageben, the publisher, is from Edo; and Tsurukin is one of the *gyōji* or censors, whose seal appears on prints published in Edo in the early 1810s.

Actors frequently toured, and during the 1780s and 1790s many prints appeared in Edo showing popular actors in roles they were performing in Osaka, Kyoto, or elsewhere. These prints often have printed inscriptions mentioning the circumstances and the popularity or success of the play, and were apparently published to sell to Edo fans of the touring actors. In the nineteenth century this practice continued, but prints like the present example were also published for sale in other cities. Osaka prints were published to commemorate provincial performances in such places as Ise, Miyajima, Kanazawa, Hagi, and Miidera, as well as performances in the larger theaters of Nagoya and Kyoto, while at least one Osaka diptych, by Kunihiro, was published for sale in Edo in 1830.

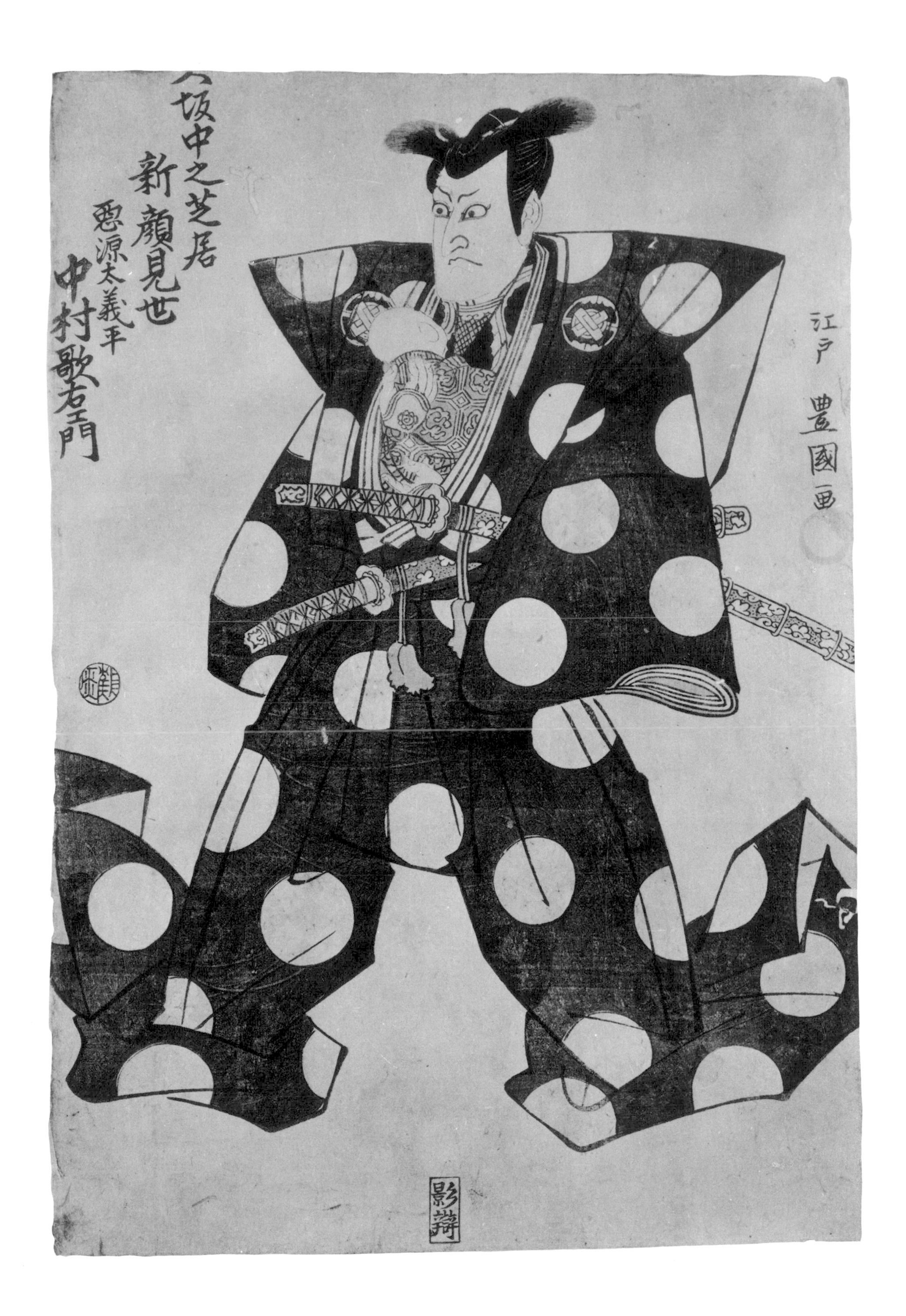

坂中之芝居
新顔見世
悪源太義平
中村歌右衛門
江戸 豊國画

11 Ashikuni and Shikan

Nakamura Utaemon III in roles depicting six months of the year
in *Matakaina Jūnibake* 3/1817
Catalogue 1

Right to left, the print portrays Utaemon III in dances he performed for the following months:

July: An old couple in the theater district who repaired pottery teapots; drawn by the actor himself. Utaemon acted the pair by using a painted fan for the woman's face. During the course of the performance he presented the old couple with a pair of matching kimonos. The pattern became a vogue, and young couples strolling together through the theater district were called "pot menders." The poem by Utahisa Renbo reads: "Morning glories blossom on the gate: water can't drip through," with puns on "theater," "full house," and the couple's profession.

August: *Tōru.* In the Noh play of this title, an old salt carrier reveals himself as a courtier, nostalgically remembers his past, and dances until he disappears in the moonlight. The poem by Nihyō reads: "Nobility above the court and clouds: crane of the moon," for Utaemon's crane-shaped crest.

September: A blind street musician; drawn by the actor himself, in Shijō style. The woman may be carrying a music stand on her back. The poem by Kakuhan reads: "Eyes cannot see the autumn wind: song of the *koto*."

October: Dancing beggar [*sutasuta-bōzu*]. Beggar monks clad in rope skirts and bandannas, accompanying their scurrilous recitations with clappers, began appearing as popular entertainers in the late eighteenth century. The poem by Shishō reads: "The music of the chestnut burr stands out in the winter rain," a pun on the beggar's unshaven pate.

November: Heron maiden. A lovesick maiden portrayed as a heron standing in the snow beside a pond. The poem by Utahisa Renbo reads: "She was twice as fair as the six-sided snowflakes in the snow

dance of the twelve changes we went to see," based on the calculation that twice six equals twelve.

December: Kuan Yu, one of the heroes of the Chinese romance, *The Tale of Three Kingdoms,* renowned for his valor, flowing beard, and fearsome mien. The Chinese poem reads: "One name of Shikan is Beautiful Beard / In loyalty as firm as iron and gold. / His noble art is a wick's free swing, / The whir of an 82-*kin* Dragon Sword," and is signed "Utahisa Renbo, for the happy third time."

Nakamura Utaemon III was a particularly accomplished dancer and throughout his career devised sets of quick changes of costume and mood known as *hengemono,* or "transformation pieces." Between his return to Osaka in 1813 and Ashikuni's death in 1818 he performed three of these plays. Ashikuni commemorated the first two in drawings preserved in the collection (Cat. 2) and the *Kyota Kyakushoku Jō,* and the last in two privately printed prints, which imitated a pair of "twelve-month" screens (*tsukinami no byōbu*), bearing a picture for each month. An impression of the right half of the pair, with three panels each by Ashikuni and Shikan, is included in the *Kyota Kyakushoku Jō*. A small stamp in the lower left corner of the Museum print identifies the publisher as Eijudō, using the same characters as the well-known Edo publisher of that name. Shikan here uses two seals: the characters of his name and a *kakihan* of an eye. Ashikuni uses three: one that can be read "Ashikuni" and two that seem to be rebuses for Naniwa.

Utaemon III was also well known as a poet, and later as a playwright, but his drawings are rare, and these are apparently the only prints he designed. This series of dances was particularly well received. The playwright Hamamatsu Utakuni pasted a copy of the program as a souvenir into his scrapbook-miscellany *Setsuyō Kiran*; and other artists including Ganjōsai Kunihiro and Ashitaka designed *ōban* that were published commercially.

12 Hokushū

Arashi Koroku IV as Oume and
Arashi Kanjūrō I as Majima Daisuke
in *Chigogafuchi Hana no Shiranami* 1/1817
Catalogue 191abc

The play describes the attempt of surviving members of the clan of Akechi Mitsuhide to usurp power from Mashiba Hisayoshi and his son Hisatsugu, with subplots describing a homosexual love affair between temple pages, and an intrigue by Saibara Kageyu, a follower of Mitsuhide, to take over the house of Kameyama. The particular scene in the present print (191c) has not been identified.

The print is the center panel of a triptych. The right and left panels of the published version are signed Shun'yō, and show Arashi Koroku IV as Oume standing at the right being threatened by Daisuke, and Arashi Kichisaburō II as her husband Takaseya Jūemon standing at the left just outside the door.

The two drawings (191a and b), carelessly drawn on thin paper, pasted onto heavier sheets folded across the middle, are noticeably different from the published prints. They are from a group of drawings related to prints signed Shunkō (Hokushū), Shun'yō, and Shunchō, which were published by Shioya Chōbei between 1815 and 1817. Despite the three signatures involved, the drawings are by the same hand, and seem to precede the prints, although the manuscript inscriptions on them were added in 1821 or later in different ink by another hand. One of the painted panels in the background of the published center panel is signed Kangetsu, the teacher of Ryūkōsai; the other is signed Shun'yū, or Harutomo, an otherwise unrecorded artist.

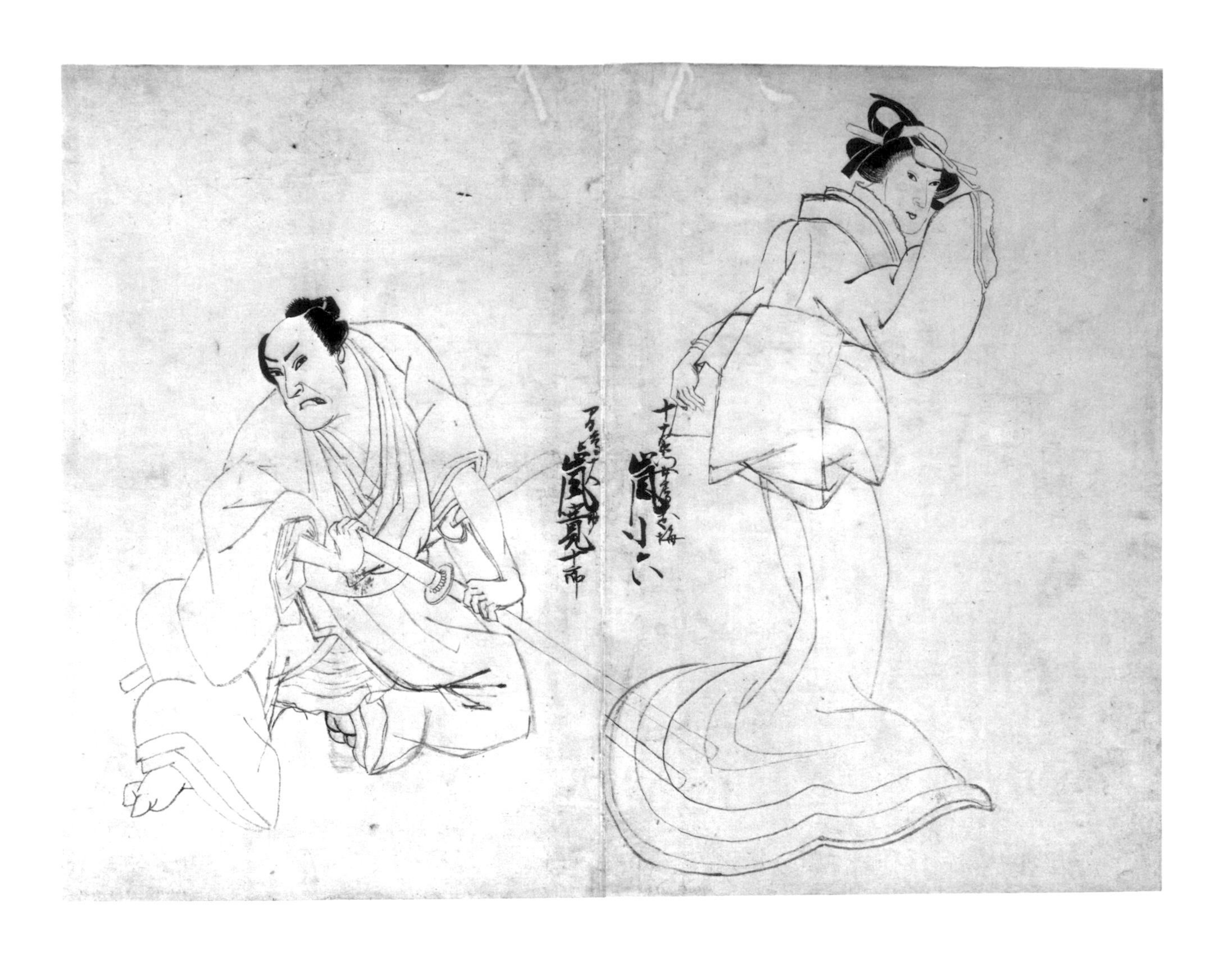
嵐小六
嵐寛十郎

13 Hokushū

Arashi Kichisaburō II as Koretaka Shinnō in *Toki wa Ima Ariwara Keizu* and Nakamura Utaemon III as Katō Masakiyo in *Hachijin Shugo no Honjō* 9/1820
Catalogue 196

Prince Koretaka, a historical figure, lived in the ninth century. He was the grandson of Ki no Natora, and the eldest son of an emperor. Historically, Koretaka's right to succession was successfully challenged by the guardians of the emperor's fourth son, Prince Korehito, whereupon he retired from the world to become a monk. In plays of the *Ariwara Keizu* cycle, Koretaka is presented as a villain who stopped at nothing to regain the disputed succession.

The model for Utaemon's role was a nearly legendary retainer of the Toyotomi clan named Katō Kiyomasa (1562–1611). In the present scene, which Utaemon apparently wrote for himself, the hero is dressed in formal robes to receive Kitabatake (Tokugawa Ieyasu) and a false Imperial Messenger. Kitabatake presents him with a ceremonial cup of sake, which Masakiyo drinks, well aware that it is poisoned. Through sheer will he lives several months longer to protect the young Toyotomi lord.

Nakamura Utaemon III and Arashi Kichisaburō II, the two actors shown together here, were rivals of long standing, and had not acted together for nearly twenty years. In the summer of 1821, fans of both actors arranged a joint shipboard banquet on the Ōkawa River. As a result, the actors agreed to appear together that September, and the theater world in Osaka bristled with excitement. Songs were composed about "the crane and the orange" (the devices used in the actors' crests), but as expectations reached their peak, Kichisaburō suddenly fell ill and died. The wish to see the actors together is reflected in this print published the previous year. They are shown as they appeared in rival performances in an imaginary confrontation.

This double half-length portrait was perhaps the first *ōban* print of its type to be published in Osaka. There are at least three states of the print, although the order of their issue is uncertain. One has a yellow ground; one has an uncolored ground and some signs of wear; another with uncolored ground bears the mark of the publisher Tamaoki.

惟喬親王
嵐吉三郎
加藤正清
中村歌右衛門
春好斎
北洲画

14 Hokushū

Nakamura Utaemon III as Katō Masakiyo
in *Hachijin Shugo no Honjō* 9/1820,
published c. 1822
Catalogue 195a

As mentioned in the description of Hokushū's earlier print of this role (Plate 13), this is the scene where Masakiyo (Katō Kiyomasa) drinks poisoned sake to protect his young lord from the machinations of Kitabatake (Tokugawa Ieyasu) and his supporters. The poem by Chōsokusai Fuminari reads: "Kiyomasa is a moon shining on the world at midday: an art of piercing insight," with puns on Kiyomasa's bull's-eye crest, his foreknowledge of Kitabatake's plot, and Utaemon's perceptive acting of the role.

This print was probably from a set of yellow-ground bust portraits published in the spring of 1822, described in Plate 21. There are at least two states: one with a blue ground and with the names of the actor and role in the upper left corner, reproduced here; another with a yellow background and lacking names (Cat. 195b).

加藤正清
中村歌右衛門
春好斎
北洲画

15 Kunisada
Ōsaka Dōtonbori Shibai Gakuya no Zu
("View of a theater backstage in Dōtonbori, Osaka") Spring 1821
Catalogue 250

Kunisada focuses attention on the dressing rooms on the lower and "middle-second" floor of an Osaka theater. Down the corridor to the right were property rooms and quarters for musicians, stagehands, and lesser actors. Rehearsal rooms were located on the floor above. The actors are making up for a performance of the "Carriage-Stopping" scene from *Sugawara Denju*. Bandō Mitsugorō III, standing at the lower right, is already dressed in the plaid costume of Matsuōmaru, while Iwai Hanshirō V, seated by a mirror at the upper right, is dressed for the role of the younger brother, Sakuramaru. This play was not performed in Osaka in 1821, nor did the Edo actors Mitsugorō and Hanshirō appear together, so it is possible that Kunisada is simply showing us a typical Osaka theater.

Osaka, like Edo, had its own traditions of acting and playwriting, which visiting authors and performers were careful to observe. In late 1820, Matsumoto Kōshirō V, Iwai Hanshirō V, Bandō Mitsugorō III, and other Edo actors traveled to Osaka and presented, for the first time, a group of Edo plays performed in pure Edo style. They were so acclaimed that Nakamura Utaemon III and other actors went to Kyoto and performed the traditional year-end plays there, rather than competing. For the New Year's and spring programs in 1821, the theaters arranged that the two superstars, Utaemon III and Mitsugorō III, should appear together at the Kado Theater to balance the rest of the Edo troupe at the Naka Theater down the way.

This triptych also shows the actor Arashi Kitsusaburō I, and was therefore designed between the

time he took this name in 3/1821 and his death six months later. It was published in Edo as a sequel to Kunisada's three backstage views of Edo theaters begun in 1813. The print is titled in the upper right corner; each actor is identified by a name slip placed nearby. Signatures, publisher's marks, and censor's seals appear on each panel. Two bands bear the devices of the powerful Sasase and Ōte fan associations. The inscriptions on the right and center panels say that Kunisada designed this triptych as a souvenir of his trip to Osaka, and explain that it is published because of the popularity of the earlier views of Edo theaters. The note on the center panel, which is signed by the publisher Nishimura, goes on to advertise other views of the Osaka theaters as well as illustrated books on Edo kabuki, theater festivals, stagecraft, etc., to be published in the near future. The left panel of the triptych is in poor condition, but shows the rest of the design.

16 Hokushū

Bandō Mitsugorō III as Daihanji Kiyozumi and Arashi Koroku IV as Koganosuke;
Nakamura Matsue III as Hinadori and Nakamura Utaemon III as Sadaka
in *Imoseyama Onna Teikin* 3/1821
Catalogue 197ab

The kabuki play *Imoseyama* was adapted from the puppet theater. It was first performed in 1771, shortly after Chikamatsu Hanji's puppet version opened at the Takemoto Theater in Osaka. The Soga clan had long ruled the nation through a regency, but a confederation of noblemen that formed around the royal prince Naka no Ōe, later the Emperor Tenchi, was able to overthrow it and make possible the Taika Reforms of 645 A.D. In the most moving and frequently performed act of the play, Soga no Iruka orders Sadaka and Kiyozumi to send their children, Hinadori and Koganosuke, to his court as hostages to insure loyalty. In spite of a feud between the two families, the children had fallen in love with each other, but hearing Iruka's orders, they decide independently to die rather than compromise themselves or their parents. Touched by their children's love and courage, the parents forgo their differences and resolve to work together to bring about the tyrant's downfall.

The scene shown takes place on the day of the Doll Festival. The two houses are set amid blossoming cherry trees on either side of a river and the action proceeds on both sides of the stage simultaneously. The actors are shown after the parents' return from Iruka's court, as each of the children resolves on suicide.

There are at least two states of this diptych: with and without the mark of the publisher Wataki. Impressions with the publisher's mark have mica on Hinadori's collar, a faint pattern on Koganosuke's collar, pink flowers and brown branches in the tree; no gold is used on the figure of the older man, whose sleeves and collar are white. On impressions without the publisher's mark, there is no mica or pattern on the children's collars, the flowers are embossed, the branches are grey, gold is used on the figure of the older man and on the youth's sword hilt, and a blue block is used for the man's sleeve, collar, eye, and chin. There are two impressions of the right panel in the Museum collection, the first with the publisher's mark and a pale, fugitive blue ground; the second lacking the publisher's mark, but before the addition of the blue block mentioned above (Cat. 197c). The left panel reproduced here lacks the publisher's mark, but seems to correspond to the impression reproduced in color in *Ukiyoe Taika Shūsei* 19 (pl. 11). Both prints appear in the *Kyota Kyakushoku Jō,* although the figures have been cut out and rearranged. Few prints published before 1822 bear engraver's names, but this group is very possibly by Kasuke.

17 Hokushū

Nakamura Utaemon III as Kanawa Gorō Imakuni
and Arashi Koroku IV as Omiwa
in *Imoseyama Onna Teikin* 3/1821
Catalogue 198

Act IV of *Imoseyama* is a domestic subplot. Omiwa, the daughter of a sake seller, falls in love with the son of Kamatari, one of the leaders of the anti-Soga party. When he refuses to reveal his identity, she attaches a spool of thread to his cloak and follows him, winding the reel. Her lover is following an unidentified princess with the same device, and all finally find themselves at Iruka's palace. Omiwa is noticed by one of Kamatari's subjects, Kanawa Gorō, who is loitering nearby disguised as Fukashichi, the fisherman. He stabs her. As she dies, he reveals that her lover was a courtier and that she will now be helping him to overthrow Iruka. Fukashichi then mixes her blood with the blood of a black-toed deer and smears it on his magic flute, making it possible to recover a certain Sacred Sword from Iruka at last, and sap his power.

The illustration, showing the confrontation between Omiwa and Fukashichi at the palace, is one of the masterpieces of Osaka printmaking. There are at least three states of the print. The first, reproduced here, is printed with a gold ground, and silver and copper pigments; it bears a seal after the signature. The second has a blue ground, blue spots on Utaemon's armor, and a yellow rope pattern. The third lacks the blue block; its background, spots, rope, chin, and hair are uncolored; the stripes on Koroku's kimono seem wider, and the overall effect is less coarse than the above. This print, as well as the two previous bust portraits, could very well have been engraved by Kasuke.

金輪五郎今国
中村歌右衛門
おみわ
嵐小六

18 Yoshikuni

Nakamura Utaemon III as Fukashichi, actually
Kanawa Gorō Imakuni
in *Imoseyama Onna Teikin* 3/1821
Catalogue 367

The illustration depicts Fukashichi discovering Omiwa on the grounds of Iruka's palace. It is the right panel of a diptych illustrating the same scene represented in Plate 17.

The left panel shows Omiwa, spool in hand, kneeling at the foot of the staircase. Yoshikuni designed another diptych for this play, a panel of which is described and illustrated as Plate 35. This print bears an unusual form of his signature, imitating Ashikuni, instead of the separate syllables for "Yoshi," which he commonly used.

中村歌右衛門
芳国画
利新

19 SHIBAKUNI

Arashi Kitsusaburō I as Gofukuya Jūbei
in *Igagoe Dōchū Sugoroku* 9/1818,
published c. 1821
Catalogue 298 (*see* Frontispiece)

Shizuma, a young man bent on avenging his father's murder by a man he has never seen, goes blind during his search, and is nursed back to health by his wife. The wife's brother, Jūbei, an itinerant clothes peddler who happened to guide the murderer in his flight to Kyūshū, leaves medicine for Shizuma in an *inrō* that belonged to the murderer. Shizuma recovers his sight, recognizes the *inrō,* but cannot locate Jūbei. Jūbei's father finds him, and by committing suicide forces him to divulge the murderer's secret whereabouts. Shizuma sets out for Kyūshū, but meets Jūbei en route and inadvertently kills him. Later, he accomplishes his revenge (*see* Plate 5).

The mirror mount in this print is decorated with orange blossoms, Kitsusaburō's decorative crest. The mirror itself bears the character "Oka," the beginning of the actor's *yagō* Okajimaya. A stylized form of the character "Kichi," the beginning of his earlier name "Kichisaburō," appears on the handle of one of the powder brushes. The books at the right are a complete five-volume script of the play *Igagoe Dōchū Sugoroku,* and a porcelain makeup bowl is placed behind the mirror at the left. The poem by Saikatei Meichoku (?) mentions the actor's skill in his role as Jūbei.

This is one of a number of bust portraits of Arashi Kitsusaburō I shown in earlier roles. Prints of this type are usually catalogued as memorial portraits and Kitsusaburō did die suddenly in September of 1821 at the height of his fame. But *ōban* bust portraits had already begun appearing in 1820 and, nothing in the poem or imagery suggesting he was dead, this portrait was probably published during his lifetime. A related portrait, of Kitsusaburō II, reflected in the mirror of his dressing table, was published the following year. Both portraits have the same imitation woodgrain on the stand.

嵐橘三郎
西花亭

20 Kunihiro

Memorial portrait of Arashi Kitsusaburō I
as Nagai Genzaburō
in *Katakiuchi Chikai no Shigarami* 9/1812,
published c. 9/1821
Catalogue 223

Here Kitsusaburō is dressed as a *komusō,* or traveling mendicant priest, a common disguise for an avenger in search of his foe. The title of the play shows that it is a story of revenge, but the plot is unknown. The poem overhead reads: "The fame of the moon remains at Komagaike Pond, after the moon has gone," an allusion to the actor's passing.

Over a dozen memorial portraits were published in Osaka on the death of Kitsusaburō I in late 1821. This particular print is based on a small unsigned drawing by Ashikuni included in volume 21 of the *Kyota Kyakushoku Jō.* The character "*ko*" before the actor's name means "deceased."

嵐橘三郎
國廣画

21 Hokushū

[Ichikawa Ebijūrō I as Tōken Jūbei]
in *Benimurasaki Ai de Someage* 8/1816,
published c. 1822
Catalogue 207a

"China Dog" Jūbei was the trusted lieutenant of Banzuin Chōbei, the famous Edo *otokodate,* and was responsible for Chōbei's family after his anticipated death at the hands of a vicious nobleman.

Ichikawa Ebijūrō I performed the role of Tōken Jūbei only once, in the eighth month of 1816, but prints of this style and technique did not appear in Osaka before 1820, and the poem by Hōrai Sanjin, "Even the goddess of Spring might be tempted: the Prawn [*ebi*] of the Island of the Immortals is the greatest actor of the spring," with its puns on the actor's and author's names could only have been written in the spring. A related portrait of Asao Gakujūrō for a performance in the spring of 1822 (Speiser, pl. 28), the date that Ebijūrō returned to Osaka from Edo, suggests that a series of yellow-ground bust portraits of actors in popular roles with poems and inscriptions above was published that spring. The series may have also included two portraits of Nakamura Utaemon III as Katō Masakiyo (*see* Plate 14) and Inanoya Hanbei (*see Ukiyoe Taika Shūsei* 19, pl. 8).

There are at least four states of the print. The first has a yellow ground, the full name of the actor, the role, and the name of the engraver, Kasuke (in *Kyota Kyakushoku Jō*). The second has a yellow ground, the name of the role, and the first two characters of the actor's name, "Ichikawa," in the upper right corner (Honolulu Academy of Arts). The third state has a yellow ground, but lacks the names upper right (Cat. 207b). The fourth state, reproduced here, has a blue ground, lacks the names in the upper right, and has the poem and signature in silver.

22 Hokushū

Nakamura Utaemon III as Ishikawa Goemon
in *Kinmon Gosan no Kiri* 2/1822,
as reissued for a performance titled
Konoshitage Hazama Gassen, 7/1826
Catalogue 203

The career of the great bandit-hero, Ishikawa Goemon, was one of the standbys of the kabuki theater, and his figure appears in countless woodblock prints, including Plate 43 where his life is briefly described. In this scene, Goemon wears the robes of an Imperial Messenger, which he has stolen as a disguise to enter the palace of the warlord Hisayoshi. Goemon intends to murder Hisayoshi to avenge his own father's death, but is surrounded by his enemy's henchmen. He escapes by magic and continues his adventures.

Hokushū's print, which may have been originally issued together with the series of bust portraits described in Plate 21, was certainly reissued for a performance of a related play in 7/1826. In this play Goemon disguises himself as an Imperial Messenger (*see* Plate 43) to steal the Imperial Seal, which is necessary to his ambition of ruling Japan. At the crucial moment he is met and foiled by Konoshita Tōkichi, another name of his enemy Hisayoshi. The encounter is shown in an undivided *chūban* diptych by Shunshi (Cat. 354ab) one of the earliest Osaka prints in this format. The right half of the Shunshi diptych is obviously copied from Hokushū's portrait. The encounter between Goemon and Tōkichi as it was actually staged is shown in an *ōban* diptych by Hokuei (Cat. 170) for yet another performance of the play several years later.

石川五右衛門
中村歌右衛門
春好斎
北洲画

23 Anonymous

Still life with porcelain vase and brush-holder
Frontispiece for a set of actor portraits
1820s or early 1830s
Catalogue 435

The still life abounds with symbols of and allusions to the actor Nakamura Utaemon III. The flowers are crane-shaped like his device, and the first characters of his name, "Naka" and "Uta," appear on the porcelain vase, along with the characters for "Ryūgyoku," the name Utaemon assumed as a playwright in 1820.

Inexpensive playbills were sold at the theaters in Osaka, but color prints were sold in shops for prints and books. The major publishers like Wataki and Honsei had stores where their own prints and illustrated books were displayed in stacks or shelves, or suspended from cords for sale. Although they sold to the public, these firms were known as "wholesalers" [*ton'ya*] to distinguish them from the "retailers" or "piece-sellers" [*kouri*] who owned small premises, or sold prints by street-hawking or from temporary stalls. Most Osaka actor prints were published for current performances. These commercially published prints were sold separately, and it was up to collectors or others to gather and bind them in albums if they wished. Certain groups of prints, including the Hokushū bust portraits and the surimono-style prints of the early 1830s, which do not bear publisher's marks, seem to have been published privately or jointly as sets. The publisher of this frontispiece for one of them is given as "Naniwa Shorin, bookseller." It bears the title *Yakusha Ezōshi* ("Color Portraits of Actors") and a long advertisement reading: "Please be so good as to purchase our color prints of actors, which are printed and sold as soon as each play is performed. We also publish albums." The shorter inscription on the inkstone reads: "An album of pictures by famous artists with poems by the actors portrayed." Since actors' poems appeared on prints most frequently in the 1830s, this may be the cover for one of the surimono-style sets engraved by Kasuke between 1831 and 1833.

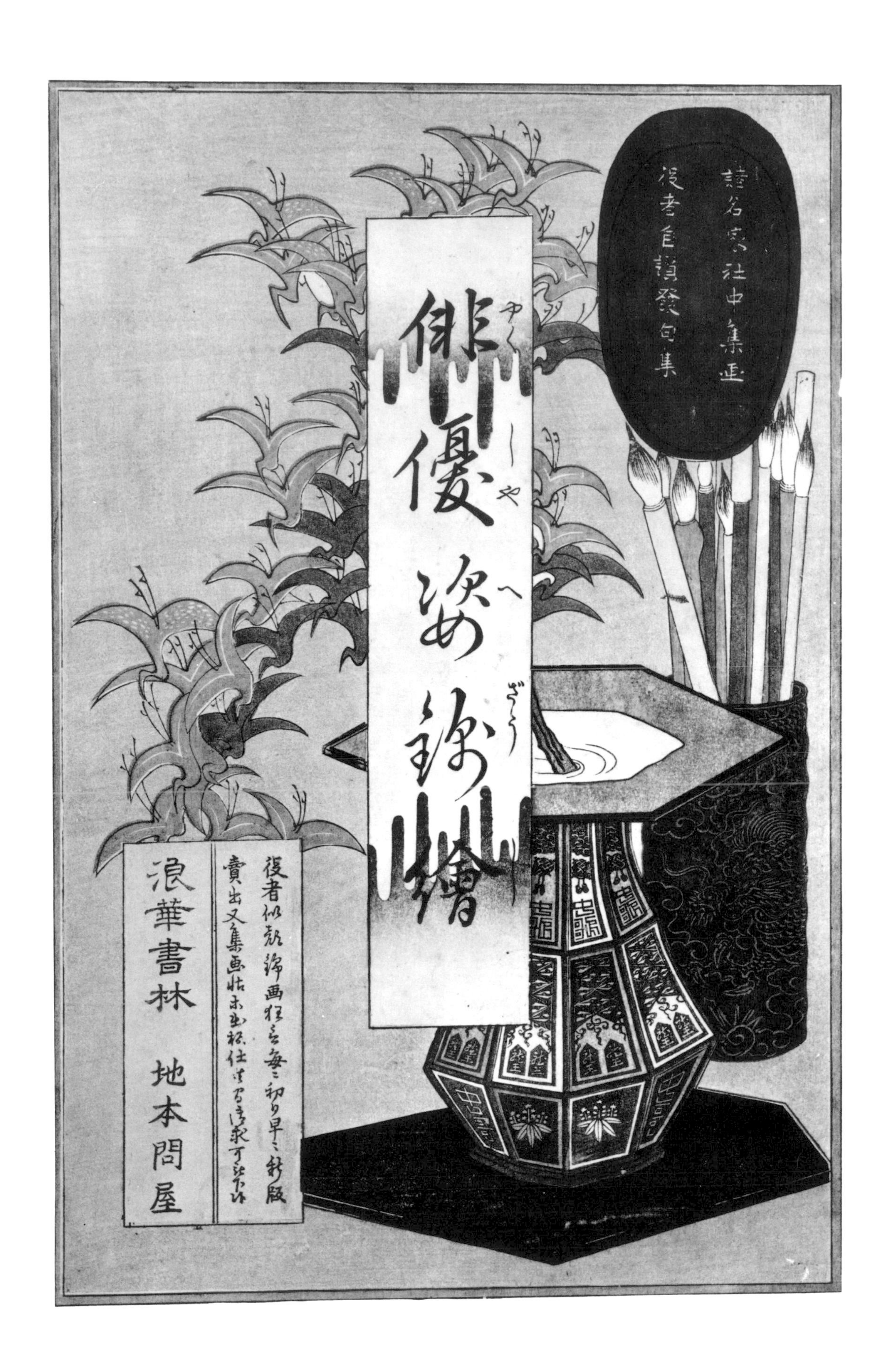
浪華書林
地本問屋

24 Shigenobu

Hatsufunedayū of Nishi-Ōgiya as a *tatebina*
in the series *Ōsaka Shinmachi Nerimono*
("Costumes in the Shinmachi district of Osaka")
c. 1822
Catalogue 340a

The courtesan in this picture is dressed as one of the dolls used in the Girls' Festival on the third of March. She is holding an oversized sake cup.

Costume parades were an annual event in the gay quarter in Osaka and Kyoto. Another set of single-sheet *hosoban* stencil prints of geisha in masquerade was designed by Harukawa, Nagahide, and others, and was published in Kyoto around this time.

This print is from a series of yellow-ground portraits of geisha costumed for the annual parade in the Shinmachi district of Osaka and published while Shigenobu was there between 1822 and 1826. The signature, "Yanagawa Shigenobu of the Eastern Capital," also appears on some actor prints designed for performances in 1822; therefore, these costume prints may have been published shortly after his arrival. This print is directly related to a square surimono with a poem by the Osaka poet Chiyo no Matsuhiko, which was undoubtedly published at about this time.

東都
柳川重信

25 Hokushū

Asao Yūjirō as Sano Genzaemon and
Ichikawa Ebijūrō I as Miura Arajirō
in *Keisei Sano no Funabashi* 5/1822
Catalogue 205ab

In 1784, Sano Zenzaemon, a minor *hatamoto* (or feudal lord), killed the son of Tanuma Okitsugu, the despised chancellor of the shogun, under severe provocation. This act broke Tanuma's power, and the grateful populace practically deified Sano, who was allowed an honorable death by his own hand. In the play based on this incident, Sano Genzaemon, (the *hatamoto*'s stage name) offers a corrupt official, Miura Arajirō, the honor of shooting down a crane in the presence of the shogun to recover a precious family genealogy in Miura's possession. Miura, however, repays this gesture by insulting Sano, who is shown here on the point of killing him.

From the Muromachi period on, there was a tradition of performing plays in shrine and temple compounds. In the seventeenth century the government restricted theater performances in Osaka, Kyoto, and Edo to the entertainment district of each city, but on occasion permitted temporary stages to be erected in shrine and temple precincts. These theaters were called *miyachi shibai* and, in Osaka, were located in Kitanoshinchi, Tenma, North Horie, Zama, and Goryō. Aside from a brief interruption in the 1840s, such performances were given throughout the Edo period, and many of them are commemorated in prints. An inscription on each panel of this print states that it was a fund-raising performance at the Goryō Shrine Theater and an unparalleled success. The play was considered appropriate to a fund-raising performance because the name of the play contains the name of the Funaba Shrine where the performance took place. *Ōban* diptychs with patterned yellow ground were common during this period in Edo and Osaka.

市川鰕十郎
御霊社

26 Yoshikuni

Ichikawa Danzō V as Tamaya Shinbei
in *Hadekurabe Tōsei Sugata* 7/1822
Catalogue 371

Tamaya Shinbei is an honest, loyal workman employed by a prodigal and undeserving master, Ukai Kujūrō. Tamaya and another man named Demura Shinbei are rivals for the love of the courtesan Kojorō. Demura lends Tamaya a sum of money to redeem a certain scroll that his master, Kujūrō, has pawned. Kujūrō embezzles the money, and Tamaya, angered beyond endurance, kills him. The scroll, a family heirloom, is finally recovered.

Ichikawa Danzō V, the adopted son of Ichikawa Danzō IV, began acting in his twenties under the name Danzaburō. In 1815, he changed his name to Ichikawa Shikō, and two years later his name began to appear on the actors' ratings. In 1819 he became Danzō V and performed in the major Osaka theaters regularly between then and his departure to Edo in 1832. He was a versatile actor, able to perform all roles except princesses and young maidens, and at times he rivaled even Nakamura Utaemon III in popularity. Considering his fame, it is perhaps surprising that he appears so rarely in prints, the present example being the only known bust portrait of him.

This is the left panel of a pink-ground diptych, the right panel of which shows Ichikawa Ebijūrō I as Ukai Kujūrō. The cartouche is formed from the first two syllables of the artist's name, "Yoshi."

市川團蔵
よし国画
本清

27 Hokushū

[Ichikawa Ebijūrō I as Wada Raihachi]
in *Appare Keisei Matsura no Tōriya* 1/1824
Catalogue 210

To encourage martial skills in the peaceful period that followed the establishment of the Tokugawa shogunate in the early seventeenth century, archery contests were held at the 390-foot hall of the Sanjūsangendō in Kyoto, the winner being the archer who shot the most arrows the full length of the hall in a twenty-four-hour period. In 1667, Hoshino Kanzaemon shot 8,009 arrows the full length in 10,542 attempts. Twenty years later, that achievement was bettered by Wasa Daihachirō, who succeeded with 8,133 arrows out of 10,053. That record was never surpassed.

A dramatization of Wasa's feat was written by Namiki Gohei, and revised by Nakamura Utaemon III for the present performance. Wada Raihachi (Wasa) is involved in a plot against Koshino Kanzaemon (Hoshino) to take over the house into which he has been adopted. The plot involves murders, love affairs, and a lost treasure arrow, and is finally resolved when Koshino exposes Wada's villainy. The present print portrays Wada during the archery contest at Sanjūsangendō at which, in Gohei's play, only a judge is present.

This is possibly the right panel of a diptych. The impression in the *Kyota Kyakushoku Jō* is cut out, as usual, and a hand-painted wall added, extending far to the left as a background. No other figures are shown. The addition of another panel of architecture at the left, printed in the luxurious, fugitive pink used here, would have been both striking and expensive.

春好斎
北洲画

28 Hokushō

[Onoe Tamizō II] reflected in the mirror of his dressing table c. 1824
Catalogue 189

The actor Tamizō is shown out of role. One of his powder brushes bears the double fan and pine-wreath crest of the Onoe family of actors, the other a stylized sparrow, which may have been his personal crest. The inverted cup at the left contained *beni,* a pink vegetable dye for makeup. The poem by Tamikuni reads: "The cherry blooms and is praised in all quarters," echoing Tamizō's new skill and popularity.

Besides marking the regular performances at the leading theaters on the Dōtonbori in Osaka, prints were published for performances in smaller theaters. Young actors often began their careers in the off-Dōtonbori "beach theaters" [*hama shibai*]. These theaters had regular performances, and capable actors like Onoe Tamizō II, Onoe Fujaku III, and Hyakumura Hyakutarō preferred playing leads to smaller audiences there to performing secondary parts in the major theaters.

Onoe Tamizō II was born in 1799 and began acting in the children's theater in Osaka under the name of Segawa Waichi. Onoe Kikugorō III, the Edo actor, saw him act during his first visit to Osaka in 1820, adopted him as a protégé, and took him back to Edo later that year. Tamizō returned to Osaka in 1823. Rather than competing with actors like Utaemon III in the big Dōtonbori theaters, he appeared in the little "beach theaters" and achieved quite a following. In the early 1830s he began appearing regularly in the main theaters and, outliving most of his contemporaries, became one of the leading actors in Osaka until his death in 1886. He was short, and in later years quite fat. His success was attributed more to showmanship than acting, but he was versatile, and could play most roles. He was also a good dancer, although to trained eyes he lacked grace.

春好斎
北洲画

29 Yoshikuni

Nakamura Utaemon III as a heavenly musician and as a nine-tailed fox
in *Yosete Aratama Kokonobake* 1/1825
Catalogue 375ab

Shown are plates 1 and 8 from a series of nine yellow-ground, full-length portraits of the roles Utaemon III danced in a set of nine changes. Following is the entire set in the order they were performed: heavenly musician; Urashima Tarō, the Japanese Rip van Winkle, riding a turtle; Negro holding a branch of coral; warrior Tomomori in full armor; shrine sorceress; courtesan, in the style of a humorous Toba-style painting; fox-witch Tamamo no Mae; nine-tailed fox; Shakkyō, a lion dancing among peonies.

Utaemon's heavenly musician holds an ancient wind instrument, the *shō*. Utaemon's poem on the print, "Spring, everywhere I look, things prospering," is suited to the season of the performance and implies a full house at the theater.

There was a legend that a magic, golden nine-tailed fox flew to Japan after several evil and mischievous adventures in China and India. Once in Japan, it transformed itself into a beautiful woman and became the mistress of the retired Emperor Toba who gave it the name of the fox-witch Tamamo no Mae (Utaemon's previous role). The Emperor doted on his concubine, but contracted a strange illness that remained incurable until the fox was exposed through the prayers of Abe no Seimei, a faithful courtier. The poem on this panel, also by Utaemon, reads: "A willow tree with branches hanging down uneven," alluding to the fox's tail.

Two weeks into the New Year's performances of 1825, Utaemon suffered a second injury to a leg he had twisted in Edo several years earlier, and on the last day of the month he fell seriously ill. A week later he had recovered enough to continue acting through the end of the second month when the New Year's performances ended, but billboards had already announced a "retirement performance" [*isse ichidai kyōgen*] for the next month.

中村歌右エ門

天人

30 Hokushū

Nakamura Utaemon III as Kyōgoku no Takumi in *Hikosan Gongen Chikai no Sukedachi* 3/1825
Catalogue 211a

To avenge his public defeat by the fencing master Ichimisai, Kyōgoku no Takumi murders him. One of Ichimisai's daughters is also killed when she encounters Takumi; but Osono, the elder daughter, and her fiancé, Keyamura Rokusuke, who was Ichimisai's prize pupil, track Takumi down and accomplish their revenge. In the portrait, Takumi seems hesitant and defiant. This may be the moment he is discovered by Rokusuke and Osono, roles that Utaemon played concurrently.

This is one of at least five bust portraits of Utaemon III on fans engraved by Kasuke and published at the time of the actor's retirement performance. Utaemon's "retirement" performance was so well received, and his spirits and health so revived, that he never left the stage, but continued acting without pause until his death at the age of sixty in 1838. During this performance Utaemon's protégé, Nakamura Tsurusuke, assumed the name of Shikan II, his master's *haigō,* and several prints were published to commemorate his name change, including a bust portrait by Yoshikuni in the same format, and a surimono signed Gochō published by Konishi, which is pasted into the *Kyota Kyakushoku Jō*. The *Ōkabuki Gedai Nenkan* (*see Naniwa Sōsho*) mentions that for this performance "two masters of portraiture, Shunkōsai (Hokushū) and Yoshikuni collaborated on the painted billboards, which were very well done."

There are at least two states of this print, with and without the name of the engraver. Most impressions are stamped "Ariharadō" in red on the handle of the fan. Ariharadō is another name of Chū, the publisher of the print, who may have put these impressions on sale. Other plates in the series portray Utaemon as Osono, Rokusuke, Gotobei, and Kumagai.

春好斎北洲画
京極内匠
中村歌右衛門
一世一代

31 Ashiyuki

Arashi Rikō as Osuma no Kata,
Arashi Kitsusaburō II as Kowari Dennai, and
Arashi Koroku IV as Okiyo
in *Katakiuchi Ura no Asagiri* 1/1826
Catalogue 13abc

The play describes an unsuccessful attempt by a villain named Karahashi, a subject of the Aboshi clan, to steal the clan treasures and install his son as leader. In act 3, Kowari Dennai, a hunter in the disguise of a pilgrim, is traveling to the Aboshi domains to settle the succession. In this scene at a roadside inn he encounters Okiyo, his fiancée, whom he has never seen before, and Osuma no Kata, the villain's daughter. He reveals to them that he is a relative of the true heir, and well aware of Karahashi's plot.

The striking feature of this triptych is the contrast between the hard-edged clarity of the three figures and the painterly Shijō-style background.

嵐橘三郎

璃寛

32 Hokuchō

Onoe Kikugorō III as Akamatsu Hikojirō Norimasa, actually Nikki Naonori in *Keisei Date no Kikiuta* 1/1826
Catalogue 139

The present play is one of many based on a historical dispute over the succession in the Date clan, who were the hereditary lords of Sendai. Because of a government ban on dramatizing events of recent history, the plot is set in the remote past. Nikki Naonori (or Nikki Danjō, as he appears in other plays on the same theme), the villain of the piece, is here shown watching a magic pheasant write out the incantations needed to make his plot against the Ashikaga shogunate succeed. The text above is Naonori's soliloquy revealing his plan to usurp the shogunate and conquer the world.

Onoe Kikugorō III was the adopted son of the Edo actor Onoe Matsusuke, and inherited from him a repertoire of ghost plays that he performed with great acclaim in Edo and in Osaka on his four tours to that city between 1820 and 1849.

There are at least two states of this print, one with the poem on the ground printed in silver, another with it printed in black. There may be a yet unrecorded earlier state with the name of the engraver, Kasuke. Other printing variations in the color of the flame at the right exist, but their order has not been determined.

赤松彦次郎則政
尾上菊五郎

33 Kunihiro

Nakayama Shinkurō IV as Tamiya Iemon and Onoe Kikugorō III as Oiwa in *Irohagana Yotsuya Kaidan* 1/1826
Catalogue 227

Tamiya Iemon, a masterless samurai, turns murderer in the bitterness of poverty and kills his father-in-law, the wife he has disfigured, and others. He is hunted down by their ghosts, and finally killed by his brother-in-law. In this scene, Iemon nails his murdered wife Oiwa, to a door panel. As he heaves the panel into the river it flips over and reveals the body of Koheiji, another victim, on the other side. Kikugorō played the ghost of both Oiwa and Koheiji, and the contrivance he used for the transformation was widely published and much admired.

This print is one of a group by various artists and publishers commemorating Kikugorō's performance of the new role of Oiwa at the beginning of his second visit to Osaka. The news of his spectacular performance in the premiere of Tsuruya Nanboku's new play, *Yotsuya Kaidan,* in 1825 preceded his visit to Osaka the following year. Interest in the play was so great that the management scheduled the summer play out of season as the finale for the New Year's program. Kikugorō had the play specially rewritten for this occasion for the Osaka audience, and it was received with tremendous acclaim.

Tsuruya Nanboku IV, the most brilliant dramatist of the early nineteenth century, created a theater of cruelty and horror that is reminiscent of *Titus Andronicus* and Jacobean tragedy. The present play, a classic of its genre, is still performed.

34 Hokushū

[Onoe Kikugorō III as the ghost of Oiwa]
in *Irohagana Yotsuya Kaidan* 1/1826
Catalogue 216

At the end of the play (*see* Plate 33) the ghost of the murdered Oiwa follows her husband to his mountain hideaway. There she haunts him until he is driven mad with fear and almost welcomes Oiwa's brother, the avenger. The inscription by Kikugorō III relating to his role in the play reads:

> Six years ago my father Shōroku's contrivance of a wicked spirit was well received, and although this is neither new nor proper to the season, I could not refuse the many people who insisted on my performing it.
>
> Happily it does not stay, but disappears: spring snow.—Baikō

At least three states of the print are known. The first, illustrated here, bears the names of the engraver Kasuke and two printers, with the writing printed in silver. The second lacks the names of the engraver and printers. A third state, coarsely printed, has the writing in black.

35 YOSHIKUNI

Nakamura Shikan II as Iruka Daijin
in *Imoseyama Onna Teikin* 4/1826
Catalogue 381

The story of *Imoseyama* has been described earlier (Plates 16-18). This scene shows the confrontation between Fukashichi and Iruka after the killing of Omiwa, when Fukashichi uses his blood-smeared flute to wrest the treasure sword from Iruka, the usurper, thus breaking his power.

This is the performance that was attended by the young German doctor Philipp Franz von Siebold on his way back to Nagasaki with the Dutch consul after an audience with the shogun in Edo. Siebold was enthralled with what he saw of the play *Imoseyama,* and had a translation made of it, which he called "The Blind Emperor," and later mentioned it to Alphonse Daudet. The morning Siebold and several Dutchmen visited the theater a painter named Kakutai made a special trip there to see them. His account is quoted in Ihara, *Kabuki Nenpyō,* vol. 6 (p. 142):

> While I was stopping in Osaka on my way back from Zōzusan in Sanuki Province, someone came to tell me that foreigners had gone to the Naka Theater [*sic*] to see the play. He took me there, and there were, indeed, three of them, as my drawing shows. They were with five or six men who looked like officials, wearing swords and black cloaks. One of them was holding a program and trying to explain. They watched, laughed, and left in the middle of the performance. When they left, they put something like a crown with a feather on their heads, and fastened a finely-made gold object on their shoulders, which differs with rank, I am told. All three wore differently colored woolen clothes. The one in black was supposed to be a doctor. Their faces were white, light pink from their eyes down, and their eyes were red. People say foreigners cannot bend their legs. This is not true. But their trousers are buttoned so tightly, it is difficult for them to kneel.

This is a reissue of the right panel of a diptych published for a performance of *Imoseyama* in 3/1821. There appear to be three states of the print. The first has a portrait of Bandō Mitsugorō III as Iruka; the signature, marks of the publishers Toshin and Ariharadō, and the name of the printer Suri Kinji appear in reserve on black under the steps at right; there is a block engraved in imitation of woodgrain for the steps, and no gold. The second has the names of Toshin and Kinji printed over in light grey, a new block for the woodwork and stairs, surface polishing on the balustrade and hairdo, and much gold. The third state, reproduced here, shows the portrait changed to Shikan II, the background screen entirely removed, the signature recarved, different color blocks, and the mark of the publisher Wataki added. The left panel shows Utaemon III as the fisherman Fukashichi.

入鹿大臣
中村芝翫
よし国画

36 Ebikane

Ichikawa Ichizō II as Gokumon no Shōbei and
Nakamura Baigyoku (Utaemon III) as
Kurofune Chūemon
in *Otoko Ippiki Sukui no Tatehiki* 8/1827
Catalogue 19

Kurofune ("Black Ship") Chūemon as an *otoko-date,* one of the free-wheeling, chivalrous champions of the urban poor, protects the weak and beautiful from the depradations of the rapacious villain Gokumon no Shōbei and his gang. In this picture, Chūemon and Shōbei pose together in defiance. Later in the play, seeing no other way of curbing him, Chūemon kills Shōbei for the good of the community, and surrenders himself to the police. Plays of this type were a stock item in the kabuki repertoire and transformations of the "Black Ship" Chūemon story appeared in various guises from its first appearance in the 1710s through the nineteenth century.

This double-bust portrait was published a month after Ichikawa Ebijūrō I's death in 1827, for a memorial performance sponsored by the actor Nakamura Utaemon III to introduce the late actor's twenty-two-year-old son to the public. It is one of two known prints by Ebikane. The other, a full-length portrait of Ebijūrō II, dates from early 1828 when Ichizō assumed his father's name. The pattern on Ichizō's kimono, a sickle, a ring, and the syllable "*nu,*" is a rebus for *kamawanu* ("I don't care"), a device of the Ichikawa family.

The titling of plays became such a mystique in the nineteenth century that some playwrights like Nishizawa Ippō simply threw up their hands. The number of syllables in a title was limited, certain conventional words or combinations had to appear, and the title had to somehow suggest the plot or the type of play the audience was to expect. In practice, authors composed resonant titles with a proper syllable count and wrote them with characters that evoked the mood of the play by combining the two regardless of how the characters would normally be pronounced. The title of this play, for example, is written with characters that would normally be pronounced *Dōjima Sukui no Irihama,* and understood as meaning something like "Salvation Entering the Port at Dōjima," although the proper reading is *Otoko Ippiki Sukui no Tatehiki* ("One Man: A Deal for Salvation").

市川市蔵
中村梅玉

37 SHIGEHARU

Nakamura Utaemon III as Ume no Yoshibei,
Ichikawa Danzō V as Chōkichi, and
Nakamura Matsue III as Oume
in *Suda no Haru Geisha Katagi* 9/1828
Catalogue 305abc

Ume no Yoshibei, an *otokodate,* undertakes to raise a hundred gold pieces to redeem a family treasure and prevent a young couple from being parted. His wife Oume secretly asks her younger brother Chōkichi to bring that amount to their house that evening. Thieves attack him on the way, but he is rescued by Yoshibei, who does not recognize him in the darkness. Without realizing what the money is for, Yoshibei begs it as a loan; when Chōkichi refuses, he kills the boy in desperation. The thieves then force Yoshibei to give them his wife as well as the money in exchange for a counterfeit of the treasure. Yoshibei is provoked beyond measure and slays the entire band, eventually recovering the genuine article. In the present scene, Yoshibei is on the point of killing Chōkichi. Oume, who usually learns of the killing much later, is shown further down the embankment watching them.

38 Shigeharu

Onoe Fujaku III as Koichirō
in an unidentified play c. 1828
Catalogue 306

In kabuki, black is a non-color. The ubiquitous, hooded stagehands called *kurogo,* or "little black men," who run on and off stage during performances placing and removing properties, arranging costumes, prompting, and helping with effects, are theoretically invisible to the audience and seldom appear in prints. Playwrights or close relatives of the actors were often appointed to the job.

Onoe Fujaku III, like Onoe Tamizō, was a popular actor who preferred acting large roles in the little theaters to playing bit parts on the Dōtonbori. He appears far less frequently in prints than Utaemon, Ebijūrō, Rikan, and other contemporaries. So few of Fujaku's performances are recorded that neither the play nor the action is identified.

Very few Osaka artists drew stage properties with any conscious sense of irony although a book illustration by Hokushū, published around this time, has a backstage view of a kabuki murder, with a series of painted hedges tacked up on wooden supports. Stage butterflies are dangled on lacquered poles in the theater to this day.

小市郎
尾上芙雀

39 Kunihiro

Nakamura Matsue III as Otami and
Ichikawa Ebijūrō II as Yokoyama Daizō
in *Asakusa Reigenki* 3/1829
Catalogue 228ab

The colorful plot of this play involves a disputed succession in the Hosokawa family, a vendetta, a miracle of the Asakusa Kannon, and a homosexual love affair, but the subject of the scene in Kunihiro's print is unidentified.

This perfectly conventional Osaka diptych is the only recorded work signed by the engraver Kōichi.

おたみ
中村松江
國廣画

40 SHIGEHARU

Ichikawa Hakuen as an ice-water seller
in *Oniwaka Nagori no Motodori* 9/1829
Catalogue 310a

Ichikawa Danjūrō VII, using the name Ichikawa Hakuen, is shown here in the role of a water seller in a dance of five quick changes performed as a farewell just before returning to Edo. The other dances, also depicted by Shigeharu, show the actor as Oniwakamaru, Musashibō Benki, Tada Kurando, and Yanone Gorō, all male roles. A print of Kurando, also with a green ground and the bat-shaped cartouche based on one of the actor's devices, is in the Museum collection (Cat. 310b).

Farewell performances [*onagori kyōgen*] were given by actors the month before they left on tour, or returned to their place of origin. The program usually included some of the actor's favorite roles and a few dances composed for the occasion.

A disastrous fire in the spring of 1829 burned all three Edo theaters and many actors went on tour until the theaters were rebuilt. Ichikawa Danjūrō VII, also known as Ichikawa Ebizō V at this time, was the leading Edo actor of the day. Hakuen was a name that had belonged to Danjūrō V, his grandfather, and Ebizō used it only for this series of performances in Osaka in 1829. The government closely supervised and restricted actors' travel and contractual agreements. If Ebizō was officially still in Edo at the time, he may have used a pseudonym to avoid government interference or prosecution, as he did in 1842 after his expulsion from Edo, using the name Hataya Jūzō for unofficial performances at Ise and elsewhere en route to Osaka.

市川白猿
氷
柳斎
重春画
ワタキ

41 Kunihiro

Onoe Tamizō II as a lion dancer performing *Shakkyō*
in *Osore ari Naniwa Shibai* 11/1831 (?)
Catalogue 230

In this Noh play a traveler falls asleep beside a stone bridge [*shakkyō*] and in a dream sees a lion gamboling among peonies. The lion dance entered the kabuki repertoire in the eighteenth century and has been performed with countless variations. In the present version, the actor changes into a lion and dances with clusters of peonies. In other versions, a maiden is possessed by the spirit of a lion mask, a mother lion and her cub dance together, a lion is tormented by butterflies, etc. In the climax of each dance, the actor swirls the great flowing mane back and forth across the stage, delighting the audience.

This print is from a series of changes, probably a set of five that Tamizō performed in 1831, and is related to, if not based on, a drawing by Ashikuni of Nakamura Utaemon III in the same role (Plate 9). It is one of the earliest prints signed by the engraver Kumazō (*see* Plate 53). The stamp "Touse," which appears on several prints in the Philadelphia Museum collection but rarely elsewhere, is probably that of an Osaka printseller. Another plate from the series, showing Tamizō as a fireman, is in the Museum of Fine Arts in Boston.

尾上多見蔵
國廣画
天喜

42 Hokuei

Nakamura Utaemon III as Asahina Saburō
in *Hōnen Uruoi Soga* 8/1832
Catalogue 156

In its fullest form, the Soga story tells how Jūrō and his younger brother Gorō manage to avenge their father, Kawazu no Saburō. Asahina Saburō, a retainer in the service of Kudō Suketsune, the villain, was usually played in Edo as a comic strongman, interceding on behalf of the brothers, and restraining them when he could. We see him here on his own, in a belligerent and vigorous, if rather confusing, pose.

Some impressions of this single-sheet print have a distinctly green background, but no actual state differences are noticeable. The poem-like inscriptions to the left of the actor give his name and role.

本清

43 Hokuei

[Nakamura Utaemon III as Ishikawa Goemon]
in *Keisei Chigogafuchi* 1/1833
Catalogue 158

Ishikawa Goemon, a legendary outlaw, magician, and popular hero, is often presented in the many plays about his life and career as the illegitimate son of the sixteenth-century warrior Takechi (Akechi) Mitsuhide, who led an unsuccessful revolt against Mashiba Hisayoshi (Toyotomi Hideyoshi) in the period of bitter warfare that preceded the founding of the Tokugawa shogunate. Hideyoshi ordered that the rebel's entire clan be exterminated, but Goemon somehow survived and was reared by a farmer in the countryside. When his foster father revealed the secret of his identity, Goemon resolved to avenge his father's death, kill Hideyoshi, and conquer Japan. To do so, he became an outlaw and was the terror of the nation before he was eventually caught and executed. In the present print, Goemon is shown in the disguise of an Imperial Messenger. He has inveigled himself into court where a hapless courtier who stood in his way is depicted in painterly Shijō style behind him.

This is from a surimono-style series of *ōban* engraved by Kasuke portraying actors in roles performed in 1833. There are at least two states of this print, the first with Kasuke's stamp, the second without. None of the prints in this series has a publisher's mark; they were either commissioned and published privately, or issued as a set with a cover. Some plates from the series have poems by the actors. This poem, printed in violet, is by Naniwa Eigan and reads: "No one has nothing to say about the cherry blossoms," alluding to Goemon's famous springtime soliloquy atop the gate at Nanzenji Temple.

44 Shigeharu

[Nakamura Utaemon III as Ishikawa Goemon]
in *Keisei Chigogafuchi* 1/1833
Catalogue 324

For the production of a play on the subject of Ishikawa Goemon in the spring of 1833, Nakamura Utaemon III, the actor who played the role of the outlaw, especially commissioned a new episode from the playwright Nishizawa Ippō. A courtesan gives birth to a child, but abandons it to his father, Kanō Shirojirō, in order to become the mistress of a wealthy lord. The father wanders through a snowy night, and the family is eventually reunited. Goemon is not mentioned in the subplot but only one baby appeared in the play. Why the bandit chief should be standing in a mountain pass at the head of his entire gang, holding the child, is unclear. The poem printed in silver at the upper left is faint and undecipherable.

This surimono-style *ōban* engraved by Kasuke is possibly from the set published in 1833, which included Plate 43. A directly related print in the Musées Royaux d'Art et d'Histoire, Brussels, shows Arashi Rikan II as Oguri Hangan (?), standing on a group of rocks printed in the same technique and colors as the cliffs in this picture, and looking down toward the left. Utaemon and Rikan were appearing at different theaters in 1833, but fictitious groupings of actors were not uncommon in Osaka prints, and the two prints may have been conceived as an oblique, diagonal diptych, Rikan's panel being placed above and to the right of the present print.

Painters of the Shijō and related schools in Osaka and Kyoto were avid designers of surimono. Their engravers and printers evolved a number of conventions and technical mannerisms to reproduce the painterly style. The conventions that were developed for the Shijō surimono were used with great effect in *ōban* portraits of actors like this and Plates 31 and 38. The Shijō-style background of the present print reveals a sense of humor seldom seen in prints of the Osaka school.

45 Hokuei

[Arashi Rikan II as Chinzei Hachirō Tametomo] and [Iwai Shijaku I as Neiwanjo] in *Shimameguri Tsuki no Yumihari* 9/1833
Catalogue 162ab

According to historical accounts, Chinzei Hachirō Tametomo, a renowned archer and warrior of the Genji clan, was born to a courtesan in 1139. By the age of fifteen he was already seven feet tall and had conquered half the castles in Kyūshū. While battling the Heike general, Kiyomori, he was captured and exiled to Ōshima, a group of islands that he subdued and set about ruling. An army was sent from the mainland to quell him once and for all, and history would have him die there in 1170. In the continuation of the tale by Takizawa Bakin, the nineteenth-century Edo novelist, Tametomo escaped from Ōshima to the Isles of Women. Later shipwrecked, he was cast ashore in Okinawa where he defended the princess of the island against usurpers, married her, brought peace, and produced a son who became king. In the present print, the castaway Tametomo has just arrived on the shore of Okinawa and is sighted by the princess of the island, Neiwanjo, who rides toward him on a water buffalo.

This performance commemorated the thirteenth anniversary of the death of Arashi Kitsusaburō I, who was known as Arashi Rikan I, or the Great Rikan [Ō-Rikan], although he never acted under that name. According to the *Ōkabuki Gedai Nenkan (see Naniwa Sōsho)*, Rikan II became ill in the middle of this performance, and the part of Tametomo was taken by Kataoka Gatō, Rikan's former pupil. Gatō later changed his name to Gadō, and became one of the leading actors of the 1840s and 1850s. This was his debut in the big theaters on the Dōtonbori.

Other impressions of this surimono-style diptych lack the stamp of the engraver Kasuke and the red stamp of Matsubaya. This was one of the last prints Hokuei designed before he changed his *gō* from Shunkōsai to Shunbaisai. It was also one of Kasuke's last prints, and is particularly interesting for the Western-style clouds appearing on the horizon.

46 Shigeharu

Nakamura Shikan II as Sōjō Henjō, Bunya no Yasuhide, Ariwara no Narihira, Kisen Hōshi, and Ōtomo no Kuronushi; and
Nakamura Baika as Ono no Komachi
in *Rokkasen Sugata no Saishiki* 1/1834
Catalogue 325

The Six Immortal Poets lived during the Heian period and included two priests (Sōjō Henjō and Kisen Hōshi), three courtiers (Bunya no Yasuhide, Ariwara no Narihira, and Ōtomo no Kuronushi), and one lady (Ono no Komachi).

The first dance play of quick changes on this theme was performed in 1789, and it remains a popular part of the kabuki repertoire today. The music for this was written and performed by Takemoto Miyoshidayū and was particularly praised at the time.

In the present version of the dance play on this theme, Narihira, Kuronushi, and the priest Henjō all fall in love with the poetess Ono no Komachi and make poetic proposals, which she refuses. Kuronushi, piqued by his rejection, accuses Komachi of plagiarism during a poetry contest and presents a forged manuscript as proof. Komachi retains her presence of mind, and washes the forged poem out of the manuscript in a tub of ceremonial sake, while Bunya no Yasuhide and the priest Kisen merrily dance. Shikan performed all five male roles in this performance and repeated them in Osaka in the spring of 1852, the last play he performed before he died.

There are at least two versions of this print: the first with the stamp of the engraver Kasuke, as here, the second lacking it. Shunbaisai Hokuei also designed a six-panel set of full-length portraits for the same performance, which are described in the following entry. The inscription gives the name of the two actors and the six roles.

小野小町　梅花
僧正遍正
文屋康秀
在原業平
喜撰法師
大伴黒主
芝翫
柳斎重春画

47 Hokuei

Nakamura Shikan II as Ariwara no Narihira,
Bunya no Yasuhide, and Kisen Hōshi,
in *Rokkasen Sugata no Saishiki* 1/1834
Catalogue 164abc

Shikan II is shown here at three successive moments of a dance of quick changes portraying three of the Six Immortal Poets described in the preceding entry. The three remaining panels show Shikan as the priest Sōjō Henjō and the courtier Ōtomo no Kuronushi, and Nakamura Baika as the poetess Ono no Komachi. The complete surimono-style hexaptych was published jointly by the three leading Osaka publishers, Tenki, Wataki, and Honsei. A single-sheet print of bust portraits of both actors in their six roles was designed by Shigeharu (Plate 46).

In the 1820s prints regularly appeared with two or more engraved marks on them. These may have been joint publications by a major publisher and a smaller or subsidiary firm, but only a few sets were published by the great Osaka print firms in collaboration, and these appeared between 1834 and 1836 only. Although the publishers' names appear on separate panels of Hokuei's hexaptych, all six sheets are uniform and were apparently engraved and printed by the same craftsmen. Another obviously expensive set of geisha in costume was published in 1836 with the names of all three publishers on each panel. Both sets may represent commercial versions of the *ōban* surimono that appeared without publisher's marks at this time.

文屋康秀
中村芝翫

在原業平
中村芝翫
本清

48 Hokuei

Nakamura Utaemon III as Komafune Hachirō, Nakamura Tomijūrō II as Okane, Arashi Rikan II as Awashima Kainosuke, Nakamura Shikan II as Amako Komawakamaru, and Iwai Shijaku I as Osamu, actually Yukari no Mae, representing a *mitate* cast for *Keisei Himehajime* or *Keisei Nazuna no Sekku* c. 1/1834
Catalogue 165a–e

The story of the Christian revolt led by Amakusa Shirō on the island of Amakusa in the late sixteenth century was often staged, and one version has been described in Plate 6. In the present version, the scene of the revolt is transferred from Kyūshū to Wakayama. The Christian rebel, Amako Komawakamaru, is using a cannon to destroy a castle commanded by Awashima Kainosuke. In earlier versions, Amako sets a wild horse loose in the courtyard of the castle to create confusion, and that scene may have been transferred here. On the verge of defeat, Awashima miraculously regains power and is able to beat off Amako's attack. The present scene is arranged like a stage-wide kabuki tableau, but may very well be a composite scene.

The play on which the print is based was not performed with this cast in 1834. It had been investigated by the government when it was performed in 1824 for its over-close similarity to a peasants' revolt in Kii Province the previous summer. In 1834, Japan was suffering a nationwide famine; discontent was widespread. Hokuei and his publisher may have been appealing to and fanning this unrest, which erupted in riots a few years later.

嵐璃寛
中村富十郎
中村歌右衛門

49 Kunimasu (signed Sadamasu)
Naniwa Tenpōzan Fūkei
("View of Tenpōzan in Osaka")
c. spring 1834
Catalogue 244a–d

The Yodo River, running down from Lake Biwa, changed its name to the Aji River and connected the harbor of Osaka with the sea. Since it had a tendency to silt, the government sponsored an immense public works project in 1832 to dredge it and prevent flooding. Townsmen organized themselves into neighborhood groups, turned out by the hundreds and thousands to help, and piled the dredged silt into a large hill at the river mouth. A lighthouse was erected, trees were planted, and the hill was named Tenpōzan, or Mount Tenpō, after the current year-period. According to Akatsuki no Kanenari, the author of one of several small books published when the dredging was finished and the mountain opened to the public, Tenpōzan was shaped like a tortoise shell in imitation of Mt. Hōrai, the abode of the Immortals. It pointed west, facing the ocean as a marker for ships entering the river, and connecting with the mainland by short bridges. Once the lighthouse was set up and trees planted, entertainers were encouraged to perform there to attract crowds whose weight would tamp down the soil. The park was well frequented, and the mountain became the subject of numerous prints: Yashima Gakutei's set of landscapes that was published in Osaka at this time, Hiroshige's view in the Edo-published *Honchō Meisho* series, and the present print, which may be the loveliest of them all. It is a view of Tenpōzan from the east, or

city side. Actors are arriving in boats where the stone landing is marked with the name "Zakoba," one of the leading actor fan clubs. Teahouses are set up, cherry blossoms are in full bloom, and Western-style clouds rise over the hilltops.

This four-panel landscape has an unusually long form of Sadamasu's signature and the publisher Tenki's address. The two red seals on the right-hand panels read Shigenao, the name of another Osaka print designer. Since they are hand-stamped apart from the signature, they may indicate that Shigenao was a printseller. Four-panel prints rarely appeared in Edo, but the format was common in Osaka. The print is often found incomplete, and the present example is mismatched because the left panel was acquired separately.

50 HOKUEI

Ichikawa Ebizō V as Inumura Daigaku Masamori and
Nakamura Tomijūrō II as
the ghost of Fusehime
in *mitate* roles for *Hakkenden* Early 1834
Catalogue 168ab

Inspired by his own translation of the Chinese novel *Sui Ho Chuan* ("All Men Are Brothers"), the novelist Takizawa Bakin labored for twenty-eight years on a fifty-three-volume epic novel entitled *Nansō Satomi Hakkenden* ("The Tale of the Eight Loyal Dogs of the House of Satomi"), which was published in parts between 1814 and 1841, illustrated by Yanagawa Shigenobu, Eisen, Sadahiro, and others. The novel was first tentatively dramatized in late 1834, and given a full production in Edo and Osaka in the spring of 1836. Many prints were published for the performance in 1836, but for unknown reasons two sets of prints by Hokuei and Shigeharu (*see also* Plate 51) appeared in the spring of 1834 showing scenes from the novel performed by fictitious (*mitate*) casts.

Bakin's story develops from the reluctant betrothal of Princess Fuse of the Satomi clan to a brave magic dog in fulfillment of a promise by her father. Shamed at becoming pregnant, she disembowels herself, and eight magic jewels scatter from her wound. The rest of the novel recounts the meetings and adventures of the human incarnations of the eight "Loyal Dogs" who sprang from the union and grew up each with a set of earthly parents and possessing a jewel and a birthmark to identify themselves to one another. Here, the ghost of Princess Fuse appears at Kōshin Mountain to help one of her sons, Inumura Daigaku, kill a magical wild cat who had disguised itself as the boy's father. The baby in her arms seems to be the child of the cat and Daigaku's terrestrial mother. The scene was not acted in the dramatization of the play in 1836.

Two other subjects from this series titled *Satomi Hakkenshi no uchi Ikko* ("One of the Eight Loyal Dogs of Satomi") by Hokuei are reproduced in Speiser (pls. 19 and 20), but no other impression of this diptych nor other plates from the set have been recorded.

51 Shigeharu

[Arashi Rikan II] as Inuzuka Shino Moritaka and [Nakamura Utaemon III] as Inukai Kenpachi Michinobu
in *mitate* roles for *Hakkenden* Early spring 1834
Catalogue 326ab

A treasure sword named Murasamemaru is entrusted to Inuzuka Shino, one of the Eight Loyal Dogs (*see* Plate 50); but it is stolen from him without his knowledge. Inugai Genpachi (written Inukai Kenpachi on this print), who is in search of the sword and realizes neither that Shino is his brother, nor that he no longer has the genuine sword, chases him to the rooftop of the Hōryūkaku Tower of Koga Castle over the Tone River and challenges him to a duel. After a spectacular battle, both slip off the roof and fall unconscious into a boat that comes loose from its moorings and carries them downstream to other meetings and adventures. The duel on the Hōryūkaku Tower was a favorite with Edo as well as Osaka artists.

According to Akatsuki no Kanenari, the Osaka writer, the first dramatization of a novel was a kabuki play entitled *Yaemusubi Jiraiya Monogatari* written by Chikamatsu Tokuzō and others after a story about the magician-thief Jiraiya by the Edo writer Kanwatei Onitake. It was performed at the Kado Theater in Osaka in the fall of 1807. The New Year's performance at both the Kado and Naka Theaters the following year was a dramatization of Santō Kyōden's novel *Inazuma Zōshi,* and from then on, the practice of dramatizing novels became established in the Osaka area. Nishizawa Ippō, the author of the stage version of *Hakkenden* performed in the spring of 1836, wrote in *Denki Sakusho Zanpen* that he began a rough draft of the play when the first five volumes of the book were published between 1814 and 1824. In the intervening years, before it was finally performed, he added to it from time to time, but until 1836 he was unable to assemble a cast that was up to performing it.

This diptych is from a series of ten surimono-style *ōban* titled *Satomike Hakkenshi no uchi Ichinin* ("One of the Eight Loyal Dogs of the House of Satomi"), which was engraved by Kasuke. There are at least two states of the print, with and without the red stamp of the engraver. A commercial version of the same scene, designed by Shunkōsai Hokuei and published by Honsei at the same date, is reproduced in Speiser (pl. 19). Aside from a series of prints sealed "Yama Ka" from around this date, Shigeharu's *Hakkenden* series seems to be the engraver Kasuke's final work.

里見家八犬士之一人
犬塚信乃戍孝
柳斎重春画
里見家八犬士之一人
犬飼見八信道
柳斎重春画

52 Shigeharu

[Nakamura Baika (?)] as a supernatural woman and [Iwai Shijaku I] as Inue Shinbei Masashi in *mitate* roles for *Hakkenden* Early spring 1834
Catalogue 327

Inue Shinbei Masashi was incarnated as the son of Nui and Fusahachi, a couple who sacrificed their own lives to save Inuzuka Shino, one of the Eight Loyal Dogs (*see* Plate 51). When Shinbei was born, his father opened the child's clenched hand and found the jewel "Benevolence." After his parents' death, Shinbei was raised by a woman with supernatural powers and later served the house of Satomi with the other "Loyal Dogs." The picture shows Shinbei as a child, growing up in the wilderness with his supernatural guardian.

Nishizawa Ippō's dramatization of *Hakkenden*, which was performed in Osaka in 1836, was in eight acts divided into two parts. The first half was performed for the New Year, and the second opened two months later. Ippō wrote: "The roles had to be assigned according to the actors' rank. Some of the actors wanted their parts rewritten to better suit their style of acting, and I had to explain that I was being as faithful as I could to Bakin's idea, and that if I rewrote their parts, the characters would be different from what the author meant them to be." Since some of the actors fell ill and one even died during the performance, Ippō found that he had to make adjustments. When Arashi Rikan II became ill, for example, the role of Fusahachi was reassigned to Kataoka Ichizō. The entire part had to be rewritten with Fusahachi as a villain, since that was the type of character Ichizō could comfortably portray. Whether due to the changes or not, the public gradually lost interest, and the March performance was poorly attended.

Another dramatization of the *Hakkenden* story was scheduled to open simultaneously in Edo, but the opening was postponed from New Year's to March. In a letter, Bakin wrote that only Onoe Kikugorō obtained the parts he wanted, and Ichikawa Ebizō was so dissatisfied that he refused to appear. Color prints that had already been printed showing Kikugorō as Keno and Princess Fuse, and Ebizō as Genpachi, had to be removed from sale, and the painted billboards advertising the Edo performance were taken down.

This print is from the set of ten surimono-style *ōban* described in Plate 51, that were engraved by Kasuke and published early in 1834, possibly the engraver's last work. Only one other impression of the print has been found, and it is the same state as this. A nearly complete set of these prints is recorded in Kuroda, *Kamigatae Ichiran,* but this plate appears never to have been included there.

重春画
里見家八犬士之一人 犬江新兵衛仁
房州行徳の任侠房八が子之幼名大八
出生して片手を開く事能ずと房八が
義死乃節初て手を開れ仁の字の玉
を出す故に名乗を仁と呼 故あつて幼
女より神女に育られ成長して武勇才
智あり後七犬士に逢侶に里見に仕ふ

53 Hokuei

[Nakamura] Baigyoku (Utaemon III) as Nyūunryū Kō Sonshō (Kung Sun Sheng),
[Nakamura] Shikan II as Kumonryū Shishin (Shin Chin),
[Nakamura] Keishi (Tomijūrō II) as Ko Sanjō Ichijōsei (I Chiao Ch'ing), and
[Arashi] Rikan II as Rōrihakuchō Chōjun (Chang Shun)
in a *mitate* cast for *Suikoden* c. 11/1835
Catalogue 176a–d

The plot of the *Suikoden* describes the adventures of a band of one hundred eight anti-government outlaws: good men in bad times. The troupe lived in an inaccessible hideout surrounded by marshes, the scene of the present print. Three of the heroes, Nine Dragons, Dragon in the Clouds, and White Stripe in the Waves (to translate the formidable names given above) have surrounded I Chiao Ch'ing, the female chief of an enemy band, and are about to capture her near their lair.

The *Suikoden,* a flamboyant translation of the great Chinese romance *Sui Ho Chuan* ("All Men Are Brothers"), was begun by Takizawa Bakin in 1805. After the appearance of the first of nine sections, Bakin disagreed with his publisher and gave up the translation, but his work was continued by Takai Ranzan. These new installments, with illustrations by Katsushika Hokusai, kept appearing in Osaka and Edo until 1828, when the translation was completed. Bits of the story of the *Suikoden* were woven into novels and plays of the period but never dramatized as a whole.

This surimono-style *mitate* tetraptych, engraved by Kumazō and an assistant, Yashichi, and printed by Toyosaburō and Tetsugorō, is one of the masterpieces of Osaka printmaking. Panels occasionally appear separately, but it is rarely found complete, as it is here. The cartouche on each print gives the name of the series, *Shibai Suikoden Hyakuhachinin no uchi* ("One Hundred Eight Heroes of the Theater Suikoden") and the role name, followed by the *haigō* (literary name) of each actor. The seal "Koshiji no ume" seems to appear only on this subject. "Koshiji" is an old name for the "Hokurikudō," or "road to the northern provinces." The character of "ume," or "plum," can also be read "bai." Susumu Matsudaira suggests that "Hoku" and "bai," which are evoked by the play on words, imply the artist's name, Shunbaisai Hokuei, as reasonable an explanation as any. The other phrased seal, "Fumoto no ume" ("Plum tree on the foothills"), written in the same style, is based on the seal of Hokuei's teacher, Shunkōsai Hokushū, which reads "Yoshinoyama." Hokushū derived his seal from Katsushika Hokusai's with the same inscription.

九紋龍史進
入雲龍公孫勝
浪裡白跳張順

54 Shigeharu

The courtesans Ei and Konami of Nakamoriken as the Emperor Shi (Kan'yō) and his concubine Kayō
c. 1836
Catalogue 338a–d

The story of the Chinese Emperor Shi and his Empress Kayō is told in the Noh play *Kan'yō Kyū* ("The Kan'yō Palace"), where the Emperor Shi is attacked by two assassins. With their swords to his chest, the Emperor begs as a last favor to hear his concubine Kayō play a piece of music on the *koto*. The assassins agree, but are lulled to sleep by the beautiful music, whereupon the Emperor is able to kill them both and save his life. In the present prints the Emperor stands on the left, crowned and holding a ceremonial drum; Kayō stands facing him, holding a branch of flowers.

This pair of diptychs, with printing variations, is titled *Shimanouchi Nerimono* ("Costumes in the Shimanouchi District"), which was published by Honsei and Tenki including prints by Sadahiro, Sadanobu, Hokuju, Hokuei, Yoshikuni, and others, showing female entertainers in costume for a parade in the Shimanouchi district of Osaka.

The official, government-controlled brothel district of Osaka was Shinmachi, but thirty or more smaller entertainment districts were scattered among the outskirts of the city in Horie, Tenma, Kitanoshinchi, Shimanouchi, and elsewhere. Shimanouchi was located just north of the Dōtonbori

Canal from the theater district, and was the largest unofficial gay quarter in Osaka. One of the annual events in Shimanouchi was a parade each June with courtesans and geisha in masquerade. The parades were banned for some time, but resumed in the summer of 1819, and were made up of large floats carrying musicians and dancers. Festival programs [*sairei banzuke*] were issued to let people know the order of the floats and what each represented. The earliest Osaka prints of the subject were designed by Yanagawa Shigenobu and published around 1822, but Edo prints, usually of large groups of figures, were designed in the 1790s and earlier by Utamaro and others for the *Niwaka* festival in the Yoshiwara district there.

These two differing impressions of each diptych were printed around the same time and represent "deluxe" and "ordinary" printings. The "regular" edition lacks certain blocks, metallic pigments, and effects of shading, and is printed with fewer and less extravagant colors than the more luxurious and expensive "deluxe" edition. The cartouche on each print is in the shape of a fan on a hanging stand. The series title is given first, followed by the geisha's role on the fan, and her name and house written beneath. The additional name, Yamamura Goto, to the right of each woman's name within the cartouche, is probably the man who conceived the idea for the costumes the women wear.

55 SADAYOSHI

Memorial portrait of Nakamura Tamasuke I (Utaemon III) by a lotus pond 7/1838
Catalogue 296

Nakamura Utaemon III was not only the most highly respected Osaka actor of his day, he was also the best loved. The *Ōkabuki Gedai Nenkan* (*see Naniwa Sōsho*) describes his funeral as follows:

> From the morning of that day a huge crowd gathered along Shimanouchi, Takatsu, and Dōtonbori to see the funeral. About two hundred theater workers in plain hemp robes and a hundred lantern bearers accompanied the gorgeous funeral procession, along with Shikan III, Tomijūrō II, Koroku, and perhaps a hundred other pupils and a hundred or so actors, including Gennosuke, Yoroku, and others. Nakamura Utaemon IV was in Edo and unfortunately unable to attend. The crowd gathered to see all the actors.

Actors and supporters, from Edo and Kyoto as well as Osaka, read poems for the occasion, and early the following year a three-volume anthology of documents, poetry and eulogistic verse, and illustrations by Shigeharu and others was published with the title *Baigyoku Yokyō* ("Baigyoku's Lingering Voice").

This *chūban* memorial portrait was one of the first prints in this format to be published in Osaka. The cartouche gives the actor's posthumous name, his death date, and the location of his tomb. His acting name is given as Tamasuke, the name Utaemon III assumed when Nakamura Shikan II became Utaemon IV two years earlier.

Memorial portraits were a common genre of Osaka printmaking. When Arashi Kitsusaburō I died in 1821 every important artist and publisher was involved in designing and issuing memorial portraits. Fifteen or more were published shortly after he died, and another six or seven appeared on the first anniversary of his death. The state of printmaking in Osaka in the aftermath of the Ōshio rebellion, when government troops were sent in to quell rioting and pacify the city, is reflected in the mere handful of memorial portraits published after the death of Utaemon III.

天保九戌年七月廿五日 行年六十一才
歌唄院宗讃日徳居士
寺ハ 高津中寺町 正法寺
俗名 中村玉助
歌川貞芳画
本清

56 SADAHIRO I

Naniwa Fūkei no uchi ("View of Naniwa")
Caulking a ship at the mouth of the Aji River
c. late 1830s
Catalogue 278

The Yodo River flows some forty miles from Lake Biwa to the sea, changing its name several times during its course. Between Osaka and the sea it becomes the Aji River. In this view Sadahiro has ignored Tenpōzan, the man-made mountain that was constructed at the mouth of the Aji in 1832 during a dredging operation, and an enormous lighthouse that was built at the same time (*see* Plate 49). The horizontal format and the Shijō style of the figures particularly recall certain plates of the "Sixty-nine Stations of the Kisokaidō" designed by the Edo artists Andō Hiroshige and Keisai Eisen, and published there in the mid-1830s.

This series of views of Osaka was designed after Sadahiro's return from Edo in 1835, and published by Tenki, whose mark appears on the high stern of the boat. Sadahiro's earliest signature, in 1830, was rather square and blocky. After his return from Edo it became more wiry and drawn out, as here. Just before the Tenpō Reforms it became even more free; on the few prints signed Sadahiro that appeared in the late 1840s, his signature was compact and much abbreviated.

浪華風景
之内
安治川口
貞廣画

57 Kunimasu

Nakayama Yoshio III as the courtesan Okon and Kataoka Gadō II as Fukuoka Mitsugi in *Iseondo Koi no Netaba* 5/1841
Catalogue 247

In 1796 Osaka was shocked by the behavior of a doctor who ran amok as he left a brothel, killing two passersby and wounding seven others. The incident was immediately dramatized with the doctor cast as Fukuoka Mitsugi, a subject of the lord of Awa, in search of a lost sword. Mitsugi's search leads him to the courtesan Okon whose patron, he feels sure, possesses the sword. The two men become rivals for Okon, who, trying to help Mitsugi, pretends to side with the villain. Mitsugi feels thwarted and goes berserk, killing everyone in sight in his frenzy. When the lost sword is finally recovered Mitsugi is ordered to commit suicide, but he cuts too shallowly, is revived, and lives happily ever after.

After the death of Nakamura Utaemon III and the departure of Utaemon IV to Edo, following a wage dispute with the theater managers in 1838, a new generation of actors appeared on stage and in prints. Kataoka Gadō II was adopted by Kataoka Nizaemon VII in 1832 and first appeared in the Dōtonbori theaters in 1837. He was short, but handsome, with a clean style of acting that brought him immediate popularity. When he returned to Osaka in 1862 after an eight-year stay in Edo, however, audiences regarded his acting as too Edo-ized for their taste. Between the time he assumed the name Gadō in 1838 and his departure for Edo in 1854, he appeared frequently in prints.

When Nakamura Tomijūrō II was banished from Osaka in 1842, Nakayama Yoshio took the name Nanshi and became the leading actor of female roles in Osaka. He was unattractive, but so skillful an actor and dancer that his homeliness went unnoticed. He performed particularly well the roles of maidens, princesses, and women in love, and exercised such elegant taste in the choice of his costumes that he tended to eclipse other actors who appeared with him on stage.

This print is from a series of horizontal double half-length portraits in *chūban* format.

福岡貢
我童
貞升画

58 SADANOBU I

Onoe Kikugorō III as Yoshida Matsuwakamaru and Nakamura Tomijūrō II as Hanako, later the nun Seigen
in *Kagamiyama Gonichi no Omokage* 3/1842
Catalogue 286ab

A series of plays was based on the passionate and degrading love of the priest Seigen for Princess Sakura, which lasts even after the monk is defrocked, dies, and becomes a ghost. The present variation on the theme, by Tsuruya Nanboku IV, reverses the story by casting Seigen as a nun. When she discovers that her younger sister's husband is her own supposed-dead fiancé, she pays a visit in disguise and, consumed with jealousy, attempts to kill her sister. The sister escapes and the nun is ravished and killed by a kidnapper. In the present scene the nun Seigen, in disguise, is visiting Matsuwakamaru, her former betrothed.

The portions of the Tenpō Reform Laws that restricted theater performances and banned the sale and production of actor prints were announced in the seventh month of 1842. This yellow-ground *ōban* diptych was one of the last prints to be published before the ban. The edicts were so strictly enforced that no actor prints of any type were published in Osaka for a full five years, between the fifth month of 1842 and about the fifth month of 1847. *Kabuki Nenpyō* mentions that two men convicted of selling actor prints during this period for two and four *mon* a sheet were fined ten thousand *mon* apiece as examples. The extremely low price of these prints suggests that the men were selling stenciled prints or *banzuke,* not full-color prints, which had been thoroughly curtailed.

Nakamura Tomijūrō II, the leading actor of female roles in Osaka at this time, was at the height of his popularity and on the verge of retirement in 1842 when the Tenpō Reforms were promulgated. His luxurious standard of living brought him under government surveillance so that in 1843 he was convicted of violations of the new sumptuary laws and banished from Osaka for life. For several years he acted in Kyoto and neighboring towns, hoping and expecting to be recalled; but the government remained firm, and in 1855 Tomijūrō died in exile.

中村富十郎
尾上菊五郎
長谷川貞信画
長谷川貞信画

59 Sadanobu I

Ranpyō Ongyoku-musha Hanagassen no Zu
("A Rough List of the Warriors in the Great Music Battle") 1848
Catalogue 293

According to Jokaku, the author of the inscription on a handscroll titled "The height of the flower, the tip of the nose," the Osaka legions of amateur chanters of *jōruri* decided to gather their ranks on Mount Kurama, northeast of Kyoto, to fight out among themselves who had best mastered the "flower" of their art, and had the right to "look down their nose." The upper half of this print gives the names of Osaka singers by district, using their crests as a decorative background. On the lower half, the opposing armies are ranged under their district banners. Among the admonitions to the combatants is an injunction against spears on the battlefield. The title is given in bold letters at the right of the print.

Sadanobu's two passionate interests, besides his work, seem to have been tea-drinking and *jōruri,* so it is entirely appropriate that he was chosen to illustrate the present print. *Jōruri* was the chanted accompaniment of puppet plays as well as some forms of kabuki. Sadanobu's amateur performing name was Rankō, perhaps the very Rankō that appears in the Uemachi section in the list of names, even though it is written with one different character, and Sadanobu was living at that time in Andōjimachi, on the opposite side of the East Canal from Uemachi.

This double *ōban* was printed on a single sheet, engraved by Uchida Torazō, and published by Iida, whose name also appears as a printer at this time.

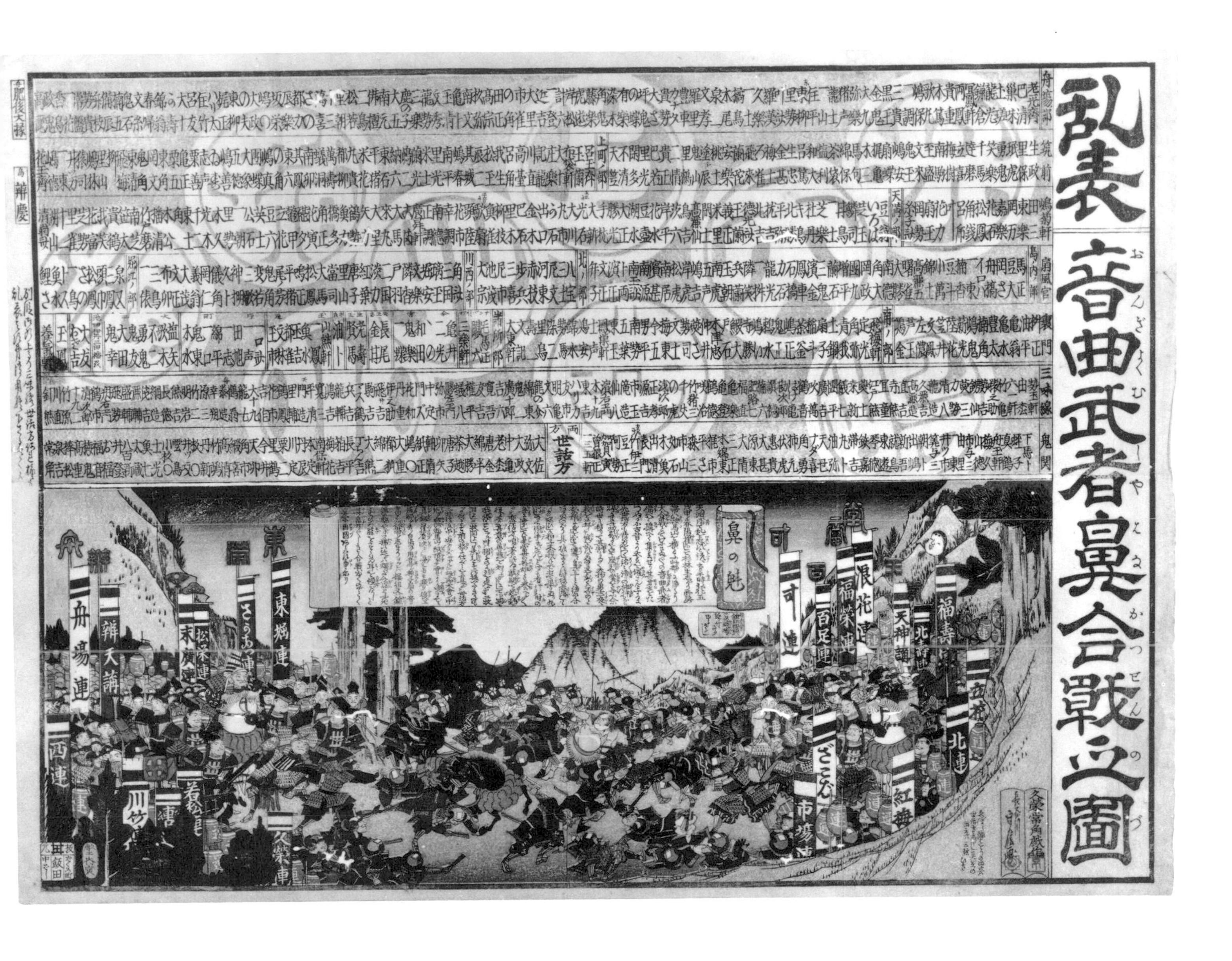
乱表 音曲武者㒵合戦立圖

60 Hirosada

[Nakamura Shikan III (?)] as Mashiba Hisayoshi in a play from the *Taikōki* cycle c. early 1847
Catalogue 33

Hashiba (or Toyotomi) Hideyoshi (1536-1598) unified Japan after a period of disruptive civil wars, and built Osaka Castle. His life was the subject of an entire cycle of plays; but because the government forbade the dramatization of recent historical events, his name on stage was changed to Mashiba Hisayoshi. In this print he is shown seated, wearing his general's regalia with his crest prominently displayed on one arm, a horned device over his courtier's cap, and his tasseled staff fluttering—perhaps in a confrontation with the rebel Akechi Mitsuhide, or some other villain.

Two plays were performed about Hisayoshi in the spring of 1847, in which his role was taken by Jitsukawa Ensaburō and Arashi Kichisaburō III. The portrait, however, seems more like that of Nakamura Shikan III, an adopted son of Utaemon III, who died later in the year. The *Kabuki Nenpyō* does not record Shikan in the role, so this may be a *mitate*, or a portrait of Kichisaburō III.

The format of bust portraits in medallions with floral backgrounds seems to have derived from "ceiling curtains" [*tenjōmaku*], a continuous series of portraits on cloth painted for presentation to actors. Prints in this format were designed by Hokuei and Sadanobu before 1842. A triptych of one of the painted strips being admired by actors was designed by Kunisada.

This print is from such a series, titled *Kōmei Buyūden* ("Tales of Brave Warriors of Renown"), portraying actors in roles played as early as 2/1847, but published later in the year. The background of each print is decorated with a different flower. Two bands of stylized clouds are printed beside the title and role cartouches above. The design for this print was reused by Hirosada for a yellow-ground *chūban* bust portrait (Plate 66). Another subject from the series is also in the collection (Cat. 32). These were among the first actor prints published after the proclamation of the Tenpō Reforms in 1842 and the severe curtailment of actor portraiture.

高名武勇傳
真柴久義
廣貞

61 Kunimasu

[Arashi Rikan III] as [Ono no] Tōfū and
[Kataoka Ichizō I] as Daroku
in *Ono no Tōfū Aoyagi Suzuri* 7/1848
Catalogue 249ab

The picture of Ono no Tōfū, the great calligrapher of the Heian period, watching a frog jumping time after time at a willow branch, has been a favorite subject of Japanese art as a symbol of perseverance. Tōfū's life is also the subject of a popular play in which, as the impoverished and illiterate son of a scholar, he works as a palace carpenter. In the play, the sight of the frog jumping for the willow branch reveals to Tōfū that Tachibana no Hayanari, a courtier, is plotting to usurp the throne. At that moment of revelation, Daroku, a carpenter for the usurper, rushes out to challenge Tōfū, hoping to draw him into the intrigue. Somehow, Tōfū miraculously gains the power to read and write, and Daroku reveals that he is the disinherited son of the poet Bunya no Yasuhide. The two of them join forces to defeat the would-be usurper.

道風
國升画

62 Hirosada

[Arashi Rikaku II] as a *harugoma* dancer,
[Nakamura Tamashichi] as a *manzai* singer, and
[Sawamura Kitō] as a *harugoma* dancer
in *Aratamaru Oshika Omoiba* 1/1849
Catalogue 53abc

It was believed in certain parts of Japan that a white horse could draw away evil, and during New Year's festivities dancers went from house to house dancing with toy horses' heads. The "spring pony" [*harugoma*] dance was adopted into the kabuki repertoire in the 1680s and often appeared in series of quick changes. In the 1790s the dance began to be woven into the Soga revenge plays traditionally performed at New Year's. Here the two pony dancers are accompanied by a *manzai* singer, another New Year's tradition.

Nakamura Tamashichi was the twelve-year-old son of Nakamura Shikan III who had died in 1847 at the age of thirty-eight. Sawamura Kitō, a homely but accomplished actor of female roles, died later in 1849.

This *chūban* triptych has seals following Hirosada's signatures that are usually associated with the red hand-stamp of the publisher Kinkadō (Tenki). The poem on the center panel reads: "We beg our fans to patronize us through the years."

63 Hirosada

[Nakamura Gizaemon] as Horiguchi Gentazaemon and
[Kataoka Gadō II] as Tamiya Genpachi
in *Osanago no Adauchi* 3/1849
Catalogue 68ab

The title of the play could be understood as "A Child's Revenge." It is based on a vendetta carried out by a youth named Tamiya Bōtarō in 1641. In the actual story, Bōtarō's father, Tamiya Genpachirō, was a swordsman serving the lord of Sanuki. Hori Gentazaemon, a former fencing instructor serving the same lord, was so mortally afraid of Genpachirō's skill that he killed him by a ruse. Bōtarō was born a few months after the murder and was raised with the sole aim of avenging his father's death, which he eventually accomplished at the age of eighteen. In the play the names of the protagonists were changed, as usual. The present subject shows Hori murdering Bōtarō's father. Another diptych by Hirosada, also in the Museum collection (Cat. 67ab), shows an earlier scene, of the men dueling with wooden practice swords.

From 1847 until the spring of 1849, in deference to the unrepealed reform edicts of 1842, a fiction was maintained that all actor portraits were either symbolic or idealized figures. Each print carried a cartouche with an edifying title like "Tales of the Loyal, Filial, Bold, and Brave" [*Chūkō Buyūden*]. In the spring of 1849 Osaka publishers decided this was unnecessary, and *chūban* bust portraits appeared without title cartouches from that time on. Cartouches were still used for some full-figure *chūban* that were published as sets. Polyptychs, from the early 1850s on, tended to have a cartouche with the title and the act of the play on their rightmost panel.

64 Kunishige

[Jitsukawa Ensaburō] as Hata no Kawakatsu
in *Shitennōji Garan Kagami* 3/1849
Catalogue 251

This play was originally written by Namiki Shōzō and first performed in 1758. The scene is set in the seventh century. Moriya Daijin, a powerful courtier, finding Prince Shōtoku too much of an obstacle to his plans for usurping the throne, blames him for the loss of the Three Imperial Treasures and has him exiled. Moriya's forces, led by Hata no Kawakatsu, win a battle against the prince's army. The defeated general, Imoko, entrusts two of the recovered Treasures to Kawakatsu, his son-in-law. Tragic deaths intervene, but in the end Moriya is defeated and peace is restored. The present print shows the young general, Kawakatsu, in his battle regalia.

Since publishers at this time could not risk putting the names of actors on their prints, artists were encouraged to introduce the actor's crest and personal devices into the decorative patterns of the design. Here, Ensaburō's crest of interlacing *aoi* leaves is used as a badge on his breastplate and headpiece. In other cases, the crests are as ingeniously devised and concealed as the date marks on calendar prints.

秦氏川勝
國重

65 Hirosada

[Ichikawa Ebizō V] as Nippon Daemon and
[Mimasu Daigorō IV] as Tsukimoto Enshū
in *Akiba Gongen Kaisen Banashi* 5/1849
Catalogue 71ab

Nippon Daemon was the leader of a gang of robbers who managed to steal a manuscript of the *Kokinshū* poetry anthology, a family treasure of the Tsukimoto clan. This was to be the first step toward displacing Enshū, the young clan heir, and taking over the household. In the present scene Daemon has disguised himself as a messenger of the shogun and orders Enshū to commit suicide to atone for the disgrace of losing the treasure. Enshū sees through his disguise, but the house is already surrounded by the soldiers of his treacherous uncle, Yūmei; Enshū is killed. Later, the treasure is recovered by a woman who defects from the Daemon camp and a loyal Tsukimoto clan retainer, who is killed by Daemon. The retainer is resurrected by a miracle of the Akiba Shrine, and lives on to overthrow the wicked band and restore the household.

Ichikawa Ebizō V was exiled from Edo in 1842 for violation of the sumptuary laws of the Tenpō Reforms. Undismayed, he traveled to Osaka, and in the absence of Nakamura Utaemon IV, who was then acting in Edo, he easily dominated the stage until his recall to Edo in early 1850. His crest showed the three concentric squares of the Ichikawa clan, while his personal device was a peony, both of which are worked into the design of the picture. Judging from his portraits, Mimasu Daigorō IV was one of the most handsome actors of his day, but very little is known about his life and personality.

6 HIROSADA and SADAHIRO

[Jitsukawa Ensaburō] as Mashiba Hisayoshi
by Hirosada and
[Jitsukawa Ensaburō] as Konoshita Tōkichi
by Sadahiro
in *Ehon Taikōki* 5/1849
Catalogue 73, 276

The *Taikōki* plays deal with the life of Toyotomi Hideyoshi: his boyhood as the son of a low-ranking samurai, his service under Oda Nobunaga, his rise to power, wars, invasion of Korea, and his eventual unification of Japan. Here in the left panel, he is shown as Konoshita Tōkichi (his pseudonym), and in the right as a general in full regalia.

Jitsukawa Ensaburō was a pupil and adopted son of Jitsukawa Gakujūrō I. He was considered handsome and acted in the grand manner. He suffered from an eye illness throughout his career, but during the 1840s and 1850s rivaled Kataoka Gadō II as the leading male actor of the Osaka stage. In 1865 he took the name Gakujūrō II, but died two years later at the age of fifty-four, on the eve of the Meiji Restoration.

This is either a diptych or two panels of a polyptych. The figure in the right panel of this triptych is shown in the same pose as the subject of a Hirosada *ōban* bust portrait of 1847 (Plate 60). Ensaburō did perform the role of Hisayoshi in 3/1847, but the present print lacks a cartouche so it cannot be earlier than the spring of 1849. The two prints are particularly interesting as evidence that Sadahiro and Hirosada were one and the same person. The style of the two prints is identical; the signatures are the same with their characters reversed, although there is no explanation why they should appear concurrently on the same polyptych. Further evidence suggesting that Sadahiro and Hirosada were the same person is presented in the Catalogue.

67 MASUHARU

[Jitsukawa Ensaburō] as [Kizu] Kansuke
in *Kizugawa Hakkei* 8/1849
Catalogue 260

Kizu Kansuke, a young hero, is a frequent subject of Osaka actor prints, but it has been impossible to locate an account of plays in which he appears.

An artistic style reaches its height in Japanese prints when there is a balance of innovation and convention between the designers and craftsmen involved: when both the engraver and the printer are sure of their techniques, but before they have gone stale and lapsed into mannerisms. In the early 1850s this point was reached; and the most ordinary amateur designs could be transformed into prints of great strength and beauty. But when technique is responsible for art, a certain amount of individuality is lost. Many of the *chūban* portraits by minor artists in this period are in recognizably different styles; but others, like this one by Masuharu, could easily be mistaken, without a signature, for another work by Hirosada.

This is possibly one panel of a polyptych. A trimmed impression, in the Hloucha collection, is reproduced in Hajek (pl. 23), with the role misidentified as a *komusō*.

68 Attributed to Hirosada

Illustrations of scenes from *Kanadehon Chūshingura* c. 1849
Catalogue 82-86, 136 (9-20)

The collection contains ninety-four unsigned drawings in color of actors in role, including eighty-eight bust portraits and six full-length figures, all in *chūban* format on thin paper, mostly related to published prints by Hirosada, Sadanobu, and Kunimasu for performances between 1847 and 1849, mounted in two albums with unlabeled paper covers. The thirty-six bust portraits reproduced here illustrate acts of the play *Chūshingura.* Most of them portray actors in a performance of the play given at the Chikugo Theater in the ninth month of 1849.

Descriptions of Japanese printmaking generally suggest that the designer produced a finished drawing called a "block-copy" [*hanshitae*], which an engraver pasted face-down on his block and destroyed as he cut through it to carve the key block. There is increasing evidence that even if this was general practice it was not invariably so. In many cases, the artist supplied only a rough sketch, and other intermediary artists seem to have transformed these sketches into finished drawings suitable for guiding the block cutter. A list of artists published around 1830 (*see* Appendix XI) shows that just such a class, called "block-copyists" [*hanshita o omo to su*], did exist. Some of these designed prints in their own names, but others are not known to have created original work.

A careful comparison between the album drawings and related prints in the Museum collection and elsewhere makes it clear that the present drawings are not tracings, or copies of prints; quite the contrary, these album portraits are invariably better drawn than their published versions. Nor do the drawings seem to be a print-related presentation set, lacking as they do, finish, signatures, and seals.

Since the drawings appear to precede the prints to which they relate, and since there was a class of copyists in Osaka who could produce block drawings without destroying the original designs, it is perhaps not unreasonable to conjecture that these are preliminary drawings by Hirosada, the artist whose name appears on the vast majority of the published prints. Unfortunately there are no other signed or attributed Hirosada drawings that would allow a comparison; in fact there seem to be no similar albums extant by any other Japanese print artist.

Sadanobu's relation to these albums is discussed in the entry for Plate 69.

Act 1

Kataoka Gadō II as Wakasanosuke,
Nakamura Daikichi III as Lady Kaoyo, and
Mimasu Daigorō IV as Kō no Moronō

In the prologue to the *Chūshingura,* Lady Kaoyo, Enya's wife, is brought to Kamakura to identify a helmet. Moronō propositions her; Wakasanosuke overhears them and becomes enraged.

Related published prints numbered 1, 2, and 4 are in the Ikeda Library. Plate 3 of the tetraptych should be a portrait of Ichikawa Shikō as Enya Hangan with title cartouche.

See Cat. 136 (9abc).

Act 2

Kataoka Gadō II as Wakasanosuke and
Kataoka Ichizō I as Kakogawa Honzō

Rather than bribe Moronō, Wakasanosuke resolves to kill him if provoked. Honzō, his steward, lops off a pine branch to show his agreement, but rushes off to try to bribe Moronō personally and avert disaster for the clan.

Ichizō acted Honzō in 1848, but no print of this subject has been located.

See Cat. 82, 136 (10ab).

Act 3

Nakamura Tomozō IV as Bannai,
Kataoka Gadō II as Hayano Kanpei, and
Sawamura Kitō as Okaru

Enya, unrestrained by his attendant Kanpei, who has been making love to Okaru, receives the brunt of Moronō's wrath and is provoked into attacking him. Hearing the commotion, Okaru and Kanpei are surrounded by Moronō's men, led by the comic figure Bannai, whom they defeat and then flee.

The print of the right panel was apparently reissued as the right panel of a diptych for an 1851 performance of a similar play, with the role altered to Shichidayū (in the Ikeda Library).

See Cat. 83, 136 (11abc).

Act 4, Scene 1

Arashi Kichisaburō III as Ishidō

The penalty for drawing a sword in the shogun's palace is death and confiscation. Two government officials are sent to supervise Enya's suicide.

At least one drawing for this scene, of Enya in ceremonial robes, is missing from the album.

See Cat. 136 (19a).

[Act 4, Scene 2]

[Kataoka Gadō II as Ōboshi Yuranosuke]

Yuranosuke, Enya's chamberlain, rushes to Kamakura, arriving as Enya commits suicide. Taking his master's dirk, he soliloquizes outside the palace gates and vows revenge.

No drawings for this scene are included in the album, but two prints, one a bust portrait, one full length, are in the Ikeda Library.

Act 5

Mimasu Daigorō IV as Ono no Sadakurō

Sadakurō, a renegade samurai, meets Kanpei's father-in-law in a rainstorm and kills and robs him. Kanpei, who is boar-hunting, kills Sadakurō and finds the money.

One drawing is lacking in the album, but prints of both panels of this diptych, the other showing Nakamura Tomozō IV as Yoichibei, are in the Ikeda Library.

See Cat. 136 (12a).

Act 6

Kataoka Gadō II as Hayano Kanpei and
Ichikawa Shikō as Senzaki Yagorō

Returning home, Kanpei believes he has killed his father-in-law and commits suicide in remorse. Before he dies, he learns the truth and is allowed to place his name on the list of avengers.

No prints of either subject are known.

See Cat. 136 (13ab).

Act 7

Kataoka Gadō II as Ōboshi Yuranosuke and
Mimasu Tanin as Ōboshi Rikiya

Yuranosuke leaves home and leads a dissolute life in a Kyoto teahouse to avoid suspicion. Rikiya, his son, brings him a letter from Enya's widow and stealthily hands it over the gate.

See Cat. 84ab, 136 (14ab).

Act 8

Nakamura Daikichi III as Tonase and
Mimasu Gennosuke II (?) as Konami

Honzō's daughter, Konami, was betrothed to Yuranosuke's son Rikiya. She and her mother, Tonase, set off to Rikiya's home to learn why he has broken off their engagement.

Gennosuke acted the role of Konami in 1849, but the identification is tentative.

See Cat. 85, 136 (15ab).

Act 9

Mimasu Daigorō IV as Kakogawa Honzō and
Sawamura Kitō as Oishi

Honzō feels responsible for his part in Enya's misfortune. He takes the tonsure and travels to Yuranosuke's country home, arriving in time to prevent Tonase from killing Konami in desperation over her broken engagement with Rikiya.

See Cat. 86ab, 136 (16ab).

Act 10

Nakamura Tomozō IV as Igo,
Kataoka Ichizō I as Fuwa Kazuemon (?), and
an unidentified actor as Yazama Jūtarō (?)

The *Rōnin* entrust the Osaka merchant Amagawaya Gihei with the task of gathering and sending weapons and armor to Edo. Two *Rōnin* visit Gihei before they leave and are met at the door by his half-witted apprentice, Igo. A print of Tomozō exists; none are known for the other two panels. Ichizō did not act in the 1849 performance.

See Cat. 136 (17abc).

Act 11, Scene 1

Ichikawa Shikō as Katō Yomoshichi,
Kataoka Gadō II as Ōboshi Yuranosuke,
Nakamura Tamashichi as Nakashiba Yoshinojō (?), and
Kataoka Ichizō I as Teraoka Heiemon

The *Rōnin,* dressed in special uniforms, attack Moronō's mansion at night. Gadō is holding a lantern, the others their weapons.

A pentaptych of this subject for a similar performance in 1848 is in the Ikeda Library, with Ebizō as Yuranosuke, Ensaburō as Ōtaka Gengo, Daigorō as Yazama Jūtarō; Tamashichi is missing.

See Cat. 136 (20a–d).

Act 11, Scene 2

Kataoka Gadō II as Ōboshi Yuranosuke

After the successful attack, the *Rōnin* retire to a nearby temple where they burn incense to their master's memory and await the government's sentence of death.

No prints of this subject are known. The album possibly lacks other panels.

See Cat. 136 (19b).

Unidentified Scene

Jitsukawa Ensaburō as Gorōta (?)
Nakayama Nanshi II as Okumi (?)

In an 1848 performance of a version of *Chūshingura,* Ensaburō plays the role of Kanpei disguised as a stonemason who asks a member of Moronō's household to obtain a plan of the mansion.

No prints of this subject are known. Ensaburō did not appear in the 1849 performance.

See Cat. 136 (18ab).

Unidentified Scene

An actor of the Sawamura family as Konami (?)

The cartouche of the *Chūshingura* series is displayed here, but no published print of this subject is known. It is bound beside the portrait of Sadakurō (Act 5) in the album and is possibly out of sequence.

See Cat. 136 (12b).

69 Sadanobu I

[Nakayama Nanshi II] as Miyuki,
[Kataoka Ichizō I] as Akizuki Yuminosuke, and
[Jitsukawa Ensaburō] as Miyagi Asojirō
in *Shōutsushi Asagao Banashi* 5/1848
Catalogue 288abc, 136 (4abc)

Miyagi Asojirō, the hero of this story, is in love with Miyuki, the daughter of Akizuki Yuminosuke. Because of a disputed succession in his household, Asojirō is forced to leave Miyuki, but sends her a marriage offer under an assumed name. Desperately in love with Asojirō, Miyuki flees from her home to avoid marrying the assumed stranger. On the verge of drowning herself, she is seized by a wicked old woman. After Miyuki goes blind, the hag releases her; later, traveling as a street singer, she encounters Asojirō. Neither recognizes the other, but Asojirō leaves her money and medicine. After his departure, Miyuki realizes that the kind man had been Asojirō. Despairing, she is upon the point of suicide when she is rescued, regains her sight, and is happily united with Asojirō, who has successfully settled the inheritance in the meantime. In this scene, Asojirō is saying good-bye to Miyuki and her father as he sets off for home.

The prints in this *chūban* triptych, titled *Giyūden* ("A Tale of Loyalty and Valor"), are based on three drawings in the album attributed to Hirosada described in the previous entry. Title cartouches have been added in the published version, the costumes of the actors have been changed, and the design of the left panel significantly altered. The crest of each actor appears as a decorative device in the cartouche of each panel as well as in their costumes: a ginkgo leaf for Ichizō, a curly leaf for Ensaburō, and paulownia for Nanshi.

Since Sadanobu copied Hiroshige bird-and-flower prints and landscapes in full as well as reduced format he has earned himself a reputation among Western collectors for being a shameless plagiarist. With the present triptych the question of plagiarism naturally arises. However, there are no Hirosada prints of these subjects, and since Sadanobu and Hirosada had a close personal relationship, it seems probable that these and certain other finished prints are based on Hirosada's designs and that Hirosada countenanced the proceedings.

義勇傳
秋月弓之助

70 Hirosada

[Nakamura Utaemon IV] as Danshichi Kurobei in *Yadonashi Danshichi Shigure no Karakasa*
5/1851
Catalogue 109

Danshichi Kurobei, a samurai, has disguised himself as a fishseller to facilitate the search for a precious sword that was once in his custody. He regains the sword with the help of a bathhouse owner, Jisuke, but the certificate that must accompany it remains in the hands of Kazuemon, a rival suitor for a bathhouse attendant, Tomi. Jisuke promises Kazuemon that Danshichi will give up Tomi in exchange for the certificate, and feigns coldness to Danshichi to gain Kazuemon's confidence. The strategem works, and Jisuke recovers the certificate, but before he can explain his pretended hostility to Danshichi, the latter kills him, enraged by his seeming disloyalty. Realizing, too late, that Jisuke had been helping him all along, Danshichi commits suicide in atonement.

In the present scene, Danshichi has just murdered Jisuke beside a well. It is a hot summer night, and sounds of a festival procession reach him from the other side of the melon patch as he douses himself with water. Utaemon actually used water on stage in this scene and this may be one reason why he was criticized for his "over-realism" (*see* below). The tattoo on his body was an innovation to the role. There is a printed program for this performance showing Danshichi stabbing Jisuke and a character named Kyūshichi in the darkness beside the well.

Nakamura Utaemon IV, who left Osaka in 1838 after a wage dispute, returned triumphantly in 1850. The tone of theatrical criticism and the height of Utaemon's acclaim at this time can be judged from a two-page broadside titled "Short Criticisms of Nakamura Utaemon" [*Nakamura Utaemon Ryaku Hyōban*], which was published in 1852 shortly after the actor's unexpected death. Discussing this play, the unnamed author wrote:

> GREAT
> TIPTOP
> SUPER
>
> *Danshichi Kurobei*: A great hit when he performed it last year at the Kado Theater. The stage sets were fine and it was a great success. But *why* was Master Utaemon so over-realistic in domestic plays? Well, at any rate, the performance played to full houses just on the strength of his personality. Very, very great!

This *chūban* diptych has a red hand-stamped seal of the publisher or retailer, Meikōdō. The title of the print, *Natsumatsuri Chūkōden* ("The Summer Festival: A Tale of Loyalty and Filial Piety"), is a curious combination of the popular title of the play, "The Summer Festival," with the edifying fictitious titles that were added to prints between 1847 and early 1849 to avoid the suspicion that they were actor portraits.

71 HIROSADA

[Mimasu Daigorō IV] as Umeōmaru,
[Nakamura Utaemon IV] as Matsuōmaru, and
[Jitsukawa Ensaburō] as Sakuramaru
in *Sugawara Denju Tenarai Kagami* 9/1851
Catalogue 113abc

The play of *Sugawara Denju* is the skillful interweaving of the semi-historical tale of the eighth-century courtier Sugawara no Michizane, who was exiled from Kyoto to Kyūshū for his part in opposing Fujiwara Shihei, a would-be usurper of the Crown. It is also the story of three brothers with divided loyalties in the service of different lords. The "Carriage-stopping" scene is one of the most brilliant in the kabuki repertoire and is still frequently performed. Two younger brothers, Umeōmaru and Sakuramaru, wearing costumes emblazoned with their symbols of plum and cherry, serve Sugawara and the Crown Prince. They wait at the Yoshida Shrine in Kyoto to ambush Shihei, the usurper, but are intercepted by his bodyguard, Matsuōmaru, their brother. As the brothers come to blows, Shihei appears from his shattered carriage and paralyzes them all with his presence. The present scene shows the tense moment just before Shihei's appearance, with his great carriage standing in the background.

Nearly all the actor prints published in Osaka in the late 1840s were *chūban* bust portraits with margins and printed borders. In 1849 some full-figure *chūban* were printed, and in the early 1850s they were published in large numbers, usually printed to the edges of the sheet. Role names were written across the entire top of prints from 1847 to 1849, but in the spring of 1850 they began to be written on small, neat, red cartouches, a practice that lasted until the end of the century.

This *chūban* triptych is from a series of polyptychs illustrating the entire play of *Sugawara Denju*. There are two editions: with the red stamp of Daijin, as here, and without; but no state differences are recorded. Other plates from the series bear different seals.

72 Hirosada

[Nakamura Utaemon IV] as Kiichi Hōgen and
[Mimasu Daigorō IV] as Chienai
in *Kiichi Hōgen Sanryaku no Maki* 11/1851
Catalogue 115ab

The play is taken from the medieval *Life of Yoshitsune.* Kiichi Hōgen, the master-strategist of the Heike clan, possesses a priceless set of scrolls of military secrets. Yoshitsune and his young retainer decide to steal these, and enter Kiichi's household disguised as gardeners. Kiichi sees through their disguises, and when they confront him one night by moonlight in his chrysanthemum garden, he explains to them that although in service to the Heike he sides with the Genji and actually taught Yoshitsune fencing on Mount Kurama, disguised as a *tengu.* He presents the treasured scrolls to his daughter, betroths her to Yoshitsune, and commits suicide to prove his fundamental loyalty to the Heike. In the present scene, Yoshitsune's retainer Chienai refuses to obey Kiichi's order to strike his young master.

This is a *chūban* diptych from an album of prints, mainly portraits of Nakamura Utaemon IV, published between 1850 and 1852, and apparently collected and bound at that time with a manuscript title, "The Fragrance of Flowers in the Pear Orchard" [*Rien Kōhō*], on the cover. "Pear Orchard" was a Chinese expression for the theater, and the title can be taken to mean "Beauties of the Stage," meaning portraits of actors. The album is complete in the Museum collection (*see* Catalogue 92, 98, 108, 110–12, 115–20, 122–24, and 291).

鬼一法眼

73 Hirosada and Sadanobu I

Memorial portrait of [Nakamura Utaemon IV]
by Hirosada 2/1852
Memorial portrait of Nakamura Utaemon IV
by Sadanobu 2/1852
Catalogue 122, 291

The print by Hirosada shows Utaemon in formal death robes and includes his farewell poem: "Returning geese, if you are going to the country of the west, please take me with you." Migrant geese often appear in memorial or farewell poems. The country of the west is Amida Buddha's Western Paradise.

In contrast to Hirosada's serious portrait, Sadanobu chose a *mitate* subject. The print is designed in imitation of a hanging scroll depicting the death of the Buddha, with Utaemon reclining on the couch in the center, surrounded by actors, fans, and other admirers.

Nakamura Utaemon IV's unexpected death in early 1852 was mourned as grievously as Utaemon III's had been fourteen years earlier. Memorial portraits were published in Edo as well as Osaka, and a special commemorative album, the *Kanjaku Tsuizen Hanashidori* with prints, sketches, and poems from friends and admirers all over Japan, was published in Edo later in the year. His death marked the end of an era in Osaka prints.

These two prints were published separately, but bound together by a contemporary collector in the *Rien Kōhō* album (*see* Plate 72). Hirosada's portrait resembles his one known signed painting, a formal seated portrait of Utaemon IV, still owned by the actor's family and exhibited at the Kabukiza in Tokyo in 1967 during the special performances marking Nakamura Fukusuke's name-change to Shikan VII.

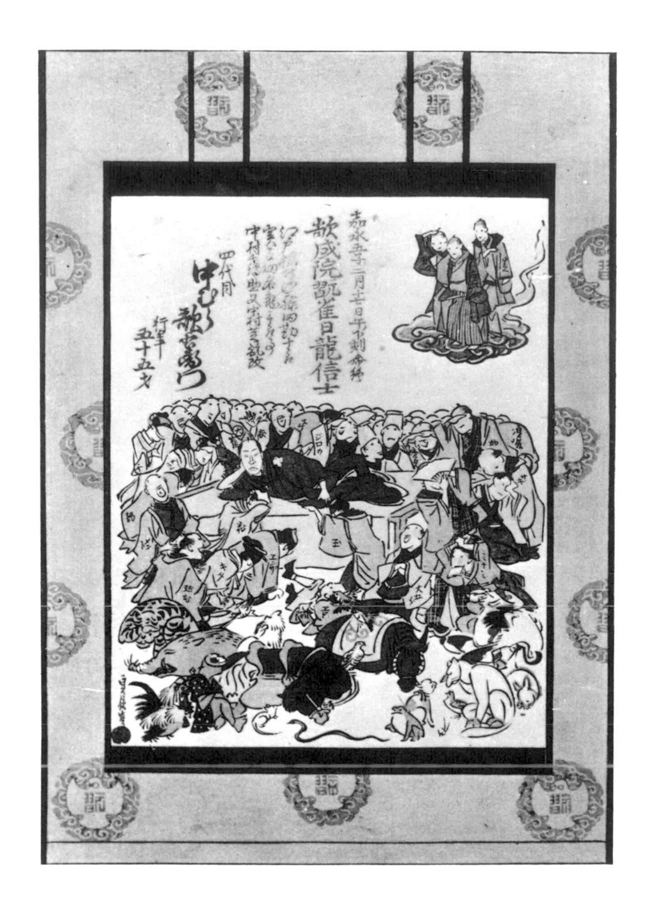

74 Yoshitoyo

[Jitsukawa Ensaburō] as Ishii Hyōsuke and
[Arashi Rikaku II] as Ishii Genzō
in *Katakiuchi Ukiki no Kameyama* 8/1855
Catalogue 429ab

In 1702 Chikamatsu Monzaemon dramatized a vendetta by Ishikawa Hyōsuke and Ishikawa Genzō at Kameyama Castle that had occurred the previous year. A certain Akabori Mizuemon had provoked Hyōsuke's father into doubting his wife's chastity and then killing her, giving Mizuemon all the excuse he needed to murder him. The disinherited Hyōsuke grew up as the assistant to a sword dealer. Joining forces with his sister, Okano, and his brother-in-law, Genzō, the three tracked Mizuemon to Kameyama Castle where they exacted their revenge. The play was rewritten many times between Chikamatsu's production and the version that was staged in Osaka a century and a half later, so it is not clear whether the two brothers-in-law are practicing their swordsmanship, have mistaken a kimono warehouse for Mizuemon's hiding place, or are fighting one another by mistake.

Yoshitoyo may be the same pupil of Kuniyoshi who designed a series of prints of an elephant exhibited in Edo in 1863. If so, he died in 1866. His actor prints display a humor that sets them quite apart from the usual straight-faced productions of the Osaka school.

75 Sadanobu I

Naniwa Hyakkei no uchi ("100 Views of Naniwa")
Rain at the mouth of the Aji River
Snow on the Matsugahana Pine
c. late 1850s
Catalogue 295 (29-30)

Matsugahana ("The Pine Nose") was the northern tip of a large island near the confluence of the Kizu and Aji Rivers. The three-hundred-year-old pine that grew there was a landmark for boatmen, and an attraction for sightseers and poets who often arranged shipboard banquets to view and extol the loveliness of the tree. A ferry that crossed the river at this point is shown in the picture. The rain scene shows the masts of boats moored at the mouth of the Aji River.

The word *sha* ("copied") as used here after a signature on a Japanese print can mean three different things. Normally it means "drawn by," but on certain portraits it means "drawn from life," and on prints derived from earlier pictures, it clearly means "copied from another original." Sadanobu seemed consistently to distinguish between his own inventions, which he signed Sadanobu *ga* or Sadanobu *hitsu,* and his copies, after Hiroshige and others, which he signed Sadanobu *sha,* with rare exceptions. Most of the landscapes in the present set are signed with *ga* or *hitsu* and are clearly Sadanobu's own designs. The two pictures that are reproduced, however, are both signed with *sha* and are very probably based on earlier book illustrations.

Landscape prints never achieved the popularity in Osaka that they had in Edo, and until the Meiji period, landscape prints by Osaka artists were rare. The title of the present set is inspired by Andō Hiroshige's *Meisho Edo Hyakkei* ("One Hundred Views of Famous Places in Edo"), which was published by Uoei in Edo between 1856 and 1858.

These pictures are from a series of small views of Osaka printed four to a horizontal *ōban* sheet and published by Wataki. Twenty-eight other subjects, originally bound together, are in the collection (Cat. 295). The catalogue of the Sadanobu Fiftieth Memorial Exhibition in 1928 lists two volumes (of three) with a total of sixty subjects; the Museum of Fine Arts in Boston owns another group of thirty. It is possible that a total of ninety subjects were published, rather than the hundred implied by the title of the set.

76 Enjaku

[Onoe Tamizō II as Kanki],
[Arashi Rikaku II as Kinshōjo], and
[Arashi Rikan III as Watōnai]
in *Kokusenya Kassen* 1/1859
Catalogue 21

The original scenario of *The Battles of Coxinga* was written by Chikamatsu for the puppet theater in 1715. It ran continuously for seventeen months, a record that was never equaled. It was revised for kabuki in 1716, and has been performed ever since.

Rō Ikkan, a Ming official, lives as a refugee in Kyūshū plotting to return to China and overthrow the newly established Ch'ing dynasty. Watōnai (Kokusenya, Coxinga), his son by a Japanese wife, lands in China where he kills a tiger with his bare hands. He then approaches his half-brother by marriage, Kanki, to obtain men and arms for his purpose. Kanki refuses to cooperate until his wife and mother-in-law both commit suicide to persuade him. Enjaku's print may show Watōnai, his half-sister Kinshōjo, and her husband Kanki meeting at Kanki's palace, Lion Castle.

77 Kunikazu

Arashi Kichisaburō III as Asahina Tōbei and Arashi Rikaku II as Terakoya Hyōsuke in *Gokusaishiki Musume Ōgi* 10/1859
Catalogue 243ab

Asahina Tōbei, an *otokodate,* promises to buy a geisha named Oshina out of service so that she can marry a temporarily disinherited samurai, Seijūrō, before his marriage to a certain Onatsu is consummated. Learning his predicament, his stepmother asks her son Hyōsuke, a blind, impoverished schoolteacher, to raise the money. Hyōsuke's wife prostitutes herself to obtain the money and Hyōsuke rushes off in a rainstorm to deliver it in time. He falls ill en route, Tōbei stumbles on him in the dark, attends him, and inadvertently discovers the money, which he begs Hyōsuke to lend him. Hyōsuke naturally refuses. Tōbei being deaf and Hyōsuke blind, before they realize their relation to one another, Tōbei kills Hyōsuke in desperation and takes the money. In the end, Seijūrō is able to marry both girls, regains his inheritance, and takes Tōbei into his service. The prints portray the murder at night.

This *chūban* diptych from the series *Nanatsu Iroha* ("Seven Syllables of the Japanese Alphabet") was published by Ishiwa. The two prints are labeled "A" and "Te," the first syllable in each role.

78 Yoshitaki

Onoe Tamizō II as Yokozō and
Arashi Rikaku II as Jihizō
in *Honchō Nijūshikō* 10/1861
Catalogue 400ab

Honchō Nijūshikō, like so many semi-historical plays in the kabuki repertoire, is complicated past telling. In the main plot, a usurper assassinates the ruling Ashikaga shogun; the powerful Takeda and Uesugi clans call a three-year truce in their bitter rivalry to hunt the assassin. Both fail, so each family is bound to kill a son as agreed upon previously. Katsuyori, the Takeda heir, is saved by a substitution and enters the Uesugi mansion disguised as a gardener to steal a magic helmet, which was the cause of the families' quarrel. The elder Uesugi sees through his disguise and sends him off to be ambushed and killed. Uesugi's daughter Yaegakihime is Katsuyori's fiancée. Learning that he is unexpectedly alive, but on the way to his death, she prays to the fox spirits of the helmet who possess her, and she runs across the frozen Lake Biwa to warn her lover in time.

Yoshitaki illustrates a subplot of the story. Jihizō, in service to one of the warring clans, goes out in the snow to dig bamboo shoots for his aged mother, whereupon he discovers a secret scroll of military strategy. Just as he discovers it his brother Yokozō, who serves the other clan, appears, and the two of them battle in the snow for possession of the scroll.

This is a *chūban* diptych from an album of theatrical polyptychs dating between 1860 and 1863 by Yoshitaki, Yoshiyuki, Hironobu, and Hirosada, which is complete in the Museum collection (*see* Catalogue 26, 27, 89, 394–407, 409–419, and 431).

79 Hironobu

Ōtani Tomomatsu as Yaegakihime
in *Honchō Nijūshikō* 3/1865
Catalogue 28

The scene this print illustrates is described in the previous entry. Princess Yaegaki, possessed by the fox spirits of the magic helmet, flees across the icy lake in the darkness to rescue her fiancé Katsuyori.

The *ōban* bust portrait was revived in the 1860s as a deluxe format for special sets and publications. The present print is one of the best of its kind.

The print is from a series of *ōban* bust portraits titled *Hanakurabe Nishiki Utsushie* ("Color Pictures of Popular Actors"), by Yoshitaki and Hironobu. Two other plates are reproduced in Kuroda, *Kamigatae Ichiran* (pls. 108-109).

大谷友松

80 Yoshitaki

Arashi Rikan IV as Toranosuke,
Onoe Tamizō II as Sarunosuke, and
Ichikawa Udanji I as Ichimatsu
in *Yukigeshiki Haru no Nigiwai* 4/1874
Catalogue 424abc

The main play performed at the Naka Theater in January 1874 dealt with two political events in the tumultuous years before the restoration of the Meiji Emperor. In one incident, Takahashi Taichirō, a samurai from Mito, committed suicide after his plans for an uprising against the shogunate were discovered and his part in the assassination of Ii Tairō before the gate of Edo Castle was revealed. The second incident dealt with an anti-shogunate revolutionary named Yoshimura Toratarō, a Tosa samurai, whose revolt was crushed and who was also forced to commit suicide. The title on the print was the name of the finale of this performance. Yoshitaki may be illustrating a dance play showing the heroes in their childhood. Another print that Yoshitaki designed for this performance is described in the entry for the play in the *Kabuki Nenpyō*.

Aniline dyes began to appear in prints in the mid-1860s and were in vogue in Edo and Osaka through the 1870s. They were used rather sparingly and tastefully at first, but they rapidly became cheaper than traditional pigments, and were used recklessly in reprints during the last quarter of the century. Yoshitaki was a devotee of the new dyes and used them to great, if rather blinding, effect as here.

This *chūban* triptych was published by Yaozen, one of the successful new publishers of the Meiji period.

Catalogue

Entries preceded by an asterisk are illustrated in this section.

Titles and actors' names are listed as they appear on prints. Bracketed names identify actors not indicated on prints.

Donors and purchase funds are identified by accession number prefix as follows:

69-208- *Purchased with donations from the Lola Downin Peck Fund; Lessing J. Rosenwald; Robert A. Hauslohner; the Trustees of the Robert L. McNeil, Jr., Trust; Dr. Emanuel Wolff; David M. Gwinn; Mrs. Bernard Behrend; Mrs. Edward G. Budd; Mrs. Meyer P. Potamkin; Dr. Ralph B. Little; Mr. and Mrs. Sidney Lipschutz; Mrs. N. William Winkelman, Jr.; the Howard A. and Martha R. Wolf Fund; and Mrs. William Wolgin*

70-36- *Purchased*

70-190- *Purchased: Lola Downin Peck Fund*

71-88- *Given by Dr. Luther W. Brady*

71-100- *Purchased with funds given by Benjamin D. Bernstein*

71-135- *Given by R. E. Lewis, Inc.*

71-136- *Purchased with funds given by Mr. and Mrs. Roderick Seidenberg*

Ashikuni (c. 1775–9/1818; active c. 1807–1818)

Ashikuni studied with the painter Suga Ranrinsai; he did not begin his career as an ukiyoe book illustrator until he was in his late twenties. His earliest books, which began to appear around 1807, were strongly influenced by Hokusai. In 1810 he illustrated a book entitled *Saten Suminoe Zōshi,* where he listed himself on the title page as a bookseller. The book contained frontispieces by Hokusai, Toyokuni I, and other Edo, Osaka, and Kyoto artists, so Ashikuni may have been responsible for assembling their work and publishing it. He apparently designed a surimono for Nakamura Utaemon III in 1808, but his first recorded single-sheet actor print is the double-bust portrait of Arashi Kichisaburō II and Asao Kuzaemon I published by Shioya Chōbei in 1811.

Between 1806 and his death in 1818, Ashikuni designed upward of forty illustrated books, but only about a dozen prints by him have been found, most of them published in the last four years of his life. Judging from the number of signatures beginning with "Ashi," he had many pupils, although only one, Ashiyuki, became an artist of note in his own right.

1. Nakamura Utaemon III in six of twelve roles representing the months of July to December by Ashikuni and Shikan (Nakamura Utaemon III)
3/1817
Double horizontal *ōban*
Publisher: Eijudō
Theater: Kado

a. Old couple
Signature: Shikan
Seal: an eye

b. Tōru
Signature: Ashikuni
Seal: Naniwa (?)

c. Blind musician
Signature: Shikan
Seal: Shikan

d. Dancing beggar
Signature: Ashikuni
Seal: Naniwa (?)

e. Heron maiden
Signature: Ashikuni
Seal: Naniwa (?)

f. Kuan Yu
Signature: Ashikuni
Seal: Ashikuni
69-208-1a-f

See Plate 11.

2. Volume 1 of two albums of drawings
Original wooden covers hand-lettered with the character "Ho," 11¼″ x 8⅜″. Thirty unnumbered sheets assembled like a scrapbook with a printed border on almost every page, within which are mounted drawings, primarily of actor portraits in color by Ashikuni and other Osaka artists, relating to performances given between 1813 and 1816, and poems by contemporary actors and writers. From the Kimura Collection.
69-208-2(1ab-30ab)

Sheet 1a
Endpaper with title *Uta no Teburi* (Dance Skill of Utaemon)

Sheet 1b
Couplet in Chinese
Signature: Shikan
Seal: an eye

Sheet 2a
Poem
Signature and seal: Shikan

Sheet 2b
Drawing of a badger dancing in the moonlight, unsigned

Sheets 3ab
Preface
Signature: Hyakugien Toboke
Seals: Nakamura and Shikan

Sheets 4ab
Poem, unsigned

Sheets 5ab-7ab
Blank pages

Sheet 8a
Drawing of a priest fording a stream
Signature: Nankō ga

Sheet 8b
Poem, unsigned

Sheet 9a
Drawing of Shikan (Nakamura Utaemon III) as a courtesan
Date: 1/1813 (misdated 1/1814 in manuscript)
Signature and seal: Ashikuni
Theater: Naka

Sheet 9b
Poems
Signatures: Hidemaro, etc.
Seal: Hidemaro

Sheet 10a
Drawing, with poem, of [Shikan] as a blind masseur
Date: 1/1813
Signature: Ashikuni
Seal: Naniwa Kuni (?)
Theater: Naka

Sheet 10b
Poems
Signatures: Kikuya and Chōsui
Seal unread

Sheet 11a
Drawing of [Shikan as Narihira]
Date: 1/1813
Signature and seal: Ashikuni
Theater: Naka

Sheet 11b
Poems, unsigned
Seal: *kakihan*

Sheet 12a
Poem
Seal unread

Sheet 12b
Drawing of [Shikan] as a *kakubei* dancer
Date: 1/1813
Signature and seal: Ashikuni
Theater: Naka

Sheet 13a
Poem
Signature: Junpūkō Minato
Seal: *kakihan*

Sheet 13b
Drawing of [Shikan as Benkei]
Date: 1/1813
Signature and seal: Ashikuni
Theater: Naka

Sheet 14a
Drawing of [Shikan] as a fisherwoman
Date: 1/1813
Signature: Ashikuni
Seal: Naniwa Kuni (?)
Theater: Naka

Sheet 14b
Poem
Signature: Hakujaku
Seal: Yonehiko

Sheet 15a
Drawing of [Shikan as Shōki]
Date: 1/1813
Signature and seal: Ashikuni
Theater: Naka

Sheet 15b
Poem
Signature: Kurasa (?)

Sheet 16a
Poem in Chinese characters
Signature: Aonisai Muchū

Sheet 16b
Blank page

Sheet 17a
Drawing of [Shikan] as a *yakko*
Date: 3/1813
Signature: Ashikuni
Seal: Naniwa Kuni (?)
Theater: Naka

Sheet 17b
Poem
Signature: Masuya
Seals: *kakihan* and two others unread

Sheet 18a
Poem
Signature: Aonisai Muchū

Sheet 18b
Drawing of cherry blossoms, unsigned, with poem signed Sukinari

Sheets 19ab
Drawing of a woman descending a staircase beneath a bridge
Signature: Masuyuki
Seal: Suiseki

Sheet 20a
Poem
Signature unread
Seal: *kakihan*

Sheet 20b
Blank page

Sheet 21a
Drawing of Shikan as a woman with a letter box
Date: 3/1816
Signature: Kyōgadō Ashikuni
Seal: Ashikuni
Theater: Kado

Sheet 21b
Poems
Signature: Tsukimado, etc.

Sheet 22a
Drawing of [Shikan] as a dancing shop clerk
Date: 3/1816
Signature and seal: Ashikuni
Theater: Kado

Sheet 22b
Poem
Signature: Randō

Sheet 23a
Poems
Signatures: Teruko, etc.
Seals: Ashiyuki, etc.

Sheet 23b
Blank page

3 (26a)

Sheet 24a
Drawing of [Shikan as Ono no Komachi]
Date: 3/1816
Signature and seal: Ashikuni
Theater: Kado
See Plate 9.

Sheet 24b
Poems
Signatures: Tosshō, etc.
Seals unread

Sheets 25ab
Poems
Signatures: Chōsui, Gessō, Randō, etc.

Sheet 26a
Poems
Signatures: Rōho, Gessō, etc.
Seal: Rōho

Sheet 26b
Drawing of [Shikan] dancing *ushiromen,* the double role of street prostitute and client
Date: 3/1816
Signature and seal: Ashikuni
Theater: Kado

Sheet 27a
Drawing of [Shikan as a courtesan at Eguchi]
Date: 3/1816
Signature and seal: Ashikuni
Theater: Kado

Sheet 27b
Poem
Signature: Gōkankyo

Sheet 28a
Drawing of Shikan as a lion dancer
Date: 3/1816
Signature and seal: Ashikuni
Theater: Kado
See Plate 9.

Sheet 28b
Poem
Signature: Chōchōtei

Sheets 29ab
Drawing of Mount Fuji and cranes
Signature: Manzan
Seal: Asayama (?)

Sheet 30a
Blank page

Sheet 30b
Endpaper
Seal: Sekkei

3. Volume 2 of two albums of drawings (*See* Cat. 2). Original wooden covers hand-lettered with the character "Ban." Preface dated 10/1818, one month after Ashikuni's death. Thirty unnumbered sheets, with illustrations of performances between 1811 and 1817. From the Kimura Collection.
69-208-3 (1ab-30ab)

Sheet 1a
Endpaper with title: *Kaomise Nahirome* (?)

Sheet 1b
Drawing of a box lettered "*Sanban,* Number 3"

Sheets 2ab
Drawing of two *manzai* singers
Signature: Masuyuki
Seal: Suiseki

Sheets 3ab-4ab
Preface
Date: 10/1818
Signature: Naotari

Sheet 5a
Drawing of Gadō (Kataoka Nizaemon VII) as Kitabatake Sukenokami
Date: c. 1812
Seal: Ashikuni

Sheet 5b
Poems
Signatures: Gadō, Kūō

Sheet 6a
Drawing of Rikan (Arashi Kichisaburō II) as Sasaki Moritsuna
Date: 10/1811
Signature and seal: Ashikuni
Theater: Kitanoshinchi

Sheet 6b
Poems
Signatures: Ippo, Fubijin, Yūri

Sheet 7a
Drawing of Shiyū (Ōtani Tomoemon II) as Wadahei
Date: 10/1811
Seal: Ashikuni
Theater: Kitanoshinchi

Sheet 7b
Poem
Signature unread
Seal: *kakihan*

Sheet 8a
Drawing of Ganshi (Bandō Jūtarō I) as Ogurusu Jūbei
Date: c. 1812
Signature: Ashikuni sha
Seal: Ashikuni

Sheet 8b
Poem, unsigned

Sheet 9a
Inscription
Signature: Jukōen Hanamaru

Sheet 9b
Drawing of Rikan (Arashi Kichisaburō II) as Sasaki Moritsuna
Date: 10/1811
Signature and seal: Ashikuni
Theater: Kitanoshinchi

Sheet 10a
Poems
Signatures: Chikei, Naotari, Kūō
Seals unread

Sheet 10b
Drawing of Shikan as Kakinoki Kinsuke
Date: 1/1813
Signature: Ashikuni ga
Seal: Ashikuni
Theater: Naka

See Plate 9.

Sheet 11a
Drawing of Fujaku (Onoe Fujaku III) in an unidentified role, unsigned
Date: c. 1812

Sheet 11b
Poems
Signatures: Naotari, etc.

Sheet 12a
Drawing of Shikan as Maiagari no Tsuru
Date: 11/1812
Seal: Ashikuni
Theater: Naka

Sheet 12b
Poems
Signatures: Hikona, etc.
Seal unread

Sheet 13a
Poems
Signatures: Suiseki, Gettō

Sheet 13b
Drawing of Shichō (Kanō Minshi I) as Osan, unsigned
Date: 3/1811
Theater: Kitanoshinchi

Sheet 14a
Drawing of Rikan (Arashi Kichisaburō II) as Ono no Tōfū
Date: 4/1813
Signature: Ashikuni sha
Seal: Ashikuni
Theater: Kado

Sheet 14b
Poems
Signature: Junsai
Seals: Shōkō, etc.

Sheet 15a
Poems
Signature: Naotari

Sheet 15b
Drawing of Shikan as Miyamoto Tomojirō
Date: 3/1814
Signature: Ashikuni sha
Seal: Ashikuni
Theater: Kado

Sheet 16a
Poems
Signatures: Chikei, etc.
Seals unread

Sheet 16b
Drawing of Shikan as Miyamoto Musashi
Date: 3/1814
Signature: Ashikuni
Seal: Naniwa (?)
Theater: Kado

Sheet 17a
Drawing of Shozan (Sawamura Tanosuke II) as Miyuki
Date: 1/1814
Signature: Ashikuni
Seal: Naniwa (?)
Theater: Kado

Sheet 17b
Poems
Signatures: Gessō, etc.
Seals unread

Sheet 18a
Drawing of Shozan (Sawamura Tanosuke II) as Miyuki, unsigned
Date: 1/1814
Theater: Kado

Sheet 18b
Poems
Signatures: Suiseki, Ryūsōdō, Shunkō, etc.
Seals unread

Sheet 19a
Drawing of Shozan (Sawamura Tanosuke II) as Suma no Kata
Date: 9/1815
Seal: Ashikuni
Theater: Naka

Sheet 19b
Poems
Seal: Enka Raiheki

Sheet 20a
Drawing of Gadō (Kataoka Nizaemon VII) as Kasahara Rōō
Date: 3/1814
Seal: Ashikuni
Theater: Kado

Sheet 20b
Poems
Signature: Tsunahiko
Seal: Dokusui

Sheet 21a
Poems
Signatures: Mamori, etc.
Seal: *kakihan*

Sheet 21b
Drawing of Shikō (Ichikawa Danzō V) as Miyamoto Musashi
Date: c. 1815
Seal: Ashikuni

Sheet 22a
Drawing of Rikan (Arashi Kichisaburō II) as Notonokami Noritsune, unsigned
Date: 8/1816
Theater: Naka

Sheet 22b
Poems
Signature and seals unread

Sheet 23a
Drawing of Shikan as Adachi Tōzaburō
Date: c. 1815
Signature: Ashikuni

See Plate 9.

Sheet 23b
Poems
Signatures: Ri Shōsō, etc.
Seal: Ri Shōsō

Sheet 24a
Drawing of Rikan (Arashi Kichisaburō II) as Sasahara Haito
Date: 9/1816
Seal: Ashikuni
Theater: Naka

6

Sheet 24b
Poems
Signatures: Issui, Fubijin

Sheet 25a
Drawing of Rikan (Arashi Kichisaburō II) as Sasaki Moritsuna
Date: 7/1817
Signature: Ashikuni
Theater: Naka

Sheet 25b
Poems
Signatures: Rikan, Shūen
Seal unread

* Sheet 26a
Drawing of Rikan (Arashi Kichisaburō II) as Aburauri Yohei
Date: 8/1816
Signature: Ashikuni
Seal: Naniwa (?)
Theater: Naka no Shibai

Sheet 26b
Poems
Signatures: Ashinomaru, Nakayo, etc.

Sheets 27ab
Drawing of Rikan (Arashi Kichisaburō II) as Yamauba; and Shikan as Kaidōmaru, unsigned
Date: c. 1815
Seal: Ashikuni

Sheets 28ab
Poems
Signatures: Tsunahiko, etc.

Sheet 29a
Poems
Signatures: Ri Shōsō, Ryūji
Seals: Ri Shōsō, Wakai Ryūji

Sheet 29b
Blank page

Sheet 30a
Drawing of a crowd of people, unsigned

Sheet 30b
Endpaper
Seal: Sekkei

Ashiyuki (active c. 1814–1833)

Ashiyuki has been unfairly neglected as an Osaka print designer. He does not seem to have been nearly as popular nor as highly regarded as Hokushū or Shigeharu, although his name appears second, between Hokushū and Kunihiro, on a broadside list of print artists that appeared around 1831 (*see* Appendix XI). Since he could not always command the services of the best engravers (Kasuke, for example, engraved few of his prints), his work is uneven and his portraits are slightly mannered. But at his best, he designed some of the masterpieces of the Osaka school and, in a quiet way, anticipated most advances of the Osaka style. He was the first person to make much use of the horizontal format; the first to exploit the contrast between the broad, painterly style of the contemporary Shijō surimono and book illustrations that were appearing at the time with the precise and brilliant actor-print style. He was the first in Osaka to employ *gofun* on his prints to create an effect of snow, the first to exploit the use of color blocks without outlines, and may have been, in fact, the first person to use the small-figure surimono style.

4. Sawamura Tanosuke as spirit of the Kankō cherry tree, 1/1815
Ōban
Signature: Gigadō Ashiyuki ga
Publisher: Shiochō
Theater: Naka
69-208-4

5. Nakamura Utaemon III as Ishida no Tsubone, 1/1817
Ōban
Signature: Ashiyuki ga
Publisher: Shiochō
Theater: Kado
Reference: Matsudaira, *Ashiyuki* 15.2
69-208-5

This is the center panel of a triptych, of which the left panel shows Ichikawa Ebijūrō I as Mashiba Hisatsugu; the right panel, Nakayama Yoshio II as Yodomachi.

*6. [Arashi Koroku IV as Otowa, and Arashi Kitsusaburō II as Iwagawa] 5/1823
Horizontal *ōban*
Signature: Ashiyuki ga
Seal: Ashiyuki
Theater: Horie Ichinogawa
69-208-6

The panel includes poems by Koroku and Rikaku (Kitsusaburō II). Another state of this print without poems was published for a performance in Kyoto (7/1823).

7. Nakamura Utaemon III as Yakanpei, 5/1824
Ōban
Signature: Ashiyuki ga
Seal: *kakihan*
Publisher: Wataki
Theater: Horie Ichinogawa
69-208-7

This is the right panel only of a triptych, of which the center panel shows Sawamura Kunitarō II as Kuzunoha; the left panel, Ichikawa Ebijūrō I as Yokanpei.

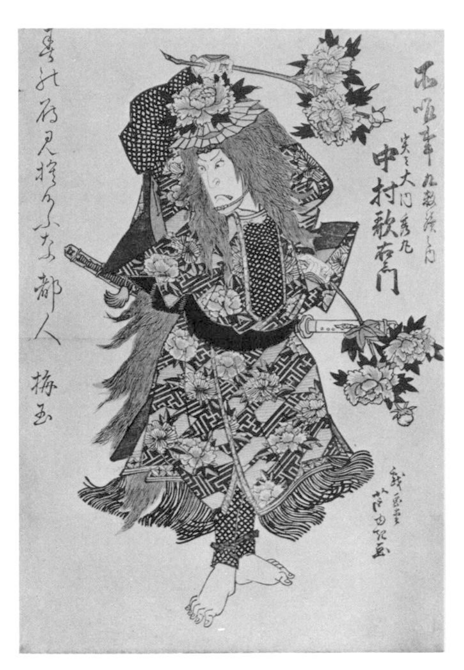

15

8. Nakamura Karoku I as Ano no Tsubone, 3/1825
   Ōban
   Signature: Ashiyuki ga
   Publisher: Wataki
   Theater: Naka
   69-208-8

9. Arashi Kitsusaburō II as Suzuki Magoichi, 3/1825
   Ōban
   Signature: Ashiyuki ga
   Publisher: Honsei
   Theater: Naka
   69-208-9

10a. Ichikawa Ebijūrō I as Kuwanaya Tokuzō
  b. Arashi Tomisaburō as the spirit of the courtesan Higaki
  c. Arashi Kitsusaburō II as Tadotsu Ikkaku, and Nakayama Bunshichi III as Takamaru Kamejirō
   8/1825
   Ōban triptych
   Signature: Gigadō Ashiyuki ga
   Publisher: Wataki
   Seal: Maeda (?)
   Theater: Kado
   69-208-10abc

11. Arashi Tomisaburō as Arimaya Ofuji, and Nakamura Karoku I as Nodaya Ofuji, 11/1825
   Ōban
   Signature: Ashiyuki ga
   Publisher: Wataki
   Theater: Kado
   69-208-11

12. Onoe Kikugorō III as Rokuzō, a carpenter, actually Matsugae Tetsunosuke; and Arashi Koroku IV as Osono, 1/1826
   Ōban
   Signature: Gigadō Ashiyuki ga
   Publisher: Honsei
   Theater: Kado
   Reference: Matsudaira, *Ashiyuki* 70
   69-208-12

13a. Arashi Rikō as Osuma no Kata
  b. Arashi Kitsusaburō II as Kowari Dennai
  c. Arashi Koroku IV as Okiyo
   1/1826
   Ōban triptych
   Signature: Gigadō Ashiyuki ga
   Publisher: Wataki
   Theater: Horie Ichinogawa
   Reference: Matsudaira, *Ashiyuki* 69
   69-208-13abc
   See Plate 31.

14. Arashi Kitsusaburō II as Miura Matazō, and Onoe Umezō as Toranosuke, 1/1827
   Ōban
   Signature: Gigadō Ashiyuki ga
   Publisher: Honsei
   Theater: Naka
   Reference: Matsudaira, *Ashiyuki* 84
   69-208-14

This is possibly one panel of a polyptych.

*15. Nakamura Utaemon III as Shakkyō, actually Ōuchi Hidemaru, 1/1827
   Ōban
   Signature: Gigadō Ashiyuki ga
   Theater: Kado
   Reference: Matsudaira, *Ashiyuki* 87.7
   69-208-15

This is plate 7 of a set of 9. The poem is by Baigyoku (Utaemon III).

16. *Arashi Rikan Somen Nōryō no Zu.* Arashi Rikan II, in summer attire, cooling himself by a river
   c. mid-1827
   Ōban
   Signature: Gigadō Ashiyuki ga
   Publishers: Honsei and Touse
   69-208-16

This left panel of a diptych is mounted with Cat. 384 (Yoshikuni).

20

17. Ichikawa Danzō V as Kajiwara Genta, 7/1827
   Ōban
   Signature: Gigadō Ashiyuki ga
   Publisher: Wataki
   Theater: Kitagawa, Kyoto
   69-208-17

This is the left panel only of a diptych, of which the right panel shows Arashi Kitsusaburō II as Kajiwara Heiji.

18a. Arashi Tomisaburō as the heavenly maiden of Itsukushima
  b. Arashi Kitsusaburō II as Ōuchi Samanosuke
  c. Bandō Jutarō I as Naruto Kōbei
   1/1828
   Ōban triptych
   Signature: Gigadō Ashiyuki ga
   Publisher: Honsei
   Theater: Naka
   Reference: Matsudaira, *Ashiyuki* 98
   69-208-18abc

Ebikane (active 1827–1828)

The characters used to write this artist's name and the fact that only two prints are known with his signature strongly suggest that he was an amateur artist, perhaps one of the wealthy merchants whose patronage supported the kabuki theater and seems to have subsidized much print production. He may even have been the actor Ichikawa Ebijūrō II, who is in the artist's two known prints.

19. Ichikawa Ichizō II as Gokumon no Shōbei, and Nakamura Baigyoku (Utaemon III) as Kurofune Chūemon, 8/1827
Ōban
Signature: Ebikane ga
Publisher: Kichi
Theater: Kado
69-208-19
See Plate 36.

Enjaku (active 1858–1865)

Enjaku could possibly be identified as the actor Nakamura (later Jitsukawa) Enjaku who was active in this period, but theatrical records indicate that the actor Enjaku was performing in Edo between 1855 and 1860, while the artist of this name was active in Osaka.

*20. [Jitsukawa Ensaburō] as Asahina Saburō, c. 1858
Chūban
Signature: Enjaku
Publisher: Daisei
69-208-20

This is one panel of a polyptych.

21. *Kokusenya.* [Onoe Tamizō II as Kanki], [Arashi Rikaku II as Kinshōjo], and [Arashi Rikan III as Watōnai], 1/1859
Chūban
Signature: Enjaku
Theater: Kado
69-208-21
See Plate 76.

22. Ichikawa Yonezō as Honchō Tsunagorō, c. 1859
Chūban
Signature: Enjaku with *kakihan* of a butterfly
69-208-22

Hikokuni (active 1821–1824)

Hikokuni may have been a pupil of Ashikuni, but nothing factual about him is known.

23. Ichikawa Ebijūrō I as Teraoka Heiemon, 3/1822
Ōban
Signature: Hikokuni ga
Publisher: Toshin
Theater: Naka
69-208-23

This is one panel of a polyptych.

*24. Asao Okujirō as Ogata Rikimaru c. 1822
Ōban
Signature: Hikokuni ga
Publishers: Toshin, Iden
69-208-24

25. *Oitomagoi Kyōgen.* Nakamura Shikan II as Kuzunoha, 10/1827
Ōban
Signature: Toyokawa ga
Publisher: Honsei
Theater: Kado
69-208-25

This is a reissue of a print for a 6/1824 performance with background, inscriptions, and signature changed.

24

Hironobu I (active 1851–1870)

Hironobu was probably a pupil of Hirosada. He designed fewer prints than his contemporary Yoshitaki, but these included comic subjects as well as actor portraits.

26. *Ōmonguchi*
*a. Arashi Kichisaburō III as Akujirō Tadazumi
*b. Onoe Tamizō II as Mino no Shōkurō

26abc

*c. Jitsukawa Ensaburō as Ise no Shinkurō
1/1862
Chūban triptych
Signatures: b. Hironobu; c. Ashinoya Hironobu
Theater: Naka
69-208-26abc

27. *Somewake Tazuna*
*a. Arashi Kichisaburō III as Saitō Kuranosuke
*b. Onoe Tamizō II as Yuruki Saemon
*c. Jitsukawa Ensaburō as Kajizō
1/1863
Chūban triptych
Signature: Hironobu ga
Engraver: Uchitora
Theater: Naka
69-208-27abc

28. *Hanakurabe Nishiki Utsushie*
Ōtani Tomomatsu as Yaegakihime
3/1865
Ōban
Signature: Hironobu ga
Printer: Surishi Horikame
Theater: Chikugo (Ōnishi)
69-208-28

See Plate 79.

*29. Nakamura Komanosuke as Isoroku, a fisherman, c. 1865
Chūban
Signature: Hironobu ga
Seal unread
69-208-29

This is possibly a proof impression with blank title cartouche.

30. *Gogyō no uchi: Mizu.* Nakamura Shijaku as Onami, a fisherwoman
c. 1865
Chūban
Signature: Hironobu ga
69-208-30

This subject illustrates "Water" from a series of five elements.

31. *Dōgi Taikōki*
a. No. 7: Shigewaka surprising Yukinoya with Magoichi watching
b. No. 8: Mashiba Hisayoshi stealing melons
c. No. 11: Farmers attacking Takechi Mitsuhide
c. 1865
Chūban
Signature: Hironobu ga
Publisher: Yaozen
69-208-31abc

These are from a series of at least eleven subjects.

Hirosada (active 1826[?]–1863; died c. 1865)

There is a strong, though unproven case for believing that Gosōtei Hirosada, the most important and prolific mid-nineteenth century Osaka print designer, was the well-known artist Sadahiro I, a cosmopolitan and well-traveled pupil of the Edo artist Kunisada. There is also reason to believe that he was for nearly fifteen years the proprietor of the major publishing firm Tenki. The facts are as follows:

Certain prints signed Hirosada are sealed Sadahiro.

Sadahiro is one of three print designers mentioned in *Ōsaka Shōkō Meika Shū,* a city directory published in Osaka in 1846 (*see* Appendix XV); Hirosada is not mentioned in this directory.

From 1847 to 1849 several hundred prints were signed Hirosada, only a handful by Sadahiro I.

The Sadahiro I prints are stylistically identical to those signed Hirosada. The signatures are identical except that the characters are reversed.

Hirosada's commonest *gō,* Gosōtei, was used by Sadahiro I.

The biography of the artist Sadahiro II states that he took his name after the death of his master, Hirosada.

Sadahiro I is recorded as a pupil of Kunisada on a monument erected in Edo in 1828.

The first print Sadahiro I signed after his return to Osaka in 1830 is sealed Tamikuni.

An artist and poet named Tamikuni worked in Osaka from 1823 to 1826.

A print signed Tomikuni, dated to the early 1820s (Cat. 360), is the only one recorded with that signature, and may be the same artist's work.

A theatrical surimono signed Gochō and sealed Konishi Gochō was published by a certain Konishi in 1826.

27abc

29

In 1835, after Sadahiro's second return from Edo, the heir of the publishing house Tenki left the firm; Tenki changed its street address and altered its name to Tenki Kinkadō Konishi.

A poem on a print published about 1840 by Tenki Kinkadō is sealed Konishi Gochō.

A *harimaze* sheet dated 1848 gives Tenki's full name as Tenmaya Kihei Gochō.

Many prints signed Hirosada are sealed Konishi Gochō; the seal is identical to those described above.

Many other prints signed Hirosada are sealed "Sada *han*," or "published by Sada."

On the one hand, there is no other recorded case of an ukiyoe artist reversing the characters of his name. We must remember, however, that between 1842 and 1847 the ban on actor portraits was strongly enforced. It is unlikely that an artist of stature would risk his career by an admitted violation of the law; with the popularity of Hirosada's work, Sadahiro may have been amused to keep the pseudonym.

Hirosada visited Edo in 1852 with his friend and teacher Utagawa Kunimasu. Both artists designed backgrounds for actor portraits by Kunimasu's teacher Kunisada, which were published in Edo that year. After his return to Osaka, Hirosada's production of prints declined sharply and only a handful of prints survive from the last decade of his life.

Mr. Kōzō Hida of the Osaka Prefectural Library has recently examined the Kikuyamachi district register (Ōsaka Kikuyamachi Shūshi Ninbetsu Chō) and finds that in 1803 Tenmaya Shōshichi, an *iemori* or rental manager, adopted a son named Shōsuke. Shōsuke established his own household in the district in 1806, married the following year and changed his name to Tenmaya Kihei in 1809. Kihei died in 11/1865. Supposing that Tenki was between twenty and twenty-five at marriage, Mr. Hida concludes that the publisher was around eighty when he died.

Kihei's death date seems to support the argument that the publisher was the artist Hirosada. If Hirosada married in 1807, however, he could hardly have been "in his twenties" around 1835, so the question of his identity with Sadahiro remains unresolved.

See the biography of Sadahiro, preceding Cat. 275.

*32. *Kōmei Buyūden.* [Kataoka Gadō II] as Chinzei Hachirō Tametomo
2/1847
Ōban
Signature: Hirosada
Seal: Konishi Gochō
Publisher: Konishi
Theater: Chikugo (Ōnishi)
69-208-32

Cat. 33 is another print from the same series.

33. *Kōmei Buyūden.* [Nakamura Shikan III (?)] as Mashiba Hisayoshi
c. early 1847
Ōban
Signature: Hirosada
Publisher: Konishi
69-208-33
See Plate 60.

Cat. 32 is another print from the same series.

34. *Hakkenden*
a. [Kataoka Gadō] as Inuzuka Shino
b. [Arashi Kichisaburō III] as Inugai Kenpachi

32

7/1847
Uncut *chūban* diptych
Signature: Hirosada
Publisher: Tenki
Theater: Naka
69-208-34ab

This diptych is mounted with Cat. 35ab.

35. *Chūkōden*
a. [Mimasu Daigorō IV] as Tōma Saburōemon
b. [Jitsukawa Ensaburō] as Hayase Iori
7/1847
Uncut *chūban* diptych
Signature: Hirosada
Engraver: Hori Toyo
Theater: Naka
69-208-35ab

This diptych is mounted with Cat. 34ab.

36. *Shiki no uchi: Fuyu*
a. [Kataoka Ichizō I] as Yokozō
b. [Jitsukawa Ensaburō] as Jihizō
7/1847
Uncut *chūban* diptych
Signature: Hirosada
Theater: Naka
69-208-36ab

This diptych is mounted with Cat. 37ab.

37. *Chūkōden*
a. [Jitsukawa Ensaburō] as Hayase Iori
b. [Ichikawa Shikō] as Hayase Genjirō
7/1847

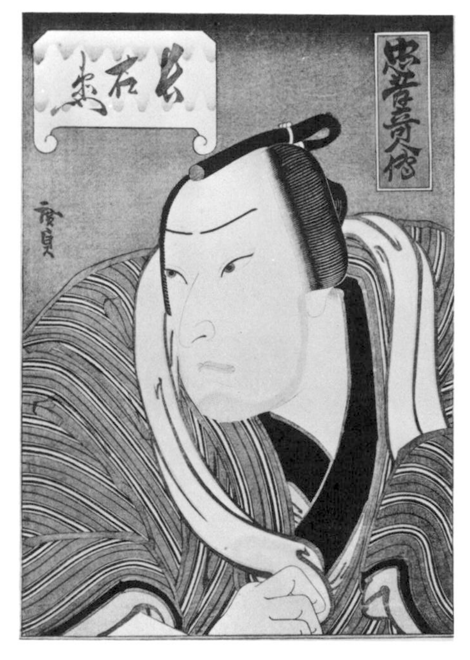

41

Uncut *chūban* diptych
Signature: Hirosada
Theater: Naka
Publisher: Tenki
69-208-37ab

This diptych is mounted with Cat. 36ab.

38. *Kokon Yūjinki.* [Kataoka Gadō II] as Washinoo Saburō, 7/1847
Chūban
Signature: Hirosada
Publisher: Kawaoto
Theater: Naka
69-208-38

Cat. 39ab bear the same cartouche.

39. *Kokon Yūjinki*
a. [Kataoka Gadō II] as Ude no Dōsuke
b. [Kataoka Gadō II] as Inagawa
7 and 10/1847
Chūban diptych
Signature: Hirosada
Publisher: Kawaoto
Printer: Suri Isa
Theater: Chikugo (Ōnishi)
69-208-39ab

Cat. 38 bears the same cartouche.

40. *Chūkō Buyūden*
a. [Ichikawa Ebizō V] as Akushichibyōe Kagekiyo
b. [Nakayama Nanshi II] as Tora Gozen
1/1848
Chūban
Signature: Hirosada
Theater: Naka
69-208-40ab

These are two panels only of a polyptych. Cat. 42ab and 43 bear the same cartouche. Cat. 137(20b) is a drawing of 40a, with another drawing of Mimasu Daigorō IV as Hatakeyama Shigetada at the right.

*41. *Chūkō Kijiden.* [Kataoka Gadō II] as Chōemon, 3/1848
Chūban
Signature: Hirosada
Theater: Chikugo (Ōnishi)
69-208-41

42. *Chūkō Buyūden*
a. [Kataoka Gadō II] as Matsugae Tetsunosuke
b. [Arashi Rikan III] as Nikki Danjō
3/1848
Chūban diptych
Signature: Hirosada
Theater: Chikugo (Ōnishi)
69-208-42ab

Cat. 40ab and 43 bear the same cartouche. There is a Hirosada diptych of the same figures, full-length.

43. *Chūkō Buyūden.* [Arashi Rikan III] as Ukiyo Tohei, 3/1848
Chūban
Signature: Hirosada
Publisher undecipherable, trimmed
Theater: Chikugo (Ōnishi)
69-208-43

Cat. 40ab and 42ab bear the same cartouche.

44. *Chūkō Buyūden.* [Arashi Rikaku II] as Kisuke, a cook, 5/1848
Chūban
Signature: Hirosada
Publisher: Kinkadō
Theater: Chikugo (Ōnishi)
69-208-44

This is the right panel only of a triptych, the center panel of which shows Sawamura Kitō as Omine; and the left panel, Kataoka Gadō II as Mitsugi. Cat. 45ab bear the same cartouche.

45. *Chūkō Buyūden*
a. [Nakayama Nanshi II] as Osono
b. [Kataoka Ichizō I] as Keyamura Rokusuke
5/1848
Chūban diptych
Signature: Hirosada
Theater: Wakadayū
69-208-45ab

Cat. 44 bears the same cartouche.

46. *Chūkō Buyūden*
a. [Asao Yoroku I] as Demura Shinbei
b. [Arashi Rikaku II] as Tamaya Shinbei
10/1848
Chūban diptych
Signature: Hirosada
Theater: Chikugo (Ōnishi)
69-208-46ab

Cat. 47 bears the same cartouche.

47. *Chūkō Buyūden.* [Jitsukawa Ensaburō] as Sasahara Haito
11/1848
Chūban
Signature: Hirosada
Theater: Chikugo (Ōnishi)
69-208-47

Cat. 46ab bear the same cartouche.

48. *Chūkō Buyūden*
a. [Mimasu Daigorō IV] as Ōmi Daijin
b. [Arashi Rikaku II] as Yawata Daijin
c. 1848
Chūban
Signature: Hirosada
Publisher: a. Kawaoto
69-208-48ab

These are right and left panels only of a hexaptych, the second of which shows Ichikawa Ebizō V as Ikyū; the third, Nakayama Nanshi II as Agemakidayū; the fourth, Kataoka Gadō II as Sukeroku (Cat. 49); and the fifth, Jitsukawa Ensaburō I as Shirosakeya.

49. *Chūkō Buyūden.* [Kataoka Gadō II] as Sukeroku, c. 1848
Chūban
Signature: Hirosada
Publisher: Kawaoto
69-208-49

This is the fourth panel only of a hexaptych including Cat. 48ab.

50. *Chūkō Gonin Otoko*
a. [Kataoka Ichizō I] as Tsuribune Sabu
b. [Kataoka Gadō II] as Kizu Kansuke
c. [Jitsukawa Ensaburō] as Goshaku Somegorō
d. [Nakamura Tamashichi] as Hanjimono no Kihei
e. [Arashi Rikaku II] as Gokumon no Shōbei

c. 1848
Chūban pentaptych
Signature: Hirosada
69-208-50a–e

These are *mitate* roles.

51. *Chūkō Jūnishi*
a. Ox [Jitsukawa Ensaburō] as Sakuramaru
b. Tiger [Arashi Rikan III] as Watōnai
c. Rabbit [Kataoka Gadō II] as Owari Dennai
d. Horse [Bandō Jutarō II] as Hinuka no Hachizō
e. Sheep [Arashi Rikaku II] as Ubuge no Tetsutarō
f. Monkey [Kataoka Ichizō I] as Gokudō Kamejirō
c. 1848
Chūban
Signature: Hirosada
Publisher: Matsuki
69-208-51a–f

These are *mitate* roles, from a set of twelve subjects.

52a. [Jitsukawa Ensaburō] as Tōsaku
b. [Ichikawa Ebizō V] as Kurando
c. [Kataoka Gadō II] as Matagorō
d. [Arashi Rikaku II] as Heiji
c. 1848
Chūban tetraptych
Signature: Hirosada
Publisher: Kitakagawa
69-208-52a–d

These are *mitate* roles.

53a. [Arashi Rikaku II] as a *harugoma* (pony) dancer
b. [Nakamura Tamashichi] as a *manzai* singer
c. [Sawamura Kitō] as a *harugoma* dancer
1/1849
Chūban triptych
Signature: Hirosada
Seal unread
Publisher: Kinkadō
Theater: Chikugo (Ōnishi)
69-208-53abc
See Plate 62.

54. [Arashi Rikaku II] as the spirit of a mandarin duck, 1/1849
Chūban
Signature: Hirosada
Theater: Chikugo (Ōnishi)
69-208-54

This is a *chūban* version of Cat. 55 and possibly one panel of a triptych.

55a. [Arashi Rikaku II] as the spirit of a mandarin duck, 1/1849
Ōban
Signature: Hirosada
Seal: Konishi Gochō
Theater: Chikugo (Ōnishi)
69-208-55a
b. A later impression with different color blocks and without the artist's seal
71-135-2

This is the center panel only of a triptych, the right panel of which shows Nakamura Tamashichi; and the left panel, Sawamura Kitō as *oshidori* dancers.

See also Cat. 54.

56. *Chūkō Buyūden*
a. [Nakamura Daikichi III] as Oren
b. [Ichikawa Sukeroku] as Akizuki Dankurō
c. [Ichikawa Shikō] as Rai Kunitoshi
1/1849
Chūban triptych
Signature: Hirosada
Publisher: Kinkadō
Theater: Kado
69-208-56abc

57. *Chūkō Buyūden*
a. An unidentified actor as Sonobe Saemon
b. [Asao Yoroku I] as Saisaki Shiganokami
c. [Arashi Rikan III] as Katsuragi Minbu
d. [Ōkawa Hashizō] as Daizen
e. [Ichikawa Sukejurō] as Sonobe Hyōe
f. [Nakamura Daikichi III] as Usuyukihime
1/1849
Chūban hexaptych
Signature: Hirosada
Publishers: a. Ueda; b. Kinkadō; c. Horio; d. Kagawa; e. Kawaoto
Theater: Kado
69-208-57a–f

58. *Chūkō Buyūden*
a. [Bandō Jutarō II] as Kiritarō
b. [Kataoka Gadō II] as Matsu Sajima
1/1849
Chūban diptych
Signature: Hirosada
Publisher: Horio

59

Theater: Chikugo (Ōnishi)
69-208-58ab

*59. *Chūkō Buyūden*. [Nakamura Gizaemon] as Tarakubō, 1/1849
Chūban
Signature: Hirosada
Publisher: Kawaoto
Theater: Chikugo (Ōnishi)
69-208-59

This is the right panel of a polyptych.

60. *Chūkō Buyūden*. [Sawamura Kitō] as Shiori, a *koshimoto*
1/1849
Chūban
Signature: Hirosada
Publisher: Kinkadō
Theater: Chikugo (Ōnishi)
69-208-60

This is the fourth panel of a polyptych.

61. *Chūkō Kyōka Awase*. [Ichikawa Ebizō V] as Ishida no Tsubone
1/1849
Chūban
Signature: Hirosada
Publisher: Tenki
Theater: Naka
69-208-61

Cat. 77 is from the same series. The poem is by Tsurunoya.

62a. [Jitsukawa Ensaburō] as Chōshimaru
b. [Kataoka Ichizō I] as Kumahei
3/1849

69

Chūban
Signature: Hirosada
Seals: a. Rankei (?); b. unread
Publisher: a. Kawaoto
Theater: Naka
69-208-62ab

These are the right and left panels only of a triptych, the center panel of which shows Mimasu Daigorō IV as Bashi Daijin.

63a. [Mimasu Daigorō IV] as Bishamonten
b. [Jitsukawa Ensaburō] as Chōshimaru
3/1849
Chūban
Signature: Hirosada
Seal: a. Rankei (?)
Publishers: a. Kawaoto; b. Ueda
Theater: Naka
69-208-63ab

These are the right and center panels only of a triptych, the left panel of which shows Ichikawa Ebizō V as Moriya Daijin.

64a. [Nakayama Nanshi II] as Koguruma Ningyō
b. [Kataoka Ichizō I] as Hidari Jingorō
3/1849
Chūban diptych
Signature: Hirosada
Seal: Konishi Gochō
Publisher: Kinkadō
Theater: Naka
69-208-64ab

65. [Nakayama Nanshi II] as Tsukimasu, 3/1849
Chūban
Signature: Hirosada
69-208-65

This is the center panel only of a triptych, the right panel of which shows Arashi San'emon as Ichinoto; the left panel, Kanō Kotobuki as Tsumaginu. *See* Cat. 136 (8abc) for related drawings.

66. [Jitsukawa Ensaburō] as Hata no Kawakatsu, 3/1849
Chūban
Signature: Hirosada
Seal: Ko
Publisher: Meikōdō
Theater: Naka
69-208-66

This is the left panel only of a diptych, the right panel of which shows Ichikawa Ebizō V as Ono no Imoko.

67a. [Kataoka Gadō II] as Tamiya Genpachi
b. [Nakamura Gizaemon] as Horiguchi Gentazaemon
3/1849
Chūban diptych
Signature: Hirosada
Seal: Ko
Theater: Chikugo (Ōnishi)
69-208-67ab

68a. [Nakamura Gizaemon] as Horiguchi Gentazaemon
b. [Kataoka Gadō II] as Tamiya Genpachi
3/1849
Chūban diptych
Signature: Hirosada
Publisher: Ueda
Theater: Chikugo (Ōnishi)
69-208-68ab

See Plate 63.

*69. [Sawamura Kitō] as Osai, 3/1849
Chūban
Signature: Hirosada
Theater: Chikugo (Ōnishi)
69-208-69

This is the right panel only of a diptych, the left panel of which shows Kataoka Gadō II as Tamiya Shinjūrō. *See* Cat. 137 (11ab) for related drawings.

70. [Asao Yoroku I] as Kimon Kihei, 4/1849
Chūban
Signature: Hirosada
Seal: Ko
Publisher: Meikōdō
Theater: Takeda
69-208-70

This is the second panel of a polyptych.

71a. [Ichikawa Ebizō V] as Nippon Daemon
b. [Mimasu Daigorō IV] as Tsukimoto Enshū
5/1849
Chūban diptych
Signature: Hirosada
Publisher: b. unread
Theater: Chikugo (Ōnishi)
69-208-71ab

See Plate 65.

72a. [Kataoka Gadō II] as Hanaregoma Chōkichi
b. [Ichikawa Ebizō V] as Nuregami Chōgorō
5/1849
Chūban diptych
Signature: Hirosada
Publisher: Kinkadō
Theater: Chikugo (Ōnishi)
69-208-72ab

73. [Jitsukawa Ensaburō] as Mashiba Hisayoshi, 5/1849
Chūban
Signature: Hirosada
Theater: Wakadayū
69-208-73

See Plate 66.

74a. [Nakamura Daikichi III] as Itoya Ofusa
b. [Ichikawa Shikō] as Itoya Sashichi
8/1849
Chūban diptych
Signature: Hirosada
Seal: b. Konishi Gochō
Publisher: Kinkadō
Theater: Chikugo (Ōnishi)
69-208-74ab

75a. [Kataoka Gadō II] as Honchōmaru Tsunagorō
b. [Ichikawa Shikō] as Kanbara Sagorō
8/1849
Chūban diptych
Signature: Hirosada
Publisher: a. Ueda
Theater: Chikugo (Ōnishi)
69-208-75ab

76. [Kataoka Gadō II] as Tsunagorō, 8/1849
Chūban
Signature: Hirosada

77

Seal: Ko
Publisher: Meikōdō
Theater: Chikugo (Ōnishi)
69-208-76

This is one panel of a polyptych.

*77. *Fūryū Hokku Awase.* [Kataoka Gadō II] as Honchōmaru Tsunagorō, 8/1849
Chūban
Signature: Hirosada
Seal: Konishi Gochō
Theater: Chikugo (Ōnishi)
69-208-77

Cat. 61 is from the same series. The poem is by Naniwa Ashiumi.

78. [Kataoka Gadō II] as Mashiba Hisayoshi, 8/1849
Chūban
Signature: Hirosada
Theater: Chikugo (Ōnishi)
69-208-78

79. [Sawamura Kitō] as Satomi Fusehime, 9/1849
Chūban
Signature: Hirosada
Seal: Chō (?)
Publisher: Ueda
69-208-79

This is a memorial portrait of the actor.

80a. [Onoe Tamizō II] as Tamaya Shinbei
b. [Kataoka Ichizō I] as Demura Shinbei
9/1849
Chūban diptych
Signature: Hirosada
Seal: a. Chō (?)
Publisher: Ueda
Theater: Kado
69-208-80ab

81. [Onoe Shōju] as Tsukasanosuke
9/1849
Chūban
Signature: Hirosada
Seal: Konishi Gochō
Publisher: Kinkadō
Theater: Kado
69-208-81

This is the left panel only of a diptych, the right panel of which shows Jitsukawa Ensaburō as Okumura Genzō.

82. *Kanadehon Chūshingura,* Act 2
[Kataoka Gadō II] as Wakasanosuke, 9/1849
Chūban
Signature: Hirosada
Seal unread
Publisher: Kitakagawa
Theater: Chikugo (Ōnishi)
69-208-82

See Plate 68.

This is the right panel only of a diptych, the left panel of which shows Kataoka Ichizō I as Honzō. *See* Cat. 136 (10ab) for related drawings.

83. *Kanadehon Chūshingura,* Act 3
[Nakamura Tomozō IV] as Bannai, 9/1849
Chūban
Signature: Hirosada
Theater: Chikugo (Ōnishi)
69-208-83

See Plate 68.

This is the right panel only of a triptych, the center panel of which shows Kataoka Gadō II as Kanpei; the left, Sawamura Kitō as Okaru. *See* Cat. 136 (11abc) for related drawings.

84. *Kanadehon Chūshingura,* Act 7
a. [Kataoka Gadō II] as Ōboshi Yuranosuke
b. [Mimasu Tanin] as Ōboshi Rikiya
9/1849
Chūban diptych
Signature: Hirosada
Seal: Ko
Publisher: Meikōdō
69-208-84ab

See Plate 68.

See Cat. 136 (14ab) for related drawings.

85. *Kanadehon Chūshingura,* Act 8
[Nakamura Daikichi III] as Tonase, 9/1849
Chūban
Signature: Hirosada
Theater: Chikugo (Ōnishi)
69-208-85

See Plate 68.

This is the right panel only of a diptych, the left panel of which shows Mimasu Gennosuke II (?) as Konami. *See* Cat. 136 (15ab) for related drawings.

86. *Kanadehon Chūshingura,* Act 9
a. [Mimasu Daigorō IV] as Kakogawa Honzō
b. [Sawamura Kitō] as Oishi
9/1849
Chūban diptych
Signature: Hirosada
Theater: Chikugo (Ōnishi)
69-208-86ab

See Plate 68.

See Cat. 136 (16ab) for related drawings.

87. *Fūryū Hokku Awase.* [Kataoka Gadō II, Mimasu Daigorō IV, and a child actor] in front of a memorial portrait of [Kataoka Nizaemon VII as Yuranosuke]
9/1849
Chūban diptych
Signature: Hirosada
Seal: Chō
Publisher: Ueda
69-208-87ab

The poem is by Naniwa Minshō, who could be the same person as Hirosada.

88. [Jitsukawa Ensaburō] as Nichiren Shōnin, 10/1849
Chūban
Signature: Hirosada
Theater: Takeda
69-208-88

89. *Nichiren Shōnin Ichidaiki*
a. [Jitsukawa Ensaburō] as the ghost of Kansaku
b. [Jitsukawa Ensaburō] as Nichiren Shōnin
10/1849
Chūban diptych
Signature: Hirosada
Theater: Takeda
69-208-89ab

This is possibly a reissue for a later performance in 10/1861.

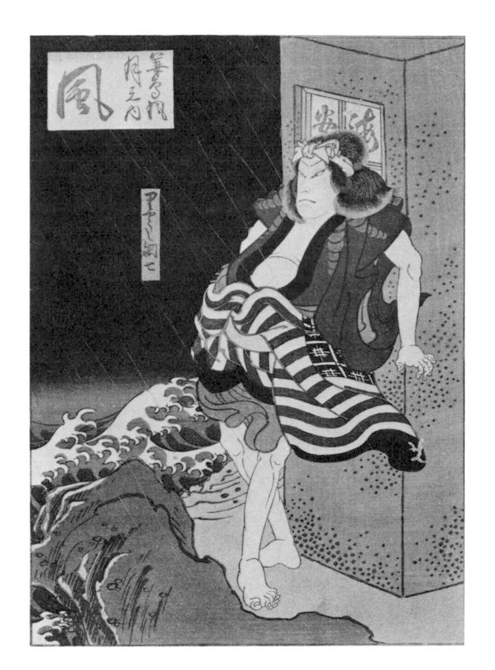

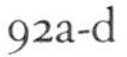

92a-d

90. [Arashi Rikaku II] as
Miuranosuke, c. 1849
Chūban
Signature: Hirosada
Seal: Konishi Gochō
Publisher: Kinkadō
69-208-90

91. [Nakamura Tamashichi] as
Sanshichirō Nobutaka, c. 1849
Chūban
Signature: Hirosada
Seal: Konishi Gochō
Publisher: Kinkadō
69-208-91

92. *Ka Chō Fū Getsu*
*a. Flower [Ichikawa Ebizō V] as
Ishikawa Goemon
*b. Bird [Jitsukawa Ensaburō] as
Jihizō
*c. Wind [Arashi Rikaku II] as
Amishichi, a fisherman
*d. Moon [Ōkawa Hashizō] as Shirai
Gonpachi
c. 1849
Chūban
Signature: Hirosada
Seals: c. Ko; d. Rankei (?)
Publishers: a. unread; b. Ueda;
c. Meikōdō; d. Kawaoto
69-208-92a–d

This is a complete series of four subjects. *See* Cat. 137 (1b, 21ab, and 22a) for related drawings.

93a. [Nakamura Utaemon IV] as
Keisei Hatsuyuki
b. [Nakamura Tamashichi] as
Yuriume, a *kamuro*
c. [Nakamura Daikichi III] as
Wakatake, a *shinzo*
d. [Nakamura Utaemon IV] as
Umanori Komakichi
1/1850
Chūban
Signature: Hirosada
Seals: abc. unread
Publisher: Isekichi
Theater: Naka
69-208-93a–d

These are four panels only of a pentaptych.

94. *Igagoe Buyūden*
a. [Nakamura Utaemon IV] as
Karaki Masaemon
b. [Mimasu Daigorō IV] as Honda
Naiki
1/1850
Chūban diptych
Signature: Hirosada
Theater: Naka
69-208-94ab

95a. [Arashi Rikaku II]as Jingohei, a
yakko
b. [Kataoka Gadō II] as Abe no
Yasunari
1/1850
Chūban diptych
Signature: Hirosada
Theater: Chikugo (Ōnishi)
69-208-95ab
c. Another impression of 95b
69-208-95c

96. *Fūryū Hokku Awase*
a. [Arashi Rikaku II] as Kitsune
Matagorō
b. [Arashi Rikan III] as Kusunoki
Masatsura
1/1850
Ōban
Signature: Hirosada
Seal: Gochō
Publisher: Tenki
Theater: Chikugo (Ōnishi)
71-135-1 (96a)
69-208-96 (96b)

These are right and center panels only of a triptych.

97. [Kataoka Gadō II] as Kizu Shingo,
1/1850
Chūban
Signature: Hirosada
Theater: Chikugo (Ōnishi)
69-208-97

*98a. [Onoe Tamizō II as Kisen Hōshi]
and [Jitsukawa Ensaburō as
Ariwara no Narihira]
*b. [Ichikawa Ebizō V as Sōjō Henjō]
and [Nakamura Utaemon IV as
Ono no Komachi]
*c. [Mimasu Daigorō IV as Ōtomo no
Kuronushi] and [Kataoka Gadō II
as Bunya no Yasuhide]
c. 1/1850
Chūban triptych
Signature: Hirosada
69-208-98abc

These are *mitate* roles.

99. [Jitsukawa Ensaburō] as
Koganosuke, 3/1850
Chūban
Signature: Hirosada
Theater: Naka
69-208-99

This is the second panel only of a tetraptych, the first panel of which shows Nakamura Utaemon IV as Daihanji; the third, Mimasu Daigorō IV as Sadaka; the fourth, Nakayama Nanshi as Hinadori.

100. [Nakamura Tamashichi] as Sutewakamaru, 8/1850
Chūban
Signature: Hirosada
Publisher: Isekichi
Theater: Naka
69-208-100

This is the left panel only of a diptych, the right panel of which shows Nakamura Utaemon IV as the ghost of Takechi Samanosuke. There is a Hirosada diptych with full-length figures of this subject.

101. [Arashi Rikaku II] as Rinpei c. 1850
Chūban
Signature: Hirosada
69-208-101

This is the seventh panel only of an octaptych.

102. [Nakamura Utaemon IV] as Katō Masakiyo, 1/1851
Chūban
Signature: Hirosada
Theater: Naka
69-208-102

103. [Kataoka Gadō II] as Shima no Koheiji, 3/1851
Chūban
Signature: Hirosada
Seal: Sada han (?)
Theater: Naka
69-208-103

This is the left panel only of a diptych.

*104. [Kataoka Gadō II] as Tamaya Shinbei, 5/1851
Chūban
Signature: Hirosada
Seal: Rankei (?)
Publisher: Kawaoto
Theater: Wakadayū
69-208-104

105. [Nakamura Utaemon IV] as Ōboshi Yuranosuke, 5/1851

104

Chūban
Signature: Hirosada
Theater: Naka
69-208-105

106. [Mimasu Daigorō IV] as Heiemon, 5/1851
Chūban
Signature: Hirosada
Seal: Rankei (?)
Publisher: Kawaoto
Theater: Naka
69-208-106

This is one panel of a polyptych.

98abc

111ab

107a. [Nakayama Nanshi II] as Ran no Kata
b. [Arashi Rikaku II] as Kōguya Yashichi
5/1851
Chūban diptych
Signature: Hirosada
Theater: Naka
69-208-107ab

108. *Chūshingura,* Act 2
a. [Jitsukawa Ensaburō] as Momonoi Wakasanosuke
b. [Kataoka Ichizō I] as Kakogawa Honzō
c. [Yamashita Kinsaku IV] as Konami, and [Nakamura Daikichi III (?)] as Ōboshi Rikiya
5/1851
Chūban triptych
Signature: Hirosada
Publisher: Kinkodō
Theater: Naka
69-208-108abc

109. *Natsumatsuri Chūkōden*
[Nakamura Utaemon IV] as Danshichi Kurobei, 5/1851
Chūban diptych
Signature: Hirosada
Publisher: Meikōdō
Theater: Naka
69-208-109ab
See Plate 70.

110. *Seisuiki,* Act 2
a. [Nakamura Utaemon IV] as Kajiwara Heiji
b. [Mimasu Daigorō IV] as Enju
c. [Jitsukawa Ensaburō] as Kajiwara Genta
d. [Nakayama Nanshi II] as Chidori, a *koshimoto*
8/1851
Chūban tetraptych
Signature: Hirosada
Seal: Rankei (?)
Publisher: Kawaoto
Theater: Naka
69-208-110a–d

111. *Seisuiki,* Act 5
*a. [Nakamura Utaemon IV] as Higuchi no Jirō
*b. [Kataoka Ichizō I] as Gonshirō, and [Mimasu Daigorō IV] as Shigetada
8/1851
Chūban diptych
Signature: Hirosada
Seal: Sada
Publisher: Kinkodō
Theater: Naka
69-208-111ab

112. *Komochi Yamauba*
a. [Mimasu Daigorō IV] as Sakata Kurando
b. [Nakamura Utaemon IV] as Yaegaki
9/1851
Chūban diptych
Signature: Hirosada
Seal: Sada
Publisher: Kinkodō
Theater: Naka
69-208-112ab

113. *Sugawara,* Act 3
a. [Mimasu Daigorō IV] as Umeōmaru
b. [Nakamura Utaemon IV] as Matsuōmaru
c. [Jitsukawa Ensaburō] as Sakuramaru
9/1851
Chūban triptych
Signature: Hirosada
Seals: bc. Sada han (?)
Publisher: b. Daijin
Theater: Naka
69-208-113abc
See Plate 71.

*114. [Kataoka Gadō II] as Yorimasa, 10/1851
Chūban
Signature: Hirosada
Theater: Chikugo (Ōnishi)
69-208-114

115a. [Nakamura Utaemon IV] as Kiichi Hōgen
b. [Mimasu Daigorō IV] as Chienai
11/1851
Chūban diptych
Signature: Hirosada
Seal: Sada han (?)
Publisher: a. Daijin
Theater: Naka
69-208-115ab
See Plate 72.

116. [Nakayama Nanshi II, Nakamura Utaemon IV, and Nakamura Tamashichi] kneeling to greet the audience at a *kaomise* performance, 11/1851
Chūban triptych
Signature: Okonomi ni tsuki Hirosada
Seal: Sadahiro
Theater: Naka
69-208-116abc

117. *Mitate Jūnishi: Saru*
a. [Nakamura Utaemon IV] as Yojirō
b. [Nakamura Tomozō IV] as Tsuriganeya Gonbei, [Nakamura Gan'emon] as Izutsuya Gorobei, and an unidentified actor as Wachigaiya Hachibei
c. 1851
Chūban diptych
Signature: Hirosada
Seal: Rankei (?)
Publisher: b. Kawaoto
69-208-117ab

These are *mitate* roles from a series of twelve subjects published with a title page listing actors and roles, engraved by Nakamura Onozō.

118a. [Arashi Rikan III] as Senzai and [Mimasu Daigorō IV] as Okina
b. [Nakamura Utaemon IV] as Sanbasō
c. [Nakamura Utaemon IV] as Urashima
c. 1/1852
Chūban triptych
Signature: Hirosada
Seals: ab. Rankei (?); c. Konishi Gochō
Publishers: ab. Kawaoto; c. Kinkadō
69-208-118abc

119. *Fūryū Rokkasen*
abcef. [Nakamura Utaemon IV] as five of the Six Immortal Poets
d. [Nakayama Nanshi II] as Ono no Komachi
1/1852
Chūban hexaptych
Signature: Hirosada
Seals: aef. Rankei (?); bcd. Konishi Gochō
Publishers: aef. Kawaota; bcd. Kinkadō
Theater: Naka
69-208-119a–f

*120a. [Nakayama Nanshi II] as Tokiwa Gozen
*b. [Nakamura Utaemon IV] as Taira no Kiyomori
*c. [Jitsukawa Ensaburō] as Taira no Munemori
1/1852
Chūban triptych
Signature: Hirosada
Seal: Sada
Publisher: Kinkodō
Theater: Naka
69-208-120abc

121. [Nakamura Utaemon IV] as Taira no Kiyomori, 2/1852
Chūban
Signature: Hirosada
69-208-121

This is a memorial portrait possibly reissued from a print of 1/1852.

122. [Nakamura Utaemon IV] 2/1852
Chūban
Signature: Gosōtei Hirosada
Seal: Gosōtei
69-208-122

See Plate 73.

This memorial portrait is mounted with a memorial portrait of Utaemon IV by Sadanobu (Cat. 291).

123. [Nakamura Tamashichi] kneeling to greet an audience, accompanied by the ghost of [Utaemon IV], 2/1852
Chūban
Signature: Hirosada
69-208-123

124. [Nakamura Tamashichi] as Bunya no Yasuhide, 2/1852

114

Chūban
Signature: Hirosada
Theater: Naka
69-208-124

In the cartouche, above left, is a memorial portrait of Utaemon IV.

*125. [Mimasu Daigorō IV] as Karigane Bunshichi, 2/1852
Chūban
Signature: Hirosada
Seal unread
Publisher: Ikekichi
Theater: Chikugo (Ōnishi)
69-208-125

120abc

125

126. [Kataoka Gadō II] as Inuzuka Shino, 2/1852
Chūban
Signature: Hirosada
Theater: Chikugo (Ōnishi)
69-208-126

This is the right panel only of a diptych, the left panel of which shows Mimasu Daigorō IV as Inuzuka Bansaku.

127. [Mimasu Daigorō IV] as Tomizawa Jūnai, 3/1852
Chūban
Signature: Hirosada
Seal: Sada han (?)
Theater: Naka
69-208-127

128. *Ise Ondo.* [Kataoka Gadō II] as Omine, 3/1852
Chūban
Signature: Hirosada
Seal: Sada
Publisher: Kinkodō
Theater: Naka
69-208-128

This is the right panel only of a diptych, the left panel of which shows Jitsukawa Ensaburō as Mitsugi. A reissue of this print signed Kunikazu appears with the portrait changed to Arashi Kichisaburō III and a new *mon*.

129. [Arashi Rikaku II] as Kamiyui Gengorō, 3/1852
Chūban
Signature: Hirosada
Theater: Kado
69-208-129

This is the left panel only of a diptych, the right panel of which shows Nakamura Tamashichi as Sutewakamaru.

130. [Arashi Rikaku II] as Sanbasō 10/1852
Chūban
Signature: Hirosada
Seal: Sada han (?)
Publisher: Isekichi
Theater: Kado
69-208-130

131a. [Nakamura Tamashichi] as Sarashi
b. [Arashi Rikaku II] as Gomidayū 10/1852
Chūban
Signature: Hirosada
Seal: Konishi Gochō
Publisher: b. Kinkadō
Theater: Kado
69-208-131ab

These are the second and fourth panels only of an octaptych, the first, fifth, and sixth panels of which show Arashi Rikaku II as Sarashi, Narihira, Sekidera Komachi, and Kajiwara Genta; the third and seventh panels show Nakamura Tamashichi as a shop clerk and soap-bubble seller.

132. [Kataoka Gadō II] as Ohatsu 10/1852
Chūban
Signature: Hirosada
Publisher: Isekichi
Theater: Naka
69-208-132

This is the left panel only of a diptych.

133. *Kagamiyama.* [Kataoka Gadō II] as Hatsu, a maid; and [Nakamura Tomozō IV] as Kannai, a gang member, 10/1852
Chūban
Signature: Hirosada
Seal: Sada
Publisher: Kinkodō
Theater: Naka
69-208-133

134. *Kagamiyama Sugata no Utsushie.* [Nakayama Nanshi II] as Onoe 10/1852
Chūban
Signature: Hirosada
Seal: Sada han (?)
Publisher: Isekichi
Theater: Naka
69-208-134

This is the right panel only of a polyptych.

135. [Kataoka Gadō II] as Oniō Dōsaburō, 1/1853
Chūban
Signature: Hirosada
Seal: Sada han (?)
Publisher: Isekichi
Theater: Kado
69-208-135

This is the right panel only of a diptych, the left panel of which shows Ichikawa Sukejurō as Oniō Shinzaemon.

Attributed to Hirosada

136. *Naniwae*
Volume 1 of two albums of unsigned color drawings. Embossed covers with handwritten title slips numbered *jō* and *ge*; 9½ x 6⅝" (blue covers) and 9⅜ x 6⅜" (pink covers). Most of the drawings, of actors in role, are related to published prints signed Hirosada and Sadanobu for performances between 1847 and 1849. They are on thin paper and are pasted, often carelessly, onto sheets that are bound to open accordion-style in polyptychs.
69-208-136 (1-20)

Sheet 1a
[Nakayama Nanshi II as Tora Gozen]
Date: 1/1848
Theater: Naka

Sheet 1b
[Kataoka Gadō II] in an unidentified role
Date and theater not established

Sheet 2a
[Mimasu Daigorō IV as Kudō Suketsune (?)]
Date: 1/1848 (?)
Theater: Naka (?)

Sheet 2b
[Arashi Rikan III as Ishikawa Goemon]
Date: 1/1848
Theater: Chikugo (Ōnishi)

Sheet 3a
[Nakayama Nanshi II as Miyuki]

Sheet 3b
[Jitsukawa Ensaburō as Miyagi Asojirō]
Date: 5/1848
Theater: Wakadayū

Sheet 4a
[Nakayama Nanshi II] as Miyuki

Sheet 4b
[Kataoka Ichizō I] as Akizuki Yuminosuke

Sheet 4c
[Jitsukawa Ensaburō] as Miyagi Asojirō
Date: 5/1848
Theater: Wakadayū

See Plate 69.

A published *chūban* version of 4abc signed Sadanobu is known.

Sheet 5a
[Mimasu Daigorō IV as Takeichi Buemon]

Sheet 5b
[Ichikawa Ebizō V as Shundō Jirōzaemon]

Sheet 5c
[Kataoka Ichizō I as Kamura Udaemon]
Date: 4/1849
Theater: Naka

A published *chūban* version of 5abc signed Hirosada is known.

Sheet 6a
[Arashi San'emon as Morokoshihime]

Sheet 6b
[Ōkawa Hashizō as Tenjiku Tokubei]

Sheet 6c
[Ichikawa Ebizō V as Nippon Daemon]
Date: 8/1848
Theater: Kado

A published *chūban* version of 6abc signed Hirosada is known.

Sheet 7a
[Arashi Kichisaburō III as Manno Hyōgo]

Sheet 7b
[Arashi Rikaku II as Miyakoichi]

Sheet 7c
[Bandō Jutarō II as Jusaku]
Date: 1/1848
Theater: Kado

A published *chūban* version of 7abc signed Hirosada is known.

Sheet 8a
[Arashi San'emon as Ichinoto]

Sheet 8b
[Nakayama Nanshi II as Tsukimasu]

Sheet 8c
[Kanō Kotobuki as Tsumaginu]
Date: 3/1849
Theater: Naka

A published *chūban* version of 8abc signed Hirosada is known. *See* Cat. 65.

Sheet 9a
[Kataoka Gadō II as Wakasanosuke]

Sheet 9b
[Nakamura Daikichi III as Lady Kaoyo]

Sheet 9c
[Mimasu Daigorō IV as Kō no Moronō]
Date: 9/1849
Theater: Chikugo (Ōnishi)

See Plate 68.

A published *chūban* version of 9abc signed Hirosada is known; a fourth published panel showing Ichikawa Shikō as Enya Hangan should exist.

Sheet 10a
[Kataoka Gadō II as Wakasanosuke]

Sheet 10b
[Kataoka Ichizō I as Kakogawa Honzō]
Date: 9/1849
Theater: Chikugo (Ōnishi)

See Plate 68.

A published *chūban* version of 10a signed Hirosada is known.

Sheet 11a
[Nakamura Tomozō IV as Bannai]

Sheet 11b
[Kataoka Gadō II as Hayano Kanpei]

Sheet 11c
[Sawamura Kitō as Okaru]
Date: 9/1849
Theater: Chikugo (Ōnishi)

See Plate 68.

A published *chūban* version of 11a signed Hirosada is known.

Sheet 12a
[Mimasu Daigorō IV as Ono no Sadakurō]

Sheet 12b
[An actor of the Sawamura family as Konami (?)]
Date: 9/1849 (?)
Theater: Chikugo (Ōnishi)

See Plate 68.

Sheet 13a
[Kataoka Gadō II as Hayano Kanpei]

Sheet 13b
[Ichikawa Shikō as Senzaki Yagorō]
Date: 9/1849
Theater: Chikugo (Ōnishi)

See Plate 68.

Sheet 14a
[Kataoka Gadō II as Ōboshi Yuranosuke]

Sheet 14b
[Mimasu Tanin as Oboshi Rikiya]
Date: 9/1849
Theater: Chikugo (Ōnishi)

See Plate 68.

A published *chūban* version of 14ab signed Hirosada is known.

Sheet 15a
[Nakamura Daikichi III as Tonase]

Sheet 15b
[Mimasu Gennosuke II (?) as Konami]
Date: 9/1849
Theater: Chikugo (Ōnishi)

See Plate 68.

A published *chūban* version of 15a signed Hirosada is known.

Sheet 16a
[Mimasu Daigorō IV as Kakogawa Honzō]

Sheet 16b
[Sawamura Kitō as Oishi]
Date: 9/1849
Theater: Chikugo (Ōnishi)

See Plate 68.

A published *chūban* version of 16ab signed Hirosada is known.

Sheet 17a
[Nakamura Tomozō IV as Igo]

Sheet 17b
[Kataoka Ichizō I as Fuwa Kazuemon (?)]

Sheet 17c
[An unidentified actor as Yazama Jūtarō (?)]
Date: 9/1849
Theater: Chikugo (Ōnishi) (?)

See Plate 68.

Sheet 18a
[Jitsukawa Ensaburō as Gorōta (?)]

Sheet 18b
[Nakayama Nanshi II as Okumi (?)]
Date: 3/1848 (?)
Theater: Naka (?)

See Plate 68.

Sheet 19a
[Arashi Kichisaburō III as Ishidō]

Sheet 19b
[Kataoka Gadō II as Ōboshi Yuranosuke]
Date: 9/1849 (?)
Theater: Chikugo (Ōnishi) (?)

See Plate 68.

Sheet 20a
[Ichikawa Shikō as Katō Yomoshichi]

Sheet 20b
[Kataoka Gadō II as Ōboshi Yuranosuke]

Sheet 20c
[Nakamura Tamashichi as Nakashiba Yoshinojō (?)]

Sheet 20d
[Kataoka Ichizō I as Teraoka Heiemon]
Date: 3/1848 (ad)
Theater: Naka
Date: 9/1849 (bc)
Theater: Chikugo (Ōnishi)

See Plate 68.

A published *chūban* version of 20ad is known as part of a pentaptych signed Hirosada for a 3/1848 performance. No published version of 20bc is known.

137. *Naniwae*
Volume 2 of two albums of drawings (*see* Cat. 136).

69-208-137 (1-22)

Sheet 1a
Blank page

Sheet 1b
Ka (flower) [Ichikawa Ebizō V as Ishikawa Goemon]
Date: 1/1849
Theater: Naka

A published *chūban* version of Sheet 1b signed Hirosada is known (Cat. 92a). 1b, 21ab, and 22a in this volume form a complete series of four subjects.

Sheet 2a
[Jitsukawa Ensaburō as Kizu Kansuke]

Sheet 2b
[Kataoka Ichizō I as Sanjūrō]
Date: 8/1849
Theater: Naka

A published *chūban* version of 2ab is known as the right and left panels of a triptych signed Hirosada, depicting Mimasu Daigorō IV as Ujiya Shichibei in the center panel.

Sheet 3a
[Arashi Rikan III as Matsuōmaru]

Sheet 3b
[Kataoka Gadō II as Umeōmaru]

Sheet 3c
[Jitsukawa Ensaburō as Sakuramaru]
Date and theater not established

A published *chūban* version of 3abc signed Hirosada is known.

Sheet 4a
[Arashi Rikō (?) as the nun Seigen]

Sheet 4b
[Onoe Shōju (?) as Matsuwaka]
Date and theater not established

A published *chūban* version of 4ab signed Hirosada is known, depicting Ichikawa Shikō as Matsuwaka and Arashi Rikan III as the nun Seigen for a performance in 1/1849.

Sheet 5a
[Arashi Rikaku II as Umeno Yoshibei]

Sheet 5b
[Nakamura Tamashichi as Chōkichi]
Date and theater not established

A published *chūban* version of 5ab signed Hirosada is known; the panels are reversed in the published version.

Sheet 6a
[Arashi Rikan III as Ishida no Tsubone]
Date: 1/1848
Theater: Chikugo (Ōnishi)

Sheet 6b
[Jitsukawa Ensaburō as Miyagi Asojirō]
Date: 5/1848
Theater: Wakadayū

A published *chūban* version of 6a is known as the right panel of a diptych signed Hirosada, the left panel of which depicts Kataoka Gadō II as Fukumasuya Daisuke. A separately published *chūban* version of 6b signed Kunimasu is also known.

Sheet 7a
[Ichikawa Ebizō V as Uji Jōetsu]

Sheet 7b
[Arashi Rikan III as Kanai Tanigorō]
Date: 8/1848
Theater: Kado

A published *chūban* version of 7a signed Hirosada is known.

Sheet 8a
[Kataoka Gadō II as Kitsune Tadanobu]

Sheet 8b
[Arashi Rikan III as Watōnai]
Date and theater not established

A published *chūban* version of 8ab signed Sadanobu is known as two panels of a triptych, the third panel of which depicts Jitsukawa Ensaburō as Sōma Yoshikado. *See* Cat. 287.

Sheet 9a
[Arashi Rikaku II] as a *rokubu*

Sheet 9b
[Kataoka Gadō II] as a *rokubu*
Date and theater not established

A published *chūban* version of 9ab signed Hirosada is known.

Sheet 10a
[Ichikawa Ebizō V as Ishikawa Goemon]

Sheet 10b
[Jitsukawa Ensaburō as Mashiba Hisatsugu]
Date: 1/1849
Theater: Naka

Sheet 11a
[Sawamura Kitō as Osai]

Sheet 11b
[Kataoka Gadō II as Tamiya Shinjūrō]
Date: 3/1849
Theater: Chikugo (Ōnishi)

A published *chūban* version of 11a signed Hirosada is known (Cat. 69).

Sheet 12a
[Ōkawa Hashizō as Nikki Danjō]
Date: 7/1848
Theater: Naka

Sheet 12b
[Ōkawa Hashizō as Hirai Gonpachi]
Date: 8/1848
Theater: Kado

A published *chūban* version of 12a signed Hirosada is known.

Sheet 13a
[Kataoka Ichizō I as Wada Raihachi]

Sheet 13b
[Mimasu Daigorō IV as Koshino Kanzaemon]
Date: 7/1848
Theater: Naka

A published *chūban* version of 13ab is known as the right and left sheets of a triptych signed Hirosada, the center sheet of which depicts Jitsukawa Ensaburō as Kitabatake.

Sheet 14a
[Mimasu Daigorō IV as Hosokawa Katsumoto]

Sheet 14b
[Arashi Rikaku II] in an unidentified role
Date and theater not established

Sheet 15a
[Jitsukawa Ensaburō] in an unidentified role

Sheet 15b
[Ichikawa Shikō] in an unidentified role
Date and theater not established

Sheet 16a
[Jitsukawa Ensaburō as Kajiwara Heiji]
Date: 5/1848
Theater: Wakadayū

Sheet 16b
[Arashi Rikaku II as Miyamoto Musashi]
Date: 3/1848
Theater: Kado

A published *chūban* version of 16a is known as the right panel of a diptych signed Hirosada, the left panel of which depicts Mimasu Daigorō IV as Matsuemon. A separately published *chūban* of 16b is also known.

Sheet 17a
[Jitsukawa Ensaburō] in an unidentified role
Date and theater not established

Sheet 17b
Three unidentified actors as Tamiya Iemon, Katō Yomoshichi, and Shinsuke Gonbei
Date: 7/1849 (?)
Theater: Takeda (?)

A published *chūban* version of 17b signed Hirosada is known.

Sheet 18a
[Mimasu Daigorō IV as Tōma Saburōemon]

Sheet 18b
[Jitsukawa Ensaburō as Hayase Iori]
Date: 7/1847
Theater: Naka

Sheet 19a
[Jitsukawa Ensaburō as Mashiba Hisatsugu]

Sheet 19b
[Ichikawa Ebizō V as Ishida no Tsubone]

Sheet 19c
[Mimasu Daigorō IV as Kohayagawa Takakage]
Date: 1/1849
Theater: Naka

A published *chūban* version of 19ab signed Hirosada is known. A separately published *chūban* version of 19c is known as the left panel of a triptych signed Sadanobu, depicting the same actors and roles.

Sheet 20a
[Mimasu Daigorō IV as Hatakeyama Shigetada]

Sheet 20b
[Ichikawa Ebizō V as Akushichi byōe Kagekiyo]
Date: 1/1848
Theater: Naka

A published *chūban* version of 20b signed Hirosada is known (Cat. 40a).

Sheet 21a
Fū (wind) [Arashi Rikaku II as the fisherman Amishichi]
Date: 1/1849
Theater: Chikugo (Ōnishi)

Sheet 21b
Getsu (moon) [Ōkawa Hashizō as Shirai Gonpachi]
Date: 8/1848
Theater: Kado

A published *chūban* version of 21ab signed Hirosada is known (Cat. 92cd). *See* Cat. 137 (1b) for series note.

Sheet 22a
Chō (bird) [Jitsukawa Ensaburō as Jihizō]
Date: 7/1847
Theater: Naka

Sheet 22b
Blank page

A published *chūban* version of 22a signed Hirosada is known (Cat. 92b). *See* Cat. 137(1b) for series note.

Hokuchō (active 1822–1830)

Although most Osaka artists mentioned their teacher's name on a single print, or on a group of prints produced at the time of their debut, if at all, Hokuchō announced that Hokushū was his teacher on practically every print that he designed between 1825 and 1826. Earlier, he had designed a few prints that he signed Shunsho. Afterward, Hokuchō designed a fair number of competent if unimaginative prints through 1830, after which he disappeared.

140

138. Nakamura Utaemon III as Karaki Mataemon, 11/1825
Ōban
Signature: Shunkō monjin Shunshosai Hokuchō ga
Publisher: Toshin
Theater: Kitagawa, Kyoto
69-208-138

139. Onoe Kikugorō III as Akamatsu Hikojirō Norimasa, actually Nikki Naonori, 1/1826
Ōban
Signature: Shunkōsai monjin Shunshosai Hokuchō ga
Publisher: Honsei
Theater: Kado
69-208-139
See Plate 32.

*140. Nakamura Utaemon III as Ōboshi Yuranosuke, 4/1827
Ōban
Signature: Shunshosai Hokuchō ga
Publisher: Honsei
Theater: Ichinogawa
69-208-140

141a. Nakamura Utaemon III as Orie
b. Seki Sanjūrō II as Yazama Jūtarō, 4/1827
Ōban diptych
Signature: Shunshosai Hokuchō ga
Publisher: Honsei
Engraver: Ka Hori
Theater: Ichinogawa
69-208-141ab

142a. Nakamura Tamanosuke as Santarō, and Nakamura Sankō as Okumi

b. Asao Kunigorō as Shōhachi, and Seki Sanjūrō II as Jinza

c. Nakamura Utaemon III as Hōkaibō, and Ogawa Kichitarō III as Yōsuke, actually Yoshida Tonoinosuke
5/1827
Ōban triptych
Signature: Shunshosai Hokuchō ga
Publisher: Honsei
Engraver: Ka Hori
Printer: a. Suri Kame
Theater: Kitanoshinchi
69-208-142abc

143a. Fujikawa Tomokichi II as the courtesan Aoyagi, actually Kōbaihime

b. Nakamura Matsue III as Sawagataya Okiku
1/1828
Ōban diptych
Signature: Shunshosai Hokuchō ga
Seal: a. Hokuchō
Publisher: Honsei
Theater: Kado
69-208-143ab

144a. Nakamura Utaemon III as Ume no Yoshibei, and Nakamura Genchō as Doburoku, an outcast

b. Nakamura Matsue III as Oume, Yoshibei's wife
9/1828
Ōban
Signature: Shunshosai Hokuchō ga
Publisher: Honsei
Theater: Naka
69-208-144ab

These may be the left and center panels of a triptych.

145a. Nakamura Utaemon III as Musashibō Benkei

b. Nakamura Matsue III as Owasa
10/1828
Ōban diptych
Signature: Shunshosai Hokuchō ga
Publisher: Honsei
Theater: Naka
69-208-145ab

*146a. Asao Gakujūrō as Sonobe Iori, and Arashi Shagan as Miroku no Sakunin

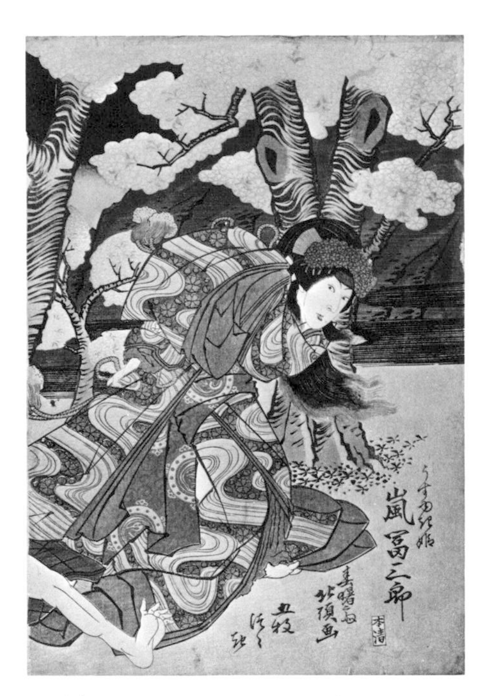

146ab

*b. Arashi Tomisaburō as Usuyukihime
1/1829
Ōban
Signature: Shunshosai Hokuchō ga
Publisher: Honsei
Engraver: Ka Hori
Theater: Kado
69-208-146ab

These are two panels only of a pentaptych.

147a. Ichikawa Ebijūrō II as Horiguchi Manzaemon

b. Nakayama Bunshichi as Hayashi Sanzaemon, and Arashi Rikan II as Kizu Kansuke

c. Asao Gakujūrō as Sanjūrō, a boatman
7/1829
Ōban triptych
Signature: Shunshosai Hokuchō ga
Publisher: Honsei
Theater: Kado
69-208-147abc

148. Nakamura Utaemon III as Shinbei, a *shirozake* seller, 3/1830
Ōban
Signature: Shunshosai Hokuchō ga
Publisher: Honsei
Theater: Kado
69-208-148

This is one panel only of a polyptych.

Hokuei (active 1824(?)–1837; died 1837)

Hokuei had one of the shortest careers of any major Osaka print designer. His earliest print, which he signed as a pupil of Hokushū, was published by Honsei around 1824; and his last print, a portrait of Nakamura Utaemon IV as a wrestler, was published posthumously in the spring of 1837 (*see* Appendix XIV). In this time he designed well over 150 single-sheet prints and polyptychs. He is listed on the broadside of artists published around 1831 (*see* Appendix XI) in eighth place among the "artists who specialized in actor portraits," yet his style did not fully mature until his collaboration with the engraver Kasuke, which began early in 1832.

149. Nakamura Utaemon III as Akizuki Daizen, 1/1829
Ōban
Signature: Shunkōsai monjin Shunkō ga
Publisher: Honsei
Theater: Kado
Reference: Matsudaira, *Hokuei* 5
69-208-149

This is the right panel only of a diptych, the left panel of which shows Ichikawa Ebijūrō I as Dankurō (Matsudaira, *Hokuei* 3)

150. Ichikawa Hakuen as Matsuemon, a boatman, 5/1829

Ōban
Signature: Shunkōsai monjin Shunkō ga
Publisher: Hyōzen
Theater: Naka
Reference: Matsudaira, *Hokuei* 6
69-208-150

151. Ichikawa Hakuen as Saeda Daigakunosuke, 9/1829
Ōban
Signature: Shunkōsai Hokuei ga
Publisher: Honsei
Theater: Naka
Reference: Matsudaira, *Hokuei* 9
69-208-151

152. Onoe Fujaku III as Hosokawa Masamoto, and Nakamura Tomozō IV as an attendant
c. 1829
Ōban
Signature: Shunkōsai Hokuei ga
Seal: Hokuei
Publisher: Honsei
69-208-152

*153. Bandō Jutarō I as Kasugano Koyoshi, and Ichikawa Danzō V as Mameshirō
3/1831
Ōban
Signature: Shunkōsai Hokuei ga
Publisher: Honsei
Theater: Kado
69-208-153

This is the left panel only of a triptych, the right panel of which shows Nakamura Utaemon III as Ki no Aritsune; the center panel, Nakamura Matsue III as Shinobu.

154. Nakamura Tatehachi as Matsuwakamaru, 7/1831 (?)
Ōban
Signature: Shunkōsai Hokuei ga
Theater: Takeda (?)
69-208-154

155a. Arashi Rikan II in a *mitate* role [Wankyū]
b. Nakamura Matsue III in a *mitate* role [Matsuyama]
c. 1831
Ōban
Signature: Shunkōsai Hokuei ga
Publisher: Honsei
Reference: Matsudaira, *Hokuei* 159
69-208-155ab

These are the left and center panels only of a triptych, the right panel of which shows Nakamura Utaemon III in a straw hat and raincoat.

156. Nakamura Utaemon III as Asahina Saburō, 8/1832
Ōban
Signature: Shunkōsai Hokuei ga
Publisher: Honsei
Theater: Kado
Reference: Matsudaira, *Hokuei* 44
69-208-156
See Plate 42.

157a. Arashi Rikan II as Hayase Iori
b. Iwai Shijaku I as Somenoi, 8/1832
Ōban diptych
Signature: Shunkōsai Hokuei ga
Publisher: Honsei
Theater: Naka
Reference: Matsudaira, *Hokuei* 47-48
69-208-157ab

158. [Nakamura Utaemon III as Ishikawa Goemon], 1/1833
Ōban
Signature: Shunkōsai Hokuei
Seal: Fumoto no Yuki
Engraver: Surimono Hori Kasuke
Theater: Kado
Reference: Matsudaira, *Hokuei* 151
69-208-158
See Plate 43.

159. Onoe Tamizō II as Miura Hitachi
1/1833
Ōban
Signature: Shunkōsai Hokuei ga
Publisher: Wataki
Theater: Kado
Reference: Matsudaira, *Hokuei* 54.2
69-208-159

This is the second panel only of a tetraptych, the first panel of which shows Nakamura Utaemon III as Sutewakamaru; the third, Nakamura Tomijūrō II as Gion Okaji; the fourth, Bandō Jutarō I as Saitō Kuranosuke.

160a. Arashi Rikan II as Oguri Hangan Kaneuji
b. Iwai Shijaku I as Kohagi, actually Terute no Mae
1/1833
Ōban
Signature: Shunkōsai Hokuei ga
Seal: b. Hokuei
Publisher: Honsei
Theater: Naka
Reference: Matsudaira, *Hokuei* 59.2, 3
69-208-160ab

153

These are the two left panels only of a triptych, the right panel of which shows Nakamura Karoku I as Okuma.

161. Iwai Shijaku I as Terute no Mae
1/1833
Ōban
Signature: Shunkōsai Hokuei ga
Publisher: Honsei
Reference: Matsudaira, *Hokuei* 60.2
69-208-161

This is the left panel only of a diptych, the right panel of which shows Arashi Rikan II as Namishichi.

162a. [Arashi Rikan II as Chinzei Hachirō Tametomo]
b. [Iwai Shijaku I as Neiwanjo]
9/1833
Ōban diptych
Signature: Shunkōsai Hokuei ga
Seals: a. Hokuei; b. Fumoto no Yuki
Publisher: Matsubaya (?)
Engraver: Surimono Hori Kasuke
Theater: Naka
70-190-1ab
See Plate 45.

163. [Nakamura Utaemon III as Awa no Jūrobei (?)], c. 1833

Ōban
Signature: Shunkōsai Hokuei ga
Seal: Shunkō
Engraver: Surimono Hori Kasuke
Reference: Matsudaira, *Hokuei* 151
69-208-162

The poem is by Baigyoku.

164a. Nakamura Shikan II as Ariwara no Narihira
b. Nakamura Shikan II as Bunya no Yasuhide
c. Nakamura Shikan II as Kisen Hōshi
1/1834
Ōban
Signature: Shunbaisai Hokuei ga
Seal: Shunbai
Publishers: a. Honsei; b. Tenki; c. Wataki
Theater: Kado
Reference: Matsudaira, *Hokuei* 77.1,3,4
69-208-163abc

See Plate 47.

165a. Nakamura Utaemon III as Komafune Hachirō
b. Nakamura Tomijūrō II as Okane, Komafune's wife
c. Arashi Rikan II as Awashima Kainosuke
d. Nakamura Shikan II as Amako Komawakamaru
e. Iwai Shijaku I as Osamu, a horse leader, actually Yukari no Mae
c. 1/1834
Ōban pentaptych
Signature: Shunbaisai Hokuei ga
Publisher: Wataki
Reference: Matsudaira, *Hokuei* 71
69-208-164a–e

See Plate 48.

166. Ichikawa Ebizō V as Akitsushima
3/1834
Ōban
Signature: Shunbaisai Hokuei ga
Seal: Hokuei
Publisher: Honsei
Theater: Kado
Reference: Matsudaira, *Hokuei* 85
69-208-165

This is probably the left panel only of a diptych, the right panel of which should show Nakamura Shikan II as Onigatake.

167. [Arashi Rikan II as Matsugae Tetsunosuke], 3/1834

169ab

Ōban
Signature: Shunbaisai Hokuei ga
Seal: Fumoto no Yuki
Publisher: Honsei
Theater: Naka
Reference: Matsudaira, *Hokuei* 86
69-208-166

168. *Satomi Hakkenshi no uchi Ikko*
a. Ichikawa Ebizō V as Inumura Daigaku Masamori
b. Nakamura Tomijūrō II as the ghost of Fusehime
Early 1834
Ōban diptych
Signature: Shunbaisai Hokuei ga
Publisher: Honsei
69-208-167ab

See Plate 50.

*169a. Nakamura Utaemon III as Kasahara Rōō
*b. Nakamura Shikan II as Miyamoto Musashi
3/1835
Ōban diptych
Signature: Shunbaisai Hokuei ga
Publisher: Wataki
Theater: Kado
Reference: Matsudaira, *Hokuei* 99
69-208-168ab

170a. Nakamura Utaemon III as Ishikawa Goemon
b. Arashi Rikan II as Konoshita Tōkichi
9/1835
Ōban
Signature: Shunbaisai Hokuei ga
Seal: Hokuei
Publisher: Honsei
Theater: Naka
Reference: Matsudaira, *Hokuei* 117.1,2
69-208-169ab

These are the two right panels only of a triptych, the left panel of which shows Nakamura Tomijūrō II as Aya no Dai.

171a. Seki Sanjūrō II as Mizuo Shirōzaemon
b. Arashi Rikan II as Sadasuke, a *yakko*
9/1835
Ōban diptych
Signature: Shunbaisai Hokuei ga
Seal: Sekka
Publisher: Tenki
Theater: Naka
Reference: Matsudaira, *Hokuei* 112
69-208-170ab

172. Arashi Rikan II as Hirai Gonpachi, 9/1853
Ōban
Signature: Shunbaisai Hokuei ga
Publisher: Honsei
Theater: Naka
Reference: Matsudaira, *Hokuei* 111.1
69-208-171

This is the right panel only of a diptych, the left panel of which shows Seki Sanjūrō II as Banzuin Chōbei.

173. *Omemie Kyōgen*
   a. Seki Sanjūrō II as Shunkan Sōzu
   b. Nakamura Tomijūrō II as Oyasu, a wife; and Arashi Kitsuzō as Koben, her daughter
   9/1835
   Ōban diptych
   Signature: Shunbaisai Hokuei ga
   Publisher: Tenki
   Theater: Naka
   Reference: Matsudaira, *Hokuei* 122.1,2
   69-208-172ab

These are the two right panels only of a triptych, the left panel of which shows Arashi Rikan II as Kameōmaru, and Asao Yoroku I as Hyakuōmaru.

*174. Nakamura Shikan II as Yasaku, a farmer, 10/1835
   Ōban
   Signature: Shunbaisai Hokuei ga
   Publisher: Tenki
   Theater: Kado
   Reference: Matsudaira, *Hokuei* 127.2
   69-208-173

This is the left panel only of a diptych, the right panel of which shows Seki Sanjūrō II as Kanpei. A handwritten slip beside the cartouche reads: "The Edo actor Shikan has changed his name to Utaemon II."

174

175a. Nakamura Tomijūrō II as Ran no Kata
   b. Seki Sanjūrō II as Mokuemon, a gardener
   c. Arashi Rikan II as Yashichi, a cosmetics seller
   10/1835
   Ōban triptych
   Signature: Shunbaisai Hokuei
   Publisher: Tenki
   Theater: Naka
   Reference: Matsudaira, *Hokuei* 124
   69-208-174abc

176. *Shibai Suikoden Hyakuhachinin no uchi*
   a. [Nakamura] Baigyoku (Utaemon III) as Nyūunryū Kō Sonshō
   b. [Nakamura] Shikan II as Kumonryū Shishin
   c. [Nakamura] Keishi (Tomijūrō II) as Ko Sanjō Ichijōsei
   d. [Arashi] Rikan II as Rōrihakuchō Chōjun
   c. 11/1835
   Ōban tetraptych
   Signature: Shunbaisai Hokuei ga
   Seals: a. Koshiji no Ume; b. Fumoto no Ume; cd. Hokuei
   Publisher: Kinkadō Konishi
   Engravers: abcd. Hori Kumazō; a. Suke Yashichi; c. Hori Yashichi
   Printers: b. Suri Toyosaburō; acd. Suri Tetsugorō
   Reference: Matsudaira, *Hokuei* 152
   69-208-175a–d

   See Plate 53.

*177. Nakamura Tamasuke I as *hanayumizukai* (a flower-arrow archer), 1/1836
   Ōban
   Signature: Shunbaisai Hokuei ga
   Publisher: Tenki
   Theater: Kado
   Reference: Matsudaira, *Hokuei* 141.1
   69-208-176

This is the right panel only of a diptych, the left panel of which shows Nakamura Utaemon IV as a monkey leader.

178. Nakamura Utaemon IV as the spirit of ivy, 1/1836
   Ōban
   Signature: Shunbaisai Hokuei ga
   Publisher: Honsei
   Theater: Kado
   69-208-177

177

179. Nakamura Utaemon IV as Asahina Tōbei, 5/1836
   Ōban
   Signature: Shunbaisai Hokuei ga
   Publisher: Tenki
   Theater: Kado
   Reference: Matsudaira, *Hokuei* 143
   69-208-178

*180. Arashi Rikan II as Aburaya Yohei 8/1836
   Ōban
   Signature: Sekkarō Hokuei ga
   Seal: Hokuei
   Publisher: Tenki
   Theater: Naka
   Reference: Matsudaira, *Hokuei* 145.1
   69-208-179

This is the right panel only of a diptych, the left panel of which shows Nakamura Tomijūrō II as the courtesan Azuma of Fujiya.

181. *Shimanouchi Nerimono.* Geisha Komine of Daisei as *hayashi* (a *samisen* player), 1836
   Ōban
   Signature: Sekkarō Hokuei ga
   Seal: Hokuei
   69-208-180

180

187

188

This is part of a series illustrated as well by Hokuei (Cat. 182-84), Hokuju (Cat. 188), Sadahiro (Cat. 277), Sadanobu (Cat. 293), and Shigeharu (Cat. 336-38).

182. *Shimanouchi Nerimono.* Geisha Emu of Matsuya as *ukai* (a cormorant fisherman), 1836
Ōban
Signature: Sekkarō Hokuei ga
69-208-181

See Cat. 181 for series note.

183. *Shimanouchi Nerimono.* Geisha Iku of Kitamoriken as *yorukanjo* (a palace attendant with fish) 1836
Ōban
Signature: Sekkarō Hokuei ga
Publisher: Honsei
69-208-182

See Cat. 181 for series note.

184. *Shimanouchi Nerimono.* Geisha Koginu of Daisei as *suehiro,* (a fan seller), 1836
Ōban
Signature: Sekkarō Hokuei ga
Costume designer (?): Yamamura Goto Kō
69-208-183

See Cat. 181 for series note.

Hokugan (active 1816–1832)

Prints are known on which Toshikuni is recorded as a pupil of Ashikuni, others where he is described as a pupil of Yoshikuni. Although it was uncommon for an Osaka artist to acknowledge two masters, Kuroda suggests that only one artist is involved, the Shun'yōdō Toshikuni who is mentioned as a portraitist in *Naniwa Shoryū Gajin Meika Annai* (*see* Appendix XI), and who became Hokugan in 1832.

185. Onoe Tamizō II as Hyakudohei 4/1826
Ōban
Signature: Juyōdō Toshikuni ga
Seal: Magari (?)
Theater: Onishi
69-208-184

186. Nakamura Fukunosuke as Ume no Yoshibei, c. 1826
Ōban
Signature: Baito Juyōdō Toshikuni ga
Seal: Toshi
Publisher: Honsei
Theater: Nagoya
69-208-185

The poem is by Fukunosuke. The actor's name and role appear in a cartouche made of the letters *toshi.*

*187. Arashi Rikan II as Aboshi Uhyōenosuke, and Asao Kuzaemon II as Matsubei, a gatekeeper 9/1832
Ōban
Signature: Toshikuni aratame Hokugan ga
Publishers: Honsei, Kawaji
Theater: Naka
69-208-186

Hokuju (active 1828[?]–1836 [1859])

Although written with the same characters, Hokuju is apparently not the Edo landscape artist of the same name.

*188. *Shimanouchi Nerimono.* Geisha Futatsuryū of Izutsuya as *hayashi* (a *samisen* player), c. 1836
Ōban
Signature: Shun'eisai Hokuju ga
Seal: Hokuju
69-208-187

See Cat. 181 for series note.

Hokushō (active 1822–1832)

Hokushō is mentioned as a portraitist in the *Naniwa Shoryū Gajin Meika Annai* (*see* Appendix XI).

189. [Onoe Tamizō II] reflected in the mirror of his dressing table, c. 1824
Ōban
Signature: Shunchōsai Hokushō ga
Seal: Hokushō
Publishers: Kichi, Tamaoki
69-208-188

See Plate 28.

Hokushū (active 1810–1832)

Hokushū, who is said to have earned his living as a paper merchant, was the only major pupil of the print designer Shōkōsai Hanbei. He was the leading Osaka actor portraitist for two decades and was responsible for many of the conventions and much of the "look" of the Osaka style. Hokushū had a long and fruitful collaboration with the great Osaka engraver Kasuke, and many of their joint works are masterpieces of the Osaka style. Hokushū is mentioned as a copyist-pupil of Hokusai's in the *Hokusai Gashiki* (1819) (*see* Appendix V) and as the first-ranked portraitist in *Naniwa Shoryū Gajin Meika Annai* (*see* Appendix XI) shortly before his death.

190. Kanō Minshi I as Okiyo, 9/1815
Ōban
Signature: Shunkō ga
Publisher: Shiochō
Theater: Naka
Reference: Matsudaira, *Hokushū* 23
69-208-189

This is the right panel only of a diptych, with Cat. 352 (Shunchō).

191a. Arashi Koroku IV (Kanō Minshi I) as Oume
b. Arashi Kanjūrō I as Majima Daisuke
1/1817
Ōban-size drawings
Unsigned
Theater: Naka
69-208-190ab
c. Arashi Kanjūrō I as Majima Daisuke, 1/1817
Ōban
Signature: Shunkō ga
Publisher: Honsei
Theater: Naka
69-208-190c
See Plate 12.

192a. Ichikawa Ebijūrō I as Kōsai Tenzō
b. Arashi Kitsusaburō I as Imaki Denshichi
c. 1817
Ōban-size drawings
Unsigned
69-208-191ab

These two drawings attributed to Hokushū have inscriptions added in 1821 or later. A published version, signed Shunkō, is known.

*193. Nakamura Matsue III as Kotani
1/1819
Ōban
Signature: Shunkōsai Hokushū ga
Publisher: Shiochō
Theater: Kado
Reference: Matsudaira, *Hokushū* 47.2
69-208-192

This is the right panel only of a diptych, the left panel of which shows Ichikawa Ebijūrō I as Kōbei.

194. Nakamura Utaemon III as Konoshita Tōkichi, 1/1820
Ōban
Signature: Shunkōsai Hokushū ga
Publisher: Honsei, Tamaoki
Theater: Kado
Reference: Matsudaira, *Hokushū* 51.3
69-208-193

This is the left panel only of a triptych, the right panel of which shows Ichikawa Ebijūrō I as Yamaguchi Kurojirō; the center Kataoka Nizaemon VII as Oda Harunaga, and Ichikawa Ichizō II as Mori no Ranmaru.

195a. Nakamura Utaemon III as Katō Masakiyo, 9/1820, published c. 1822
Ōban
Signature: Shunkōsai Hokushū ga
Seal: Hokushū
Theater: Kado
Reference: Matsudaira, *Hokushū* 59
69-208-194a
See Plate 14.
b. An earlier impression
69-208-194b

196. Arashi Kichisaburō II as Koretaka Shinnō, and Nakamura Utaemon III as Katō Masakiyo, 9/1820
Ōban
Signature: Shunkōsai Hokushū ga
Theaters: Ichinogawa and Kado
Reference: Matsudaira, *Hokushū* 58
69-208-195
See Plate 13.

197a. Bandō Mitsugorō III as Daihanji Kiyozumi, and Arashi Koroku IV as Koganosuke
b. Nakamura Matsue III as Hinadori, and Nakamura Utaemon III as Sadaka

193

3/1821
Ōban diptych
Signature: Shunkōsai Hokushū ga
Publisher: a. Wataki
Theater: Kado
Reference: Matsudaira, *Hokushū* 66
70-190-3 (197a)
69-208-196a (197b)
See Plate 16.
c. Another impression of 197a
This impression lacks the publisher's name and the blue ground.
69-208-196c

198. Nakamura Utaemon III as Kanawa Gorō Imakuni, and Arashi Koroku IV as Omiwa
3/1821
Ōban
Signature: Shunkōsai Hokushū ga
Seal: Yoshinoyama
Reference: Matsudaira, *Hokushū* 67
69-208-197
See Plate 17.

199. Arashi Koroku IV as Kichisaburō
9/1821
Ōban
Signature: Shunkōsai Hokushū ga
Publisher: Toshin
Theater: Naka
Reference: Matsudaira, *Hokushū* 71.1
69-208-198

This is the right panel only of a diptych, the left panel of which shows Iwai Hanshirō V as Yaoya Oshichi

*200. Arashi Kitsusaburō I as Mashiba Hisayoshi, 9/1821
Ōban
Signature: Shunkōsai Hokushū ga
Publisher: Fujita
Reference: Matsudaira, *Hokushū* 76
69-208-199

This is a memorial portrait. The poem and inscription are by Shikan (Utaemon III).

201. *Ton-Ton-Ton.* Nakamura Utaemon III as Tabakokiri Sankichi, 1/1822
Ōban
Signature: Shunkōsai Hokushū ga
Publisher: Honsei, Tamaoki
Theater: Naka
Reference: Matsudaira, *Hokushū* 86
69-208-200

202. Nakamura Sankō as Keisei Hananoto, 1/1822
Ōban
Signature: Shunkōsai Hokushū ga
Publisher: Tenki
Theater: Naka
Reference: Matsudaira, *Hokushū* 84.2
69-208-201

This is the left panel only of a diptych, the right panel of which shows Ichikawa Ebijūrō I as Kuranosuke.

203. *Konoshitage Hazama Gassen* Nakamura Utaemon III as Ishikawa Goemon, 2/1822
Ōban
Signature: Shunkōsai Hokushū ga
Theater: Naka
Reference: Matsudaira, *Hokushū* 92
71-100-11
See Plate 22.

204a. Nakamura Utaemon III as Kanda Yogorō
b. Ichikawa Ebijūrō I as Teraoka Heiemon
3/1822
Ōban
Signature: Shunkōsai Hokushū ga
Publishers: a. Toshin; b. Honsei, Yamaichi
Theater: Naka
Reference: Matsudaira, *Hokushū* 95.1, 3
69-208-202ab

200

These are the right and left panels only of a triptych, the center panel of which shows Nakamura Sankō as Kashiwagi.

205a. Asao Yūjirō as Sano Genzaemon
b. Ichikawa Ebijūrō I as Miura Arajirō
5/1822
Ōban diptych
Signature: Shunkōsai Hokushū ga
Publisher: Toshin
Theater: Goryō
Reference: Matsudaira, *Hokushū* 98
69-208-203ab
See Plate 25.

206. Sawamura Kunitarō II as Ayame no Mae, and Arashi Kitsusaburō II as Hyōgonokami Yorimasa
9/1822
Ōban
Signature: Shunkōsai Hokushū ga
Publisher: Yamaichi
Theater: Naka
Reference: Matsudaira, *Hokushū* 102
69-208-204

An early state of this print appears with poems, gauffrage, and silver on the woman's head ornament, but without actors' names and roles.

207a. [Ichikawa Ebijūrō I as Tōken Jūbei], 8/1816, published c. 1822
Ōban
Signature: Shunkōsai Hokushū ga
Reference: Matsudaira, *Hokushū* 145
69-208-205a
See Plate 21.
b. An earlier impression
Seal: Hokushū
69-208-205b

208. Fujikawa Tomokichi II as Nagisa, Katsumoto's wife, 1/1823
Ōban
Signature: Shunkōsai Hokushū ga
Theater: Kado
Reference: Matsudaira, *Hokushū* 110.1
69-208-206

This is the left panel only of a triptych, the right panel of which shows Sawamura Kunitarō II as Shigarami (Shinkurō's wife); and the center, Nakamura Karoku I as Kochō (Shōkurō's wife).

209a. Nakamura Utaemon III as Danshichi Kurobei
b. Ichikawa Ebijūrō I as Issun Tokubei
4/1823
Ōban diptych
Signature: Shunkōsai Hokushū ga
Seal: a. Hokushū
Publishers: Tenki, Yamaichi
Theater: Kado
Reference: Matsudaira, *Hokushū* 115
69-208-207ab
c. Another impression of 209b
Signature: Shunkōsai Hokushū ga
Seal: Hokushū
Publishers: Tenki, Touse
69-208-207c

On 209c the mark of the publisher Yamaichi has been removed and the green color block altered.

210. [Ichikawa Ebijūrō I as Wada Raihachi], 1/1824
Ōban
Signature: Shunkōsai Hokushū ga
Seal: Hokushū
Theater: Kado
69-208-208
See Plate 27.

211a. *Isse Ichidai Atari Kyōgen* Nakamura Utaemon III as Kyōgoku no Takumi, 3/1825
Ōban
Signature: Shunkōsai Hokushū ga
Seal: Hokushū
Publisher: Ariharadō, Chū
Theater: Kado
Reference: Matsudaira,

Hokushū 133.1
69-208-209a
See Plate 30.
b. Another impression
69-208-209b

212. *Isse Ichidai Atari Kyōgen*
Nakamura Utaemon III as
Kumagai Jirō Naozane, 3/1825
Ōban
Signature: Shunkōsai Hokushū ga
Seal: Hokushū
Publisher: Ariharadō, Chū
Theater: Kado
Reference: Matsudaira,
Hokushū 133.3
69-208-210

See Cat. 211 for print from same series.

*213. *Isse Ichidai*. Ichikawa Ebijūrō I as
Izumi no Saburō, and Nakamura
Utaemon III as Gotobei, 3/1825
Ōban
Signature: Shunkōsai Hokushū ga
Seal: Shunkō
Publishers: Tenki, Iden
Theater: Kado
Reference: Matsudaira,
Hokushū 131
69-208-211

214. [*Isse Ichidai*]. Ichikawa Ebijūrō I
as Keyamura Rokusuke, 3/1825
Ōban
Signature: Shunkōsai Hokushū ga
Seal: Shunkō
Publisher: Chū
Printer: Suri Zakoba
Theater: Kado
Reference: Matsudaira,
Hokushū 126
69-208-212

This is the left panel only of a diptych, the right panel of which shows Nakamura Utaemon III as Osono, with the title *Isse Ichidai*.

215a. Nakamura Matsue III as Shizuka
no Mae
b. Nakamura Utaemon III as
Kitsune Tadanobu, and Asao
Danzō as Hayami no Tōda
9/1825
Ōban diptych
Signature: Shunkōsai Hokushū ga
Publisher: Honsei, Tamaoki
Theater: Ōdera, Sakai
69-208-213ab

216. [Onoe Kikugorō III as the ghost
of Oiwa], 1/1826
Ōban
Signature: Shunkōsai Hokushū ga

213

Seal: Hokushū
Engraver: Horikō Kasuke
Printers: Matsumura, dō Hanji
Theater: Kado
70-190-2
See Plate 34.

217. Nakamura Utaemon III as
Hōkaibō, 4/1827
Ōban
Signature: Shunkōsai Hokushū
Theater: Horie Ichinogawa
Reference: Matsudaira,
Hokushū 54
69-208-214

218. Ichikawa Ebijūrō I, 7/1827
Ōban
Signature: Shunkōsai Hokushū
Seal: Hokushū
Reference: Matsudaira,
Hokushū 143
69-208-215

This is a memorial portrait. The poems are by Shinshō (Ebijūrō I) and Baigyoku (Utaemon III).

219a. Asao Utashirō as Shinbei, a clerk,
and Ichikawa Ichizō II as
Gokumon no Shōbei
b. Nakamura Utaemon III as
Kurofune Chūemon
c. Nakamura Matsue III as Omaki,
Kurofune's wife
8/1827
Ōban triptych
Signature: Shunkōsai Hokushū ga
Publisher: Honsei
Engraver: ab. Ka Hori
Printers: a. Oto Suri, b. Taki Suri
Theater: Kado
Reference: Matsudaira,
Hokushū 141
69-208-216abc

220. Nakamura Matsue III as Otaka
c. 8/1827
Ōban
Signature: Shunkōsai Hokushū ga
Publisher: Honsei
Theater: Miyajima
69-208-217

The poem is by Baika (Matsue III).

Hokuyō (active 1819–1830s)

Hokuyō is mentioned as a copyist-pupil of Katsushika Hokusai in the colophon of *Hokusai Gashiki* of 1819 (*see* Appendix V), and his rare signed prints appear around this date. He is mentioned again as a block-copyist in *Naniwa Shoryū Gajin Meika Annai,* c. 1831 (*see* Appendix XI) and probably pursued this vocation during the intervening years.

*221. *Yaezakura.* A woman standing
under a cherry tree, early 1820s
Vertical *ōban* diptych
Signature: Hokuyō ga
Publisher: Sujiharaya Shōemon
71-135-3

Kiyoharu (active 1820s–1830s)

Kiyoharu was chiefly a book illustrator, but is listed as a block-copyist in *Naniwa Shoryū Gajin Meika Annai* (*see* Appendix XI) and mentioned in *Keisetsu Gesakusha Kō* (*see* Appendix XVII).

*222. *Sesshū Ōsaka Tenmangū
Gosairei Zu* ("View of the
festival at Tenmangū Shrine in
Ōsaka"), c. mid-1830s
Ōban
Signature: Hishikawa
Kiyoharu ga
Publisher: Shioki
69-208-218

Kunihiro (active 1816–1841 [?])

Kunihiro's first prints were published by Wataki and Honsei in 1816. The following year a set was published by Hirooka, and immediately afterward

221

he designed his first print for Tenki. From that day until he gave up print designing in 1841, practically every Kunihiro print, except for a few collaborations, was published by Tenki. The reasons for this unparalleled loyalty to one publisher may lie in the fact that around 1830 Kunihiro lived in the same Osaka ward as the publisher Tenki, and in a novel published in 1835 he is actually called Tenmaya Kunihiro, as though he were in fact the proprietor of the publishing firm.

Kunihiro apparently had some special relation to Ashikuni, the Osaka painter and illustrator who died in 1818. Several of Kunihiro's prints are based on drawings or are altered versions of privately issued prints by the senior artist.

223. Arashi Kitsusaburō I as Nagai Genzaburō; 9/1812, published c. 9/1821
Ōban
Signature: Kunihiro ga
Publisher: Tenki
Reference: Matsudaira, *Kunihiro* 25
69-208-219
See Plate 20.

*224. *Isse Ichidai*. Nakamura Utaemon III as Shunkan, 4/1825
Ōban
Signature: Kunihiro ga
Seal: Kunihiro
Publisher: Tenki
Theater: Kado
Reference: Matsudaira, *Kunihiro* 26
69-208-220

*225. Nakamura Utaemon III addressing the audience at his "retirement" performance, 4/1825
Ōban
Signature: Kunihiro ga
Publisher: Tenki
Theater: Kado
69-208-221

The packet before the actor contains ginseng sold by his son, Hashinosuke, a druggist.

226. Sawamura Kunitarō II and Ichikawa Ichizō II pulling young pines for a New Year's festival 1/1826
Ōban
Signature: Kunihiro ga
Publisher: Tenki
69-208-222c

This is the left panel only of a triptych, with Cat. 300ab (Shigeharu).

227. Nakayama Shinkurō IV as Tamiya Iemon and Onoe Kikugorō III as Oiwa, 1/1826
Ōban
Signature: Kunihiro ga
Publisher: Tenki
Theater: Kado
70-190-4
See Plate 33.

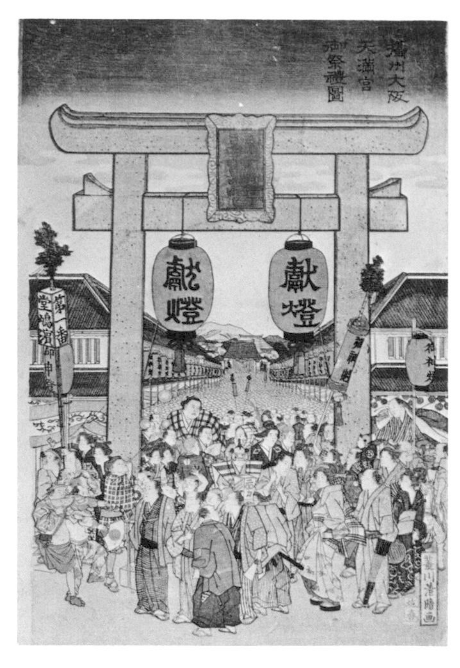

222

228a. Nakamura Matsue III as Otami
b. Ichikawa Ebijūrō II as Yokoyama Daizō
3/1829
Ōban diptych
Signature: Kunihiro ga
Publisher: Tenki
Engraver: b. Hori Kōichi
Theater: Kado
Reference: Matsudaira, *Kunihiro* 77
69-208-223ab
See Plate 39.

229. Ichikawa Hakuen as Kajiwara Heiji, 5/1829
Ōban
Signature: Sanshōtei Kunihiro gasan
Publisher: Tenki
Theater: Naka
69-208-224

230. Onoe Tamizō II as a lion dancer performing *Shakkyō*, 11/1831 (?)
Ōban
Signature: Kunihiro ga
Publishers: Tenki, Touse
Engraver: Hori Kuma
Printer: Suri Ichi
69-208-225
See Plate 41.

231. *Mitate Yamatoya Shijaku*. Yamatoya (Iwai) Shijaku I in summer attire at a cage shop c. mid-1832
Ōban
Signature: Kunihiro ga

224

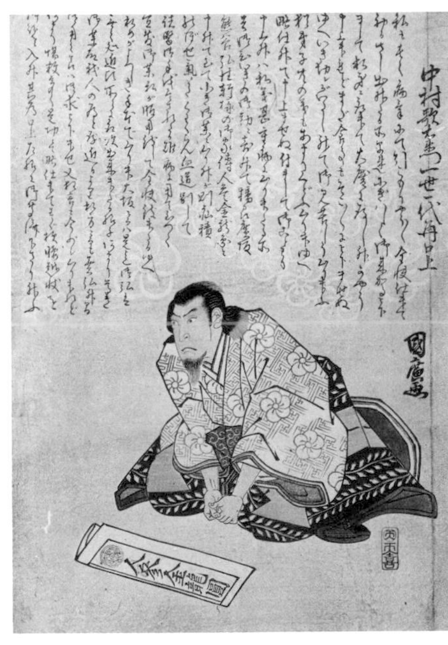

225

Publisher: Tenki
Engraver: Hori Kuma
Printer: Suri Nao
69-208-226

232. *Naniwa Shimanouchi Nerimono.*
Geisha Kiju of Kyōki as Yūgao
c. 1833
Ōban
Signature: Kunihiro ga
Publisher unidentified
69-208-227

This is part of a series illustrated as well by Kunihiro (Cat. 233-34), Shigeharu (Cat. 332-34), and Yoshikuni (Cat. 390c).

233. *Naniwa Shimanouchi Nerimono.*
Geisha Take of Matsutsuruya as the Bodhisattva Fugen, c. 1833
Ōban
Signature: Kunihiro
Publisher unidentified
69-208-228

See Cat. 232 for series note.

234. *Naniwa Shimanouchi Nerimono.*
Geisha Maki of Zenigen as Sekidera Komachi, c. 1833
Ōban
Signature: Kunihiro ga
Publisher unidentified
69-208-229

See Cat. 232 for series note.

Kunikage (active 1831)

Kunikage was an Edo artist listed as a block-copyist in *Naniwa Shoryū Gajin Meika Annai* (*see* Appendix XI) and listed as a pupil of Toyokuni I on that artist's memorial monument (*see* Appendix IX).

*235. *Naniwa Shinmachi Shimaisarae Bangumi no uchi.* Geisha Shizuka of Kamiya as Okina, and Hisai and Ayame as Senzai and Sanbasō
1/1831
Ōban
Signature: Eisai Kunikage
Seal: Kunikage
Publisher: Senri
69-208-230

This is one panel from a series. The poem is by Hokusō Baikō.

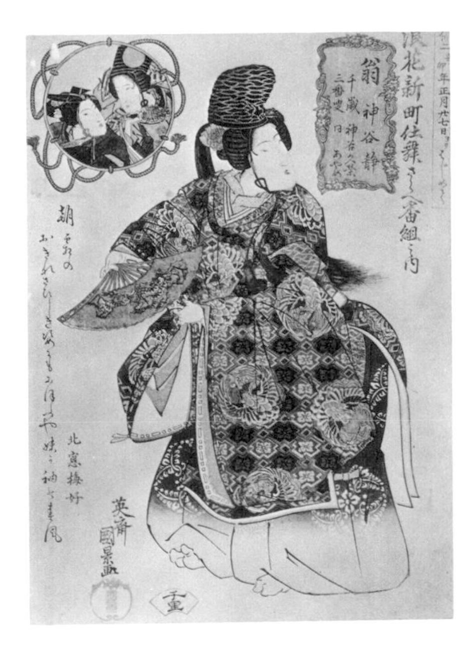

235

Kunikazu (active 1849–1867)

Kunikazu was a prolific print designer whose career spanned the years between Hirosada's retirement around 1853 and the appearance of Yoshitaki in the early 1860s. He was able to ride the crest of technical accomplishment that had been achieved by the time of Nakamura Utaemon's death in 1852, and some of his prints are remarkably beautiful for their time.

236. *Ōtōnomiya Asahi no Yoroi*
a. [Ichikawa Ebizō V] as Tarōzaemon
b. [Jitsukawa Ensaburō] as Umanokami
c. [Arashi Rikan III] as Hanazono
8/1857
Chūban triptych
Signature: Kunikazu
Publisher: Ishiwa
Theater: Kado
69-208-231abc

237. [*Hanamomiji Ōmi Hakkei*].
[Ichikawa Ebizō V] as Mishima Genzō, 8/1857
Chūban
Signature: Kunikazu
Publisher: Ishiwa
Theater: Kado
69-208-232

This is the left panel only of a triptych, the right panel of which shows Mimasu Daigorō IV as Shimada Heiemon, with title; the center, Jitsukawa Ensaburō as Tagami Saemon.

*238. Arashi Rikaku II as a *kamuro*
1/1858
Chūban
Signature: Kunikazu
Theater: Kado
69-208-233

This is the center panel only of a triptych.

238

242

239. *Jūnishi no uchi.* Nakamura Tamashichi as Tabakoya Sankichi, 1/1858
Chūban
Signature: Kunikazu
Theater: Chikugo (Ōnishi)
69-208-234

This is one panel of a polyptych.

240. *Kagamiyama,* Act 4. Nakamura Tamashichi as Motomitsu, c. 1858
Chūban
Signature: Kunikazu
Seal: Kunikazu
69-208-235

This is the right panel only of a polyptych.

241. Nakamura Seijirō as Musashi and Gengobei, c. 1858
Chūban
Signature: Kunikazu
Seal: Kunikazu
Publisher: Ishiwa
69-208-236

*242. *Senbon Zakura. Michiyuki.* Onoe Tamizō II as Kitsune Tadanobu
10/1859
Chūban
Signature: Kunikazu
Seal: Kazu
Publisher: Kinkodō
Theater: Kado
69-208-237

This is the right panel only of a polyptych.

243. *Nanatsu Iroha*
a. Arashi Kichisaburō III as Asahina Tōbei
b. Arashi Rikaku II as Terakoya Hyōsuke
10/1859
Chūban diptych
Signature: Kunikazu
Publisher: Ishiwa
Theater: Horie
69-208-238ab
See Plate 77.

Kunimasu (active 1834–1852)

Kunimasu was a wealthy artist who is said to have spent his fortune on advancing his own school of print design. He had many pupils, and seems to have been at least partly responsible for the vogue of *chūban* bust portraits in the late 1840s and early 1850s, but relatively few prints were published after his own designs then. He is mentioned as a woodblock-print artist in *Ōsaka Shōkō Meika Shū* (*see* Appendix XV).

After Utagawa Kunisada, his teacher, changed his name to Toyokuni in 1844, Sadamasu changed his name to Kunimasu. In 1852 he visited Edo with his pupil Hirosada; the two of them collaborated with other pupils of Kunisada on the backgrounds of a set of half-length portraits of actors by the Edo master. After this trip Kunimasu seems to have given up print designing and begun painting in the Shijō style.

244. *Naniwa Tenpōzan Fūkei* ("View of Tenpōzan in Osaka")
c. spring 1834
Ōban tetraptych
Signatures: abc. Utagawa Sadamasu ga; d. Tōbu Gototei Kunisada monjin Utagawa Sadamasu
Seals: ab. Shigenao; d. Sada
Publisher: Tenki
69-208-239abc (244abc)
71-135-4 (244d)
See Plate 49.

245a. Nakamura Baigyoku (Utaemon III) as Tsujikaze Happei
b. Arashi Rikan II as Ushiwaka Saburō
c. Nakamura Shikan II as Inaba Tarō
d. Iwai Shijaku as Inaba
c. 1834
Ōban tetraptych
Signature: Gochōtei Sadamasu ga
Publisher: Tenki
69-208-240a–d

246. Nakamura Shikan III as Minamoto Ushiwakamaru
3/1837
Ōban
Signature: Gochōtei Sadamasu ga
Publisher: Honsei
Theater: Naka
69-208-241

247. Nakayama Yoshio III as Okon, and Kataoka Gadō II as Fukuoka Mitsugi, 5/1841

248

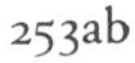

253ab

Horizontal *chūban*
Signature: Sadamasu ga
Theater: Naka
69-208-242
See Plate 57.

*248. Jitsukawa Ensaburō holding a makeup brush, c. 1841
Ōban
Signature: Gochōtei Sadamasu ga
Seal: Sadamasu
Publisher: Honsei
Seal: Jukyū (?)
69-208-243

249a. [Arashi Rikan III] as [Ono no] Tōfū
b. [Kataoka Ichizō I] as Daroku
7/1848
Chūban diptych
Signature: Kunimasu ga
Publisher: Konishi
Engraver: a. Horikō Uchida Torazō
Theater: Wakadayū
69-208-244ab
See Plate 61.

Kunisada (1786–1864; active c. 1807–1864)

By 1821 when he visited the kabuki theaters in Osaka, Kunisada had outstripped his teacher, Toyokuni I, and become the leading actor-print designer in Edo. His visit to Osaka was brief, and none of his designs seems to have been published in that city. Nor is there anything to suggest he taught, met artists, or accepted pupils during his visit. A flurry of Edo-style actor prints were published in the early 1820s, with imitations of censor's seals, and Edo-like signatures, but these were probably prompted by the arrival in 1822 of Hokusai's son-in-law, Yanagawa Shigenobu, who designed Osaka prints in that year and subsequent years.

250. *Ōsaka Dōtonbori Shibai Gakuya no Zu* ("View of a theater backstage in Dōtonbori, Osaka")
Spring 1821
Ōban triptych
Signature: Gototei Kunisada ga
Publisher: ab. Nishimura
Censor: ab. kiwame
69-208-245ab (250ab)
71-135-6 (250c)
See Plate 15.

Kunishige (active 1847–1851)

This is possibly the same artist as Shigeharu (*see* biography preceding Cat. 300).

251. [Jitsukawa Ensaburō] as Hata no Kawakatsu. 3/1849
Chūban
Signature: Kunishige
Theater: Naka
69-208-246
See Plate 64.

*252. [Nakayama Nanshi II] as Koina
3/1849
Chūban
Signature: Kunishige
Theater: Naka
69-208-247

253. *Hankajin Yūden*
*a. [Sawamura Kitō] as Otsuyu
*b. [Arashi Rikaku II] as Zundohei
c. [Kataoka Gadō II] as Tamiya Shinjūrō
3/1849
Chūban triptych
Signature: Kunishige
Publisher: bc. Daisei
Theater: Chikugo (Ōnishi)
69-208-248abc

254. *Chūgiden.* [Kataoka Gadō II] as Jūrobei, 3/1849
Chūban
Signature: Kunishige
Engraver: Ningyōichi
Theater: Chikugo (Ōnishi)
69-208-249

255. *Hankajin Yūden.* [Kataoka Gadō II] as Izaemon, 3/1849
Chūban
Signature: Kunishige
Printer: Horikame
Theater: Chikugo (Ōnishi)
69-208-250

256. [Arashi Rikaku II] as Hisamatsu
4/1849

252

259

261ab

Chūban
Signature: Kunishige
Engraver: Ningyōichi
Theater: Takeda
69-208-251

257. [Arashi Rikaku II] as Yoichibei
4/1849
Chūban
Signature: Kunishige
Engraver: Ningyōichi
Theater: Takeda
69-208-252

258a. [Ichikawa Ebizō V] as Nuregami Chōgorō
b. [Kataoka Gadō II] as Hanaregoma Chōkichi
4/1849
Chūban diptych
Signature: Kunishige
Engraver: a. Ningyōichi
Theater: Chikugo (Ōnishi)
69-208-253ab

*259. [Kataoka Gadō II] as Tokushima Gohei, 4/1849
Chūban
Signature: Kunishige
Theater: Chikugo (Ōnishi)
69-208-254

Masuharu (active late 1840s–1850s)

Masuharu was one of the many pupils of Utagawa Kunimasu who designed *chūban* bust portraits in the late 1840s and early 1850s after the revival of actor printmaking that followed the Tenpō Reforms.

260. [Jitsukawa Ensaburō] as Kizu Kansuke, 8/1849
Chūban
Signature: Masuharu
Theater: Naka
69-208-255
See Plate 67.

Masunobu (active 1849–1853)

A pupil of Utagawa Kunimasu, Masunobu also designed *chūban* bust portraits during the revival of actor printmaking after the Tenpō Reforms.

261. *Kokon Kijinden*
*a. [Kataoka Gadō II] as Yoshikawa Kageto
*b. [Arashi Rikaku II] as Kakusuke, a *yakko*
1/1849
Chūban diptych
Signature: Masunobu
Publisher: Junshi Suri Shin (?)
Theater: Chikugo (Ōnishi)
69-208-256ab

262. [Kataoka Gadō II] in an unidentified role, c. 1849
Chūban
Signature: Masunobu
Publisher: Kawaoto
69-208-257
An unsigned poem appears above.

Munehiro (active 1848–1867)

Munehiro was probably a pupil of Hirosada, but nothing more about him is known.

263. *Chūshingura*
*a. [Mimasu Daigorō IV] as Kiheiji
*b. [Kataoka Gadō II] as Kimura Jirōemon
3/1853
Chūban diptych
Signature: Munehiro
Theaters: Kado and Naka
69-208-258ab

264. Nakamura Hashinosuke as Akamatsu Man'yūmaru, c. 1858
Chūban
Signature: Munehiro
Publisher undecipherable
69-208-259

Nagahide (active c. 1805–1842 [?])

A Kyoto artist who often worked in Osaka, this is possibly the same person as Naraya Ihachi, a Kyoto artist who resided north of Tazaemonbashi in Osaka. He is listed as a portraitist and block-copyist in *Naniwa Shoryū Gajin Meika Annai* (*see* Appendix XI).

265. Sawamura Tanosuke II [as Oryū], 10/1806

Octagonal fan colored by stencils
Signature: Nagahide ga
Publisher: unidentified (Kyoto)
Theater: Kitanoshinchi, Kyoto
71-136-1

See Plate 7.

266. Arashi Kichisaburō II [as Yojirō, a monkey leader], 4/1807

Hosoban colored by stencils
Signature: Nagahide
Publisher: Hakusō (Kyoto)
Theater: Naka
71-136-2

See Plate 8.

*267. Calendar print, 1/1819

Quarter-block format colored by stencils
Signature: Nagahide ga
Publisher: Wataki
71-135-7

The New Year's poem is by Utayoshi. The long months are designed into the standing figure; the short months are listed on the open book.

Nobukatsu (active 1824–1841)

Nobukatsu was a pupil of Sadamasu, whose career as a print designer ended with the promulgation of the Tenpō Reform edicts.

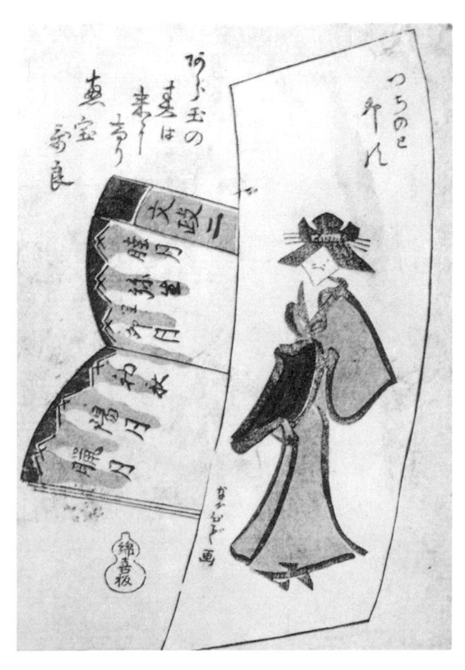

267

263ab

268. *Nanayaku no uchi.* Ichikawa Hakuen as Yorikane and Kinugawa Tanizō, 8/1829

Ōban
Signature: Shigeharu monjin Shigenao ga
Publisher: Wataki
Theater: Naka
69-208-260

*269. Ichikawa Hakuen as Dōtetsu 8/1829

Ōban
Signature: Shigenao ga
Publisher: Tenki
Theater: Naka
69-208-261

The poem is by Hakuen (Danjūrō VII).

270. Ichikawa Hakuen as Oniwakamaru of Shoshazan 9/1829

Ōban
Signature: Shigenao aratame Nobukatsu ga
Publisher: Tenki
Theater: Naka
69-208-262

The poem is by Hakuen (Danjūrō VII).

Nobusada (active 1823–1832 [?])

Nobusada became a pupil of Yanagawa Shigenobu in 1822 when the Edo artist came to Osaka, changing his name from Yukinobu. Very few prints signed by him are known.

*271. Arashi Kitsusaburō II as Awa no Jūrobei, and Ichikawa Shinnosuke as Otsuru, his daughter; 4/1827

Ōban
Signature: Nobusada ga
Seal unread
Publisher: Wataki
Censor: kiwame
Theater: Naka
69-208-263

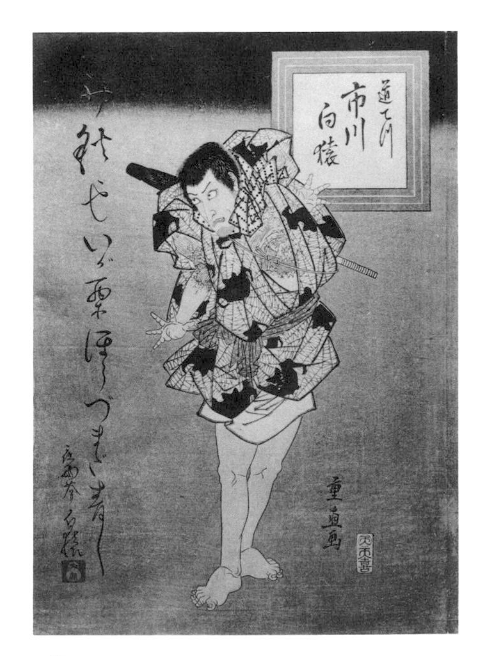

269

271

274

275

Rankōsai (active 1805)

A follower of Ryūkōsai, Rankōsai is known by one *hosoban* triptych, two panels of which are in the Museum collection.

272a. Kataoka Nizaemon VII as Karaki Masaemon
b. Arashi Isaburō I as Ishidome Busuke
8/1805
Hosoban
Publisher: Shiochō
Theater: Kado
69-208-264ab
See Plate 5.

Ryūkōsai (active 1770s–1809)

Ryūkōsai received formal training with Shitomi Kangetsu, the son and pupil of Tsukioka Settei, but gave up academic painting in the late 1770s or early 1780s to become an actor portraitist. He was active through the first years of the nineteenth century, being reasonably considered the founder of the Osaka style. Ryūkōsai was famous in his own day as a portrait painter and book illustrator. He designed, however, a certain number of woodblock prints, most of them *hosoban* full-length portraits of actors published by Shioya Chōbei in 1792 and 1793. Nishizawa Ippō, a playwright reminiscing in the 1840s about the beginnings of actor portraiture in Osaka, says that Ryūkōsai designed "nothing but sets of three," which could only mean *hosoban* triptychs (*see* Appendix XVI). In many cases he signed only one panel, so that several of Ryūkōsai's prints have been misattributed to Shōkōsai, or have been described as anonymous. Even allowing for this, no more than about two dozen of his single prints have been discovered. He probably designed no more than twenty triptychs and a handful of single-sheet prints altogether.

Ryūkōsai has often been compared with his illustrious contemporary Sharaku. Both shared an impulse to accurate and unflattering portraiture, but Ryūkōsai's bold, simplified drawing style and broad use of color is far closer to that of the Edo artist, Katsukawa Shun'ei, whom he may have influenced. There is a tradition linking Shun'ei with Osaka, and his striking transformation of style, after the death of his teacher Shunshō in 1792, came at the same time that Ryūkōsai's single-sheet prints began to appear.

273. Onoe Shinshichi I (Fujaku) [as Isshiki Yūkinokami], 1/1793
Hosoban
Unsigned
Publisher: Shiochō
Theater: Naka
70-36-3
See Plate 3.

*274. Suketakaya Takasuke II in an unidentified role, c. 1790s
Color drawing, $7\frac{3}{4}$ x $5\frac{3}{8}$″
Signature: Ryūkōsai
Seal: Ryūkōsai
69-208-265

Sadahiro (active 1830–1851)

Until recently very little was known about Sadahiro. He was a pupil of Utagawa Kunisada in Edo in 1828, designed prints that were published in Osaka in 1830, from 1835 to 1842, and again in the late 1840s. He illustrated books in Edo in the early 1830s, and designed the frontispieces for Heitei Ginkei's novelette *Chimata no Uwasa,* which was published in 1835. In a section of this book on ukiyoe artists, he was singled out as a promising young artist (*see* Appendix XIII). In 1846 "Gorakutei Sadahiro" was one of three ukiyoe artists listed in a city directory and shopping guide, *Ōsaka Shōkō Meika Shū* (*see* Appendix XV). From 1851 his name disappears altogether on prints until 1864 when Hirokane, "a pupil of Hirosada," took the name

Sadahiro II after his teacher's death, as directed by his will.

It now appears that Sadahiro did, in fact, change his name briefly to Hirokuni in mid-1847, immediately afterward changing it to Hirosada. It also appears that he was the proprietor of the publishing firm Tenki from 1835, shortly after his return from Edo, until 1852 or later. Sadahiro may have begun his career early in the 1820s with a print in the Museum collection signed Kōgadō Tomikuni. Catching the eye of the poet and print designer Yoshikuni, he became his pupil, signing prints and poems Kōgadō Tamikuni between 1823 and 1826. In 1826 he seems to have studied with the Shijō painter, Ueda Kōchō. He published a surimono of his own that year, signed and sealed Konishi Gochō, leaving soon afterward for Edo where, as a pupil of Kunisada, he received the name Sadahiro. The evidence for this theory is presented under Hirosada's biography preceding Cat. 32.

*275. Kataoka Gadō II as Terakoya Genzō, 4/1841
Ōban
Signature: Gorakutei Sadahiro ga
Publisher: Tenki
Theater: Naka
69-208-266

276. [Jitsukawa Ensaburō] as Konoshita Tōkichi, 5/1849
Chūban
Signature: Sadahiro
Theater: Wakadayū
69-208-269
See Plate 66.

277. *Shimanouchi Nerimono*
a. Geisha Tora II of Nakamoriken as *wakanatsumi* (gatherer of spring herbs)
b. Geisha of Nakamoriken as *hashitame* (a maid)
c. 1836
Ōban diptych
Signature: Gochōtei Sadahiro ga
Seal: Sada
Publisher: Tenki
69-208-268ab
See Cat. 181 for series note.

278. *Naniwa Fūkei no uchi: Ajikawaguchi.* Caulking a ship at the mouth of the Aji river
c. late 1830s
Horizontal *ōban*
Signature: Sadahiro ga
Publisher: Tenki
69-208-270
See Plate 56.

279. *Daishinpan Iroha Datoe No. 2.* Alphabet with proverbs and illustrations, c. 1840s
6⅜ x 14¼″ (plus margins)
Signature: Sadahiro ga
69-208-267

This is the second sheet only of two.

Sadamasu II (active 1849)

Teruji Yoshida states in *Ukiyoe no Ura to Omote* that there is a *chūban* recording Sadamasu as a pupil of Kunimasu. Since Sadamasu I changed his name to Kunimasu in 1848, the example in the Museum collection should be a work of the second artist of this name.

*280. [Bandō Jutarō II] as Kurofune Chūemon, 4/1849
Chūban
Signature: Sadamasu ga
Publisher: Horikō Kawaoto
Theater: Kado
69-208-271

This is the center panel only of a triptych, the right panel of which shows Onoe Tamizō II as Gokumon no Shōbei; the left, Ichikawa Shikō as Kamakuraya Gorohachi.

Sadanobu I (1809–1879; active 1834–1879)

Sadanobu I began his career as a pupil of the Shijō painter Ueda Kōchō. In the early 1830s he became a pupil of Utagawa Sadamasu (later Kunimasu), his first actor prints appearing in 1834. By 1840 he was the most active of the Osaka print designers. In 1843, that is, shortly after the Tenpō Reforms, he was adopted briefly into the family of Tenmaya Kihei, the hereditary owner of the publishing firm Tenki. At this time he designed a series of half-length figures of children, which he signed Konishi Sadanobu and Kinkadō Sadanobu, but the association was short-lived; the subsequent year he left the Tenki household. He seems to have had a close and long-standing relationship with the artist Hirosada and may have used some of Hirosada's drawings of actors for prints published around 1850. Later in his career, Sadanobu designed landscapes, bird-and-flower prints, and a series of miniature copies of prints by Hiroshige, which have earned him an undeserved reputation as an unimaginative plagiarist. His descendants carried on his work and the present head of the family, Sadanobu V, may be the last living artist with a direct link to the ukiyoe tradition.

280

281. *Shōgai Onagori Kyōgen*
Nakamura Tamasuke I as Shindō Saemon and Kajiwara Heizō
7/1838
Ōban
Signature: Hasegawa Sadanobu ga
Publisher: Tenki
69-208-272

This is a memorial portrait.

282a. Nakamura Tomijūrō II as Otaki
b. Kataoka Gadō II as Funaya Gengorō
1/1839
Ōban diptych
Signature: Hasegawa Sadanobu ga
Publisher: Honsei
Theater: Kado
69-208-273ab

*283. Nakamura Tomijūrō II as Fusano, a *koshimoto*, 1/1840
Ōban
Signature: Hasegawa Sadanobu ga
Publisher: Tenki
Theater: Naka
69-208-274

This is probably part of a polyptych.

284. *Kyōfuku Tōsei Kurabe,* Kataoka Gadō II as Oguri Hangan, 8/1840
Ōban
Signature: Hasegawa Sadanobu ga
Publisher: Tenki
Theater: Naka
69-208-275

This is part of a series.

*285a. Kataoka Gadō II as Yodoya Tatsugorō
*b. Nakamura Tomijūrō II, as Omatsu
1/1841
Ōban diptych
Signature: Hasegawa Sadanobu ga
Publisher: Tenki
Theater: Naka
69-208-276ab

285ab

286a. Onoe Kikugorō III as Yoshida Matsuwakamaru
b. Nakamura Tomijūrō II as Hanako, later the nun Seigen
3/1842
Ōban diptych
Signature: Hasegawa Sadanobu ga
Publisher: Tenki
Theater: Naka
69-208-277ab
See Plate 58.

287. *Ryūkō Isamashiya Kenkurabe.* [Kataoka Gadō] as Kitsune Tadanobu, spring 1848
Chūban
Signature: Sadanobu
Engraver: Ono Hori
69-208-278

This is one panel only of a triptych, other panels of which show Arashi Rikan III as Wotōnai, and Jitsukawa Ensaburō as Sōma Yoshikado. It is related to a Hirosada drawing (Cat. 137 [8a]).

288. *Giyūden*
a. [Nakayama Nanshi II] as Miyuki
b. [Kataoka Ichizō I] as Akizuki Yuminosuke
c. [Jitsukawa Ensaburō] as Miyagi Asojirō
5/1848
Chūban triptych
Signature: Sadanobu
Theater: Wakadayū
69-208-279abc
See Plate 69.

289. *Chūkō Giyūden*
*a. [Jitsukawa Ensaburō] as Mashiba Hisayoshi
*b. [Ichikawa Ebizō V] as Ishida no Tsubone
1/1849
Chūban
Signature: Sadanobu
Engraver: Horikō Ningyō
Theater: Naka
69-208-280ab

These are the two right panels only of a triptych, the left panel of which shows Mimasu Daigorō IV as Kohayakawa Takakage.

290. *Sangoku Yōfuden.* [Arashi Rikan III] as Tamamo no Mae, 1/1850
Chūban
Signature: Sadanobu
Theater: Chikugo (Ōnishi)
69-208-281

This is the left panel only of a diptych, the right panel of which shows Kataoka Gadō II as Abe no Yasunari.

291. Memorial portrait of Nakamura Utaemon IV surrounded by mourners, 2/1852
Chūban
Signature: Sadanobu sha
69-208-283
See Plate 73.

This is mounted with a memorial portrait of Utaemon IV by Hirosada (Cat. 122).

283

292. *Shimanouchi Nerimono*. Geisha Kinuha of Kyōki as Hagoromo c. 1836
Ōban
Signature: Hasegawa Sadanobu ga
Seal: Nansōrō
Publisher: Honsei
69-208-284

See Cat. 181 for series note.

293. *Ranpyō Ongyoku-musha Hanagassen no Zu* ("A Rough List of the Warriors in the Great Music Battle"), 1848
Double *ōban*
Signature: Hasegawa Sadanobu ga
Publisher: Iida
Engraver: Uchitora
69-208-285

See Plate 59.

294. *Yoshitsune Senbon Zakura* ("The Thousand Cherry Trees of Yoshitsune"), c. 1850s
Small format
Signatures: Nansō, Kageaki, Sadanobu, Sadanobu hitsu, Sekkaen, Hasegawa hitsu, Sadanobu Kageaki
Publisher: Ikekichi
69-208-286ab

These two horizontal sheets each have six uncut prints illustrating acts 1 to 12 of the play *Yoshitsune Senbon Zakura.*

295. *Naniwa Hyakkei* ("100 Views of Naniwa"), c. late 1850s
30 horizontal *chūban*
Signature: variously signed Sadanobu ga, Sadanobu sha, Sadanobu hitsu
Seals: variously sealed Shinten'ō, Hasegawa, Sadanobu
Publisher: Wataki

No. 1. Night market at Shinsaibashi
No. 2. Snow at the Hirota Shrine
No. 3. Soldiers crossing Kōrai Bridge
No. 4. Net fishing at the Octopus Pine, Nakanoshima
No. 5. The Five Hundred Rakan Temple
No. 6. Rain at Ume Bridge, Kitanoshinchi
No. 7. Yasui Tenjin Shrine
No. 8. Bridge at Crab Island, Tsukiji
No. 9. View to the east from Kappa Bridge
No. 10. Plum blossoms at the Umeyashiki
No. 11. Pavilion at the Tamatsukuri Inari Shrine
No. 12. Storehouse at Nanbamura
No. 13. Cherries at the Suiryūji Temple
No. 14. Tsuyu no Tenjin Shrine
*No. 15. Hōfukuji Temple
No. 16. Lighthouse at Sumiyoshi
No. 17. Curved bridge at Sumiyoshi
No. 18. Yotsubashi Bridge
No. 19. Canal by the Tenmangū Shrine
No. 20. Bishamon Temple at Nagamachi
No. 21. Eastern Gate of Shitennōji Temple

289ab

295 (15)

299ab

No. 22. Higashi Honganji Temple

No. 23. Mitsu Hachiman Shrine

No. 24. Urae Giten Temple

No. 25. Cherry blossoms at Hinokuchi

No. 26. Kakumanji Temple

No. 27. Morning at Jianji Temple

No. 28. Full moon at the Shinmei Shrine

No. 29. Snow on the Matsugahana Pine

See Plate 75.

No. 30. Rain at the mouth of the Aji River

See Plate 75.

69-208-282 (1-30)

Sadayoshi (active 1837–1853)

Sadayoshi was a writer as well as a print designer. Besides his various names, however, little else about him is known.

296. Memorial portrait of Nakamura Tamasuke I (Utaemon III) by a lotus pond, 7/1838
Chūban
Signature: Utagawa Sadayoshi ga
Seals: Utagawa, Sadayoshi
Publisher: Honsei
70-190-5
See Plate 55.

Shibakuni (active 1821–1826)

Shibakuni is mentioned as a portraitist in *Naniwa Shoryū Gajin Meika Annai* (*see* Appendix XI). He may have been a pupil of Yoshikuni's, but practically nothing is known about him.

297. Arashi Koroku IV as Okuma
5/1821
Ōban
Signature: Shibakuni ga
Publishers: Chū, Toshin
Theater: Kado
69-208-287

The scroll in the actor's hand gives the date, theater, play title, and names of actors for the performance.

298. Arashi Kitsusaburō I as Gofukuya Jūbei; 9/1818, published c. 1821
Ōban
Signature: Saikōtei Shibakuni ga
70-190-8
See Plate 19.

This may be a memorial portrait. The poem above the mirror may be by the artist.

*299a. Nakamura Shikan II as Nikki Saburō Kunisada

*b. Nakamura Matsue III as Okoma, a lame woman
7/1826
Ōban diptych
Signature: Saikōtei Shibakuni ga
Publisher: Honsei
Theater: Naka
69-208-288ab

Shigeharu (1803–1853; active in Osaka 1821–1841 or later)

Shigeharu, a native of Nagasaki, is mentioned in contemporary accounts as being the only full-time professional actor-print designer in Osaka. His first print, signed Nagasaki Kunishige, was published in Osaka when he was seventeen. In 1825 and early 1826 he collaborated with Ganjōsai Kunihiro on polyptychs. Later that year, apparently around the time that Yanagawa Shigenobu returned to Edo, he combined the first characters of that artist's names and changed his name to Ryūsai Shigeharu. Within months he was rivaling Hokushū as the leading print designer in Osaka. On the broadside of ukiyoe print artists published around 1831 (*see* Appendix XI), he was placed at the top of the list of artists who specialized in block-copies, with a note adding that he was a portraitist as well. Besides prints, he painted billboards, and designed over fifteen illustrated books. His last known Osaka print was designed for a performance early in 1838, but at least one of his books was published there as late as 1841. There is a tradition that Shigeharu returned to Nagasaki after the economic and civil disturbances that occurred in Osaka in the mid-1830s. He remained there until his death in 1853, although he could conceivably have returned briefly to the city in the late 1840s and, reverting to his earlier name, designed the many handsome bust portraits signed Kunishige that have survived (*see* Cat. 251-59).

300a. Onoe Kikugorō III and Nakamura Shikan II

b. Ichikawa Ebijurō I and Asao Kunigorō pulling young pines for a New Year's festival
1/1826
Ōban
Signature: Kunishige ga
Publisher: Tenki
69-208-222ab

These are the two right panels only of a triptych, the third panel of which is Cat. 226 (Kunihiro).

301. Nakamura Utaemon III as Ishikawa Goemon, 7/1826
Ōban
Signature: Kunishige aratame Ryūsai Shigeharu ga
Publishers: Toshin, Daiki
Theater: Naka
69-208-289

302. Onoe Fujaku III as Awashima Kainosuke, 1/1827
Ōban
Signature: Ryūsai Shigeharu ga
Publishers: Touse, Wataki, Hyōzen
Engraver: Ka Hori
Theater: Ōnishi
69-208-290

303. Nakamura Utaemon III as Fujiwara Shihei, 1/1828
Ōban
Signature: Ryūsai Shigeharu ga
Publisher: Kichi
Engraver: Ka Hori
Theater: Kado
69-208-291

304. Nakamura Utaemon III as Musashibō Benki, 3/1828
Ōban
Signature: Ryūsai Shigeharu ga
Theater: Naka
69-208-292

305a. Nakamura Utaemon III as Ume no Yoshibei
b. Ichikawa Danzō V as Chōkichi
c. Nakamura Matsue III as Oume
9/1828
Ōban triptych
Signature: Ryūsai Shigeharu ga
Publisher: Wataki
Theater: Naka
69-208-293abc
See Plate 37.

306. Onoe Fujaku III as Koichirō
c. 1828
Ōban
Signature: Ryūsai Shigeharu ga
Publisher: Kichi
69-208-294
See Plate 38.

307. Asao Gakujūrō as Sonobe Iori
1/1829
Ōban
Signature: Ryūsai Shigeharu ga
Publisher: Wataki
Theater: Kado
69-208-295

308. Ichikawa Hakuen as Higuchi no Jirō, 5/1829
Ōban
Signature: Ryūsai Shigeharu ga
Publisher: Wataki
Engraver: Kasuke Hori
Theater: Naka
69-208-296

309. Ichikawa Hakuen as Banzui Chōbei, 8/1829
Ōban
Signature: Ryūsai Shigeharu ga
Publisher: Tenki
Theater: Naka
69-208-297

310. *Onagori*
a. Ichikawa Hakuen as an ice-water seller
b. Ichikawa Hakuen as Monokawa Kurando
9/1829
Ōban
Signature: Ryūsai Shigeharu ga
Publisher: Wataki
Theater: Naka
69-208-298ab
See Plate 40 for Cat. 310a.

311. Nakamura Utaemon III as Sanni Goroshichi, 1/1830
Ōban
Signature: Gyokuryūtei Shigeharu ga
Publisher: Tenki
Theater: Kado
69-208-299

*312a. Ichikawa Hakuen as Teraoka Heiemon
*b. Nakamura Matsue III as Okaru
3/1830
Ōban diptych
Signature: Gyokuryūtei Shigeharu ga
Publisher: Wataki
Theater: Kado
69-208-300ab

313. Ichikawa Hakuen as Sukeroku
3/1830
Ōban
Signature: Gyokuryūtei Shigeharu ga
Publisher: Wataki
Theater: Kado
69-208-301

This is the center panel only of a triptych, the right panel of which shows Nakamura Matsue III as Agemaki; the left, Nakamura Utaemon III as a *shirozake* seller.

312ab

314. *Naniwa Date Kurabe*

a. Ichikawa Hakuen as an *otokodate*

b. Arashi Rikan II as an *otokodate*
3/1830
Ōban diptych
Signature: Gyokuryūtei
Shigeharu ga
Publisher: Wataki
69-208-302ab

315a. Arashi Rikan II as Furuteya Hachirobei

b. Ichikawa Ebijūrō III as Kōguya Yahei
8/1830
Ōban diptych
Signature: Gyokuryūtei
Shigeharu ga
Publishers: Wataki, Touse
Theater: Naka
69-208-303ab

The title cartouche is formed from the syllables "Shige."

316a. Arashi Rikan II as Furuteya Hachirobei

b. Sawamura Kunitarō II as Otsuma, his wife
8/1830
Ōban diptych
Signature: Gyokuryūtei
Shigeharu ga
Publishers: Honsei, Touse
Theater: Naka
69-208-304ab

317. Nakamura Matsue III as Osono, Ichimisai's daughter, 8/1830
Ōban
Signature: Gyokuryūtei
Shigeharu ga
Publisher: Wataki
Theater: Naka
69-208-305

318a. Arashi Rikan II as Osome

b. Ichikawa Danzō V as Hisamatsu, and Nakamura Utaemon III as Yamagaya Seibei
9/1820
Ōban diptych
Signature: Gyokuryūtei
Shigeharu ga
Publisher: Tenki
Theater: Kado
69-208-306ab

319a. Onoe Kikugorō III as Shizuka Gozen

b. Nakamura Utaemon III as Kitsune Tadanobu
11/1830
Ōban diptych
Signature: Gyokuryūtei
Shigeharu ga
Publisher: Tenki
Theater: Kado
69-208-307ab

*320. Nakamura Utaemon III as Matsunami Kurando, 1/1831
Ōban
Signature: Gyokuryūtei
Shigeharu ga
Publisher: Honsei
Theater: Naka
69-208-308

321. Nakamura Utaemon III as Oboko no Ginta, 1/1831
Ōban
Signature: Gyokuryūtei
Shigeharu ga
Publisher: Wataki
Theater: Naka
69-208-309

This is one panel only of a polyptych.

322. Onoe Fujaku III as Karukaya Dōshin, and Onoe Otomatsu as Ishidōmaru, 1/1831 (?)
Ōban
Signature: Gyokuryūtei
Shigeharu ga
Publisher: Honsei
69-208-310

This may be a memorial portrait of Onoe Fujaku.

323a. Arashi Rikan II as Miyagi Asojirō

b. Iwai Shijaku I as Miyuki
3/1832
Ōban diptych
Signature: Gyokuryūtei
Shigeharu ga
Publishers: Tenki, Touse
Theater: Ōnishi
69-280-311ab

324. [Nakamura Utaemon III as Ishikawa Goemon], 1/1833
Ōban
Signature: Ryūsai Shigeharu
Seal: Ryūsai
Engraver: Surimono Hori Kasuke
Theater: Kado
70-190-7
See Plate 44.

325. Nakamura Shikan II as five of the Six Immortal Poets, and Nakamura Baika as Ono no Komachi, 1/1834
Ōban
Signature: Ryūsai Shigeharu ga
Seal: Ryūsai (?)
Engraver: Kasuke
Theater: Kado
69-208-312
See Plate 46.

326. *Satomike Hakkenshi no uchi Ichinin*

a. [Arashi Rikan II] as Inuzuka Shino Moritaka

b. [Nakamura Utaemon III] as Inukai Kenpachi Michinobu
Early 1834
Ōban diptych

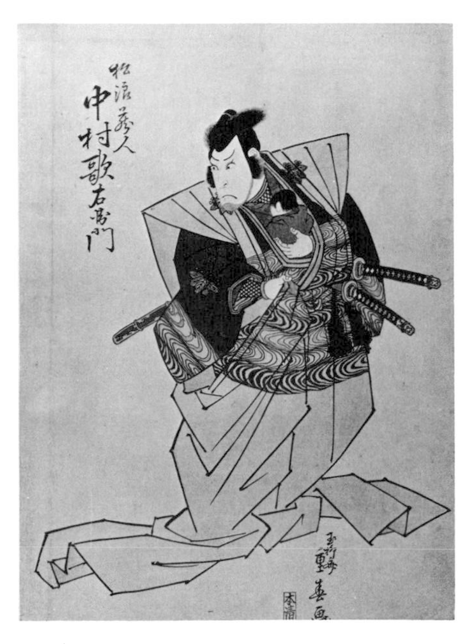

320

328

329abc

Signature: Ryūsai Shigeharu ga
Engraver: Yama Saiku Kasuke
69-208-313ab
See Plate 51.

These are from the same series as Cat. 327 and 328.

327. *Satomike Hakkenshi no uchi Ichinin.* [Nakamura Baika (?)] as a supernatural woman, and [Iwai Shijaku I] as Inue Shinbei Masashi, early spring 1834
Ōban
Signature: Ryūsai Shigeharu ga
Seal: Yamaguchi uji Shigeharu
Engraver: Yama Saiku Kasuke
69-208-314
See Plate 52.

This is from the same series as Cat. 326 and 328.

*328. *Satomike Hakkenshi no uchi Ichinin.* [Bandō Jutarō I] as Inuzuka Keno Tanetomo
Early 1834
Ōban
Signature: Ryūsai Shigeharu ga
Seal: Yamaguchi uji Shigeharu
Engraver: Yama Saiku Kasuke
69-208-315

This is from the same series as Cat. 326 and 327.

*329a. Seki Sanjūrō II as Hangan
*b. Arashi Rikan II as Wakasanosuke
*c. Nakamura Utaemon III as Moronō
10/1835
Ōban triptych
Signature: Ryūsai Shigeharu ga
Publisher: Wataki
Theater: Naka
69-208-316abc

*330. *Nijūshi Kō no uchi* ("Twenty-four filial pieties") showing three Chinese brothers: Denshin, Denkō, and Denki, late 1820s
Horizontal *ōban*
Signature: Ryūsai Shigeharu ga
69-208-317

This is one panel only from a series that probably numbers 24.

331. *Naniwa Horie Kinki Tōrō Odori* Geisha Koyuka of Umeya with a flowery hat, holding two drumsticks, c. 1830
Ōban
Signature: Gyokuryūtei Shigeharu
Publisher: Wataki
69-208-318

330

339a-f

332a. *Naniwa Shimanouchi Nerimono*
Geisha Yana of Daisei as Ama no Ukihashi (the goddess Izanami)
c. 1833
Ōban
Signature: Ryūsai Shigeharu ga
Publisher unidentified
69-208-319a

This impression has gauffrage in the cartouche. *See* Cat. 232 for series note.

b. Another impression with printing variations and lacking gauffrage
69-208-319b

333. *Naniwa Shimanouchi Nerimono*
Geisha Shima and Fusa of Ōmiya as *hanairo-goromo* (a woman in a flowery kimono) and *zenmon* (a boy as a Zen priest), c. 1833
Ōban
Signature: Ryūsai Shigeharu ga
Publisher unidentified
69-208-320

See Cat. 232 for series note.

334. *Naniwa Shimanouchi Nerimono*
Geisha Miyo of Izutsuya as *hachitataki* (a Buddhist devotee)
c. 1833
Ōban
Signature: Ryūsai Shigeharu ga
Publisher unidentified
69-208-321

See Cat. 232 for series note.

335. *Shichihon'yari no uchi*
a. Fukushima Ichimatsu
b. Katagiri Sukesaku
c. Hirano Hyōhei
c. 1834
Ōban
Signature: Ryūsai Shigeharu ga
Seal: Yamaguchi uji Shigeharu
Engravers' seals: b. Aburaka, Yamaka
69-208-322abc

These are three panels only from a heptaptych.

336. *Shimanouchi Nerimono.* Geisha Konabe of Itamigoma as *kesōbumi* (bearer of love letters), c. 1836
Ōban
Signature: Ryūsai Shigeharu ga
69-208-323

See Cat. 181 for series note.

337. *Shimanouchi Nerimono.* Geisha Chō of Kyō-Ōgiya as *yuagari* (after the bath), c. 1836

Ōban
Signature: Ryūsai Shigeharu ga
Seal: Yamaguchi uji Shigeharu
69-208-324

See Cat. 181 for series note.

338. *Shimanouchi Nerimono*
a. Courtesan Ei of Nakamoriken as Kayō Fujin
b. Courtesan Konami of Nakamoriken as Kan'yō
c. 1836
Ōban diptych
Signature: Ryūsai Shigeharu ga
Seal: Yamaguchi uji Shigeharu
69-208-325ab
c,d. later impressions
69-208-325cd

See Plate 54.

See Cat. 181 for series note.

Shigehiro (active c. 1865–1878)

As with most Osaka print designers, Shigehiro's biography is obscure.

*339a. Ichikawa Udanji I as Miyamoto Musashi
*b. Nakamura Sennosuke as Kohagi
*c. Kataoka Gatō II as Kusunoki Masatsura
*d. Ichikawa Udanji I as Eji Matagorō
*e. Arashi Hinasuke as Zubora no Denkichi
*f. Jitsukawa Enjaku I as Mohei, a clerk
3/1870
Sheet 15 x 6½"
Signature: Shigehiro
Publisher: Tamanoi
Seal: aratame
Theater: abcd. Kado; ef. Chikugo (Ōnishi)
69-208-326a–f

These three diptychs are printed on one uncut sheet.

Shigenobu (1787–1832; active in Osaka 1822–1825)

Shigenobu, an Edo artist, was the son-in-law of Katsushika Hokusai, and designed book illustrations and single-sheet prints. He is particularly well known as a designer of surimono. Shortly after his arrival in Osaka in 1822 he became involved with the engraver and printer and print designer

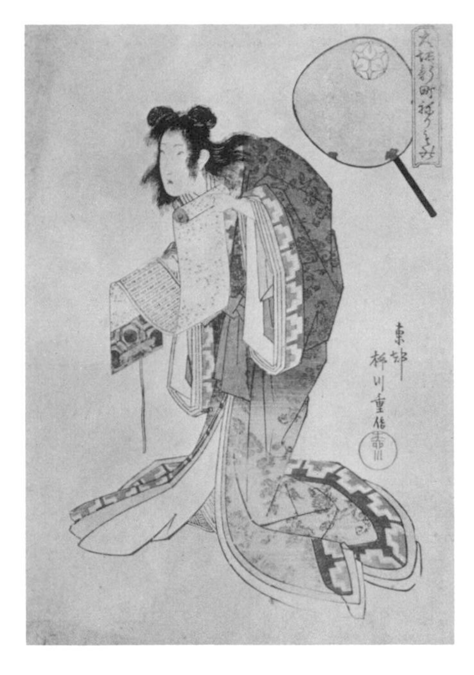

342

Tani Seikō, and many of Shigenobu's surimono that were published in Osaka at this time bear Tani's red gourd-shaped seal. Shigenobu was the first of a series of Edo surimono artists, including Yashima Gakutei and Katsushika Taito II, who worked in Osaka and found the Osaka preoccupation with technique and craftsmanship congenial to their style.

340a. *Ōsaka Shinmachi Nerimono*
Geisha Hatsufunedayū of Nishi-Ōgiya as a *tatebina* (a standing doll), c. 1822
Ōban
Signature: Tōto Yanagawa Shigenobu
Seal: Yanagawa
70-36-4
See Plate 24.

This is from the same series as Cat. 341-45.

b. Another impression
69-208-327

341. *Ōsaka Shinmachi Nerimono*
Geisha Hatsuhanadayū of Naka-Ōgiya dancing *Genjōraku*, (a *bugaku* dance), c. 1822
Ōban
Signature: Tōto Yanagawa Shigenobu
Seal: Yanagawa
70-36-7
See Cat. 340a for series note.

343

*342. *Ōsaka Shinmachi Nerimono*
Geisha Manjudayū of Naka-Ōgiya as Kanzan, c. 1822
Ōban
Signature: Tōto Yanagawa Shigenobu
Seal: Yanagawa
70-36-6
See Cat. 340a for series note.

*343. *Ōsaka Shinmachi Nerimono*
Geisha Yaegumo of Kataya as *Fujidaiko* (dancer with folded fan), c. 1822
Ōban
Signature: Tōto Yanagawa Shigenobu
Seal: Yanagawa
70-36-5
See Cat. 340a for series note.

344. *Ōsaka Shinmachi Nerimono*
Geisha Kotozurudayū of Nishi-Ōgiya as *Asazumabune* (dancer with a cap and folded fan), c. 1822
Ōban
Signature: Tōto Yanagawa Shigenobu
Seal: Yanagawa
69-208-328
See Cat. 340a for series note.

345. *Ōsaka Shinmachi Nerimono*
Geisha Emi of Tsunoi as *atobayashi* (dancer with a hand drum), c. 1822
Ōban
Signature: Tōto Yanagawa Shigenobu
Seal: Yanagawa
70-36-9
See Cat. 340a for series note.

346. Two dancers in butterfly costumes 1820s
Horizontal *aiban*
Signature: Yanagawa Shigenobu
Seal: Yanagawa
69-208-329

SHIMAMARU (active 1830)

The son of the actor Kataoka Nizaemon VII, and a *zamoto,* or troupe leader, at two theaters in 1828 and 1829, Shimamaru was strictly an amateur as a print designer and, like other Shijō surimono artists, may have designed no more than an occasional print.

*347. [Nakamura Utaemon III as Ōboshi Yuranosuke], 3/1830
Horizontal surimono
Signature: Shimamaru ga
Seal: Shima
Theater: Kado
69-208-330

This is a Shijō-style surimono, with a poem by Kataoka Nizaemon VII.

SHŌKŌ OR SHŌKŌSAI (active 1795–1809)

Shōkōsai took up as a print designer where his teacher, Ryūkōsai, left off. Very few of his prints have survived, but following the advertisements at the end of Shōkōsai's first illustrated book, *Ehon Futaba Aoi,* published in 1798, the publisher Shioya Chōbei says: "Besides these we have many different full-color single-sheet prints of actors' portraits. Please inform us of your needs, and we will be pleased to accommodate your requirements." Ryūkōsai had practically stopped designing single-sheet prints by 1798, and since Shōkōsai's pupils did not become active until the 1800s, the quotation must refer to Shōkōsai's prints, which Shioya Chōbei also published. Shōkōsai also wrote his next book, *Gakuya Zue,* an illustrated guide to the Osaka kabuki and puppet theaters, and contributed poems to his album of bust portraits, *Ehon Masukagami,* which appeared in 1806. He was active through 1809, designing books in collaboration with Shunkō (later Hokushū), his most important pupil, and probably died shortly thereafter, since Shunkō briefly assumed his name in 1811.

348. Arashi Sangorō II as Kosobe no Tomoharu, 5/1795
Hosoban
Signature: Shōkō, with *kakihan* of pine needles
Publisher: Shiochō
Theater: Kado
70-190-6
See Plate 4.

349. *Keisei Nazuna no Sekku*
Nakamura Utaemon III as Hanazono Mitchitsune, 1/1806
Hosoban
Signature: Kōnan Shōkōsai ga
Publisher: Shiochō
Theater: Naka
69-208-331
See Plate 6.

*350. *Ehon Kawasaki Ondo*
An illustrated kabuki script, in four volumes, bound as five, with dark blue covers and handwritten title slips; 8¾ x 6¼″. Volume 1, 1-26, with five double-page illustrations; Volume 2, 1-31 (one sheet not numbered), with four double-page illustrations; Volume 3, 1-20, with three double-page illustrations; Volume 4, 21-38 (one sheet not numbered), with two double-page illustrations; Volume 5, 1-16, with three double-page illustrations and unnumbered advertisement for five publications by Hachimonjiya at the end.

350

Signature: Shōkōsai on poem
(Vol. 1, p. 2a)
Date: 1806 on preface
(Vol. 1, p. 1b)
Publisher: not given, but probably
Hachimonjiya
69-208-332

After Shōkōsai

351. *Kōhon Shibai Ehon Ōsaka Kawachiya Taisuke Hanshitabon*

A manuscript copy of illustrations by Shōkōsai for a kabuki scenario, *Kyōhabutae Kawari Hinagata,* published in 1806. Orange covers and modern handwritten title slip; 8⅝ x 6¼″. Fourteen unnumbered sheets with six colored half-length portraits of actors with decorative borders, and ten and one-half black-and-white double-page illustrations; handwritten colophon on final page inscribed *"Shibai Mono Hon'ya. Yakusha Kaonise Shō-utsushi Nishikie Rui Iroiro Ari"* (Theatrical booksellers. Various color prints of actors' likenesses drawn from life), with names and addresses of the Edo publishers Tsuruya Kiemon and Nishimura Yohachi, the Nagoya publisher Matsuya Zenbei, the Kyoto publisher Namariya Yasubei, and the Osaka publishers Shioya Chōbei and Kawachiya Tasuke.

An 1813 reissue of this book signed Ashikuni contains an additional illustration by that artist, but lacks several publishers' names in the colophon.

69-208-333

Shunchō (active 1815–1823)

Shunchō was a pupil of Shunkō. He changed his name to Hokushō, perhaps in deference to his master, who had become Hokushū.

*352. Arashi Kichisaburō II as Kowari Dennai, 9/1815
Ōban
Signature: Shunchō ga
Publisher: Shiochō
Theater: Naka
Reference: Matsudaira, *Hokushū* 23.1
71-135-5

This is the left panel only of a diptych with Cat. 190 (Hokushū).

352

Shunsei (active mid-1820s)

Shunsei was a pupil of Gakōken Shunshi. His life-span is unknown. Judging from his few prints, he supported himself some other way.

*353. *Kokonobake no uchi.* Onoe Tamizō II as Genta and a fisherman, c. 1827
Ōban
Signature: Gayūken Shunsei ga
Publishers: Tamaoki, Kichi
69-208-334

This is from a series of nine changes, along with Cat. 356 (Shunshi) and others.

Shunshi (active 1826–1828)

This is possibly the same artist as Shunpu Haruko who died in 1860.

354a. Nakamura Utaemon III as Ishikawa Goemon
b. Ichikawa Ebijūrō I as Konoshita Tōkichi
7/1826
Chūban diptych
Signature: Shunshi ga
Theater: Naka
69-208-335ab

*355. Onoe Fujaku III as Katsuma Gengobei, and Nakayama Isshi as Kikuno, a geisha, c. 1827
Ōban
Signature: Seiyōsai Shunshi ga
Publisher: Hyōzen
Theater: Shijō, Kyoto
69-208-336

The poems are by Fujaku and Isshi.

353

SHUNSHI (active mid-1820s)

Shunshi was a pupil of Shunkō (later Hokushū) and is mentioned as a portraitist in *Naniwa Shoryū Gajin Meika Annai* (*see* Appendix XI).

*356. *Kokonobake no uchi*. Onoe Tamizō II as an Edo night watchman and as a Chinese princess, c. 1827
Ōban
Signature: Gakōken Shunshi ga
Publishers: Tamaoki, Kichi
69-208-337

This is from a series of nine changes, with Cat. 353 (Shunsei) and others.

SUIFUTEI (active 1782)

There is a painting of peacocks signed Kunitaka at Suifutei, with the seals Kunitaka and Shitō, dated 1783, otherwise there are no known or related works by an artist of this name. His one book, *Suifutei Gigafu,* an album of actor portraits, marks the beginning of the Osaka style.

357. *Suifutei Gigafu*
"The Suifutei Sketchbook," with original light blue covers and printed yellow title slip; 10⅜ x 6½". Pink title page inside front cover with date 3/1782, false publisher's mark, red seal with portrait of theater announcer, and two inscriptions in seal script. Sheet numbered 1 with Chinese-style preface signed Geiki Kasen with a seal; view of crowd before Kyoto theater and two lines of seal script by Mugen Koji with two seals. Thirty-six half-length portraits of actors in role on sheets numbered 1-18. Japanese postscript signed Suikyōrō with a seal and Chinese postscript by Tokushinshu Genmoku with three seals on sheet numbered 19. Three-page Chinese-style postscript signed Kaigeisha (?) and calligraphy by Shinkatsu Sanjin with three seals, followed by one blank sheet numbered 1-2. Seal of the collector Tadamasa Hayashi on first page of preface and second page of last postscript. Japanese owner's name cut out from inside back cover. The actors are named on each sheet with hand-stamped seals, usually giving their *haigō*.
71-88-1
See Plate 2.

Sheet 1a
Arashi Hinasuke I
Seals: Minshi, Minshi

Sheet 1b
Yamamoto Giemon
Seal: Goto
See Plate 2.

Sheet 2a
Nakayama Raisuke
Seal: Sharyū
See Plate 2.

355

356

Sheet 2b
Nakamura Jirozō
Seal: Ganshi

Sheet 3a
Anegawa Minato
Seal: Ikkō

Sheet 3b
Nakamura Noshio
Seals: Rankō and Shūka

Sheet 4a
Asao Kunigorō
Seal: Gadō

Sheet 4b
Nakayama Ihachi
Seal: Shisei

Sheet 5a
Mimasu Daigorō II
Seal: Ikkō

Sheet 5b
Asao Monzō
Seal: Kōzan

Sheet 6a
Sawamura Kunitarō I
Seal: Kitō

Sheet 6b
Hanagiri Tomimatsu
Seals: Shisei, and one unread

Sheet 7a
Asao Tamejūrō I
Seal: Okuyama

Sheet 7b
Nakamura Jūzō
Seals: Koyū and Daisetsu

Sheet 8a
Arashi Bungorō
Seal: Issen

Sheet 8b
Onoe Shinshichi
Seal: Fujaku

Sheet 9a
Yamashita Yaozō
Seal: Tōwa

Sheet 9b
Fujikawa Sango
Seal: Gorei

Sheet 10a
Onoe Kikugorō I
Seal: Baikō

Sheet 10b
Shibazaki Rinzaemon
Seal: Shigaku

Sheet 11a
Arashi Sanjūrō
Seal: Shōta

Sheet 11b
Otowa Jirozō
Seal: Kakō

Sheet 12a
Arashi San'emon
Seals: Hakō, and one unread

Sheet 12b
Mimasu Tokujirō
Seal: Ryōkō

Sheet 13a
Mioki Gizaemon
Seal: Sohō

Sheet 13b
Arashi Sangorō
Seals: Raishi and one unread

Sheet 14a
Yamashita Kamenojō
Seal: Tōko

Sheet 14b
Yamashita Jinkichi
Seal: Kinshō

Sheet 15a
Fujikawa Hachizō
Seal: Happo

Sheet 15b
Yamashita Shungorō
Seal: Moshi

Sheet 16a
Sawamura Kamegiku
Seals: Kamegiku, and one unread

Sheet 16b
Yoshizawa Iroha
Seal: Kōho

Sheet 17a
Nakamura Kyōjūrō
Seal: Sangyō

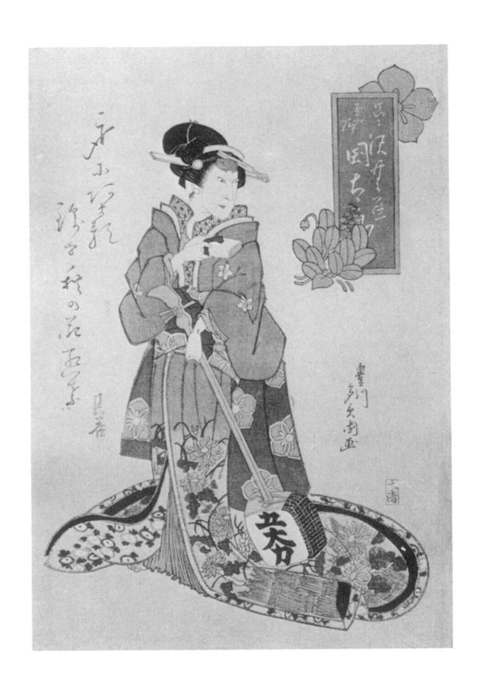

359

Sheet 17b
Nakayama Bunshichi I
Seals: Yoshio and Sanrin

Sheet 18a
Yamashita Kinsaku II
Seal: Rikō

Sheet 18b
Nakamura Tomijūrō I
Seals: Keishi, and one unread

Tamikuni (active 1823–1826)

This is possibly an early name of Sadahiro who used the name Tamikuni as a seal in 1830 (*see also* Hirosada).

358. Asao Gakujūrō as Chōgorō, and Nakayama Hyakuzō as a policeman, 11/1823
Ōban
Signatures: Tamikuni ga, Yoshikuni ga
Publisher: Honsei
Theater: Naka
Reference: Matsudaira *Yoshikuni* 64.2
69-208-338

This was completed jointly with Yoshikuni and is cross-listed under his name (Cat. 373). It is the left panel only of a diptych, the right panel of which is signed Ashiyuki and shows Arashi Kichisaburō II as Hanaregoma Chōkichi.

*359. Sawamura Kunitarō II as Kikuno, a geisha, 9/1826

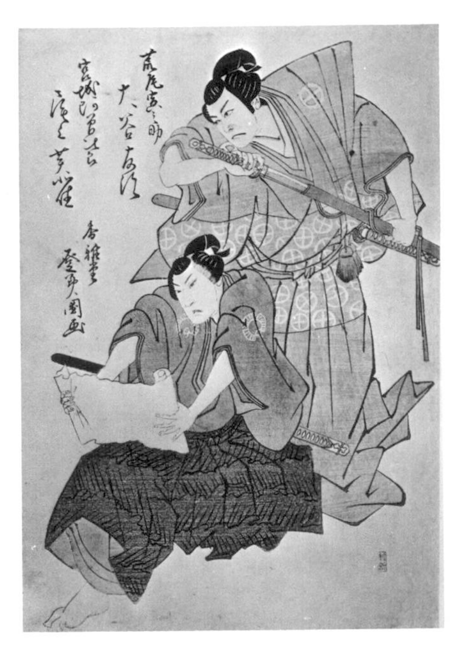

360

Ōban
Signature: Toyokawa Tamikuni ga
Publisher: Honsei
Theater: Naka
69-208-339

The poem is by Kitō (Kunitarō).

Tomikuni (active c. 1821–1822)

This is possibly an early name of Sadahiro (*see also* Hirosada).

361

*360. Ōtani Tomoji as Arao Toranosuke and Onoe Fujaku III as Miyagi Asojirō, early 1820s
Ōban
Signature: Kōgadō Tomikuni ga
Publisher: Toshin
69-208-340

Tōun (active c. 1800)

Tōun was a provincial artist, perhaps active in Aizu. His work has no relation to the Osaka school or style.

*361. The puppeteer Bandō Kamejirō handling a puppet in the role of Ofude, c. late 1790s
Ōban
Signature: San Tōun
Publisher undecipherable
Seal: Kai
69-208-341

This was possibly published in Aizu (collector's mark on verso: Akino).

Toyokuni I (1769–1825; active 1786–1825)

Toyokuni I was the most important and influential actor-print designer in Japan after the retirement of Shun'ei and Kunimasa in the early 1800s. When new publishers proliferated and the quality of engraving began to decline in Edo around 1800, Toyokuni altered his style and made the best of the changes. His prints were a direct source of inspiration to Osaka artists of the mid-1810s, who combined his expansive poses, boldly patterned costumes, and descriptive backgrounds with blocky portraits inherited from Shōkōsai. He made some prints for Osaka performances.

362. Nakamura Utaemon III as Akugenta Yoshihira, 11/1812
Ōban
Signature: Edo Toyokuni ga
Seal: Toshidama
Publisher: Kageben (Edo)
Censor: Tsuruki
Theater: Naka
69-208-342
See Plate 10.

363

Umekuni (active 1823–1826)

A surimono signed Umekuni (Baikoku) has been attributed to Ryūkōsai's son Shiken, who may be the same artist. Umekuni changed his poetry name to Kensan (?) in 1824.

*363. Sawamura Gennosuke II as Shirai Gonpachi, c. 1824
Ōban
Signature: Jugyōdō Umekuni ga
Seal: Umekuni
Publishers: Tenki, Iden
69-208-343

364. Geisha Koyoshi of Itamikō at Sakamachi, Naniwa, c. 1824
Ōban
Signature: Umekuni ga
Publisher: Iden
69-208-344

The printed inscription beside the signature reads: "Upon request while drunk at a brothel in Kōnan."

Yoshikuni (active 1800 [?], 1813–1832)

Yoshikuni was active as a print designer between 1813 and 1830, but is equally important as a poet. He may have been the son of Hakuensai Baikō, the late eighteenth century Osaka poet who was the proprietor of the publishing firm Shioya Saburobei. Yoshikuni may have begun his career in 1800 with a poetry anthology, and could have designed two or three prints that appeared with the signature Jukō in 1813. Although his career as a print designer ended around 1832, he seems to have continued his activity as a poet, leading the Jukōsha poetry group whose members designed actor prints (*see* Appendixes VI and VIII). Some of his poems appear in Akatsuki no Kanenari's unpublished mid-nineteenth-century manuscript on Osaka geography and history, which is printed in *Naniwa Sōsho,* volumes 7 and 8.

365. Nakamura Utaemon III and attendant entering Kado Theater in Osaka, 1/1821
Ōban
Signature: Jukōdō Yoshikuni ga
Publishers: Toshin, Arihara, Chū
Reference: Matsudaira, *Yoshikuni* 8
69-208-345

There are at least three panels in this series. Two others show Bandō Mitsugorō III, and Asao Okuyama II with Nakamura Karoku I. The poem is by Shikan (Utaemon III).

366. Nakamura Utaemon III as a *yakko,* 1/1821
Ōban
Signature: Yoshikuni ga
Seal: Yoshi
Publisher: Wataki
Seal: Maeda (?)
Reference: Matsudaira, *Yoshikuni* 13.2
69-208-346

This is the left panel only of a diptych, the right panel of which shows Bandō Mitsugorō III as another *yakko.*

367. Nakamura Utaemon III as Fukashichi, actually Kanawa Gorō Imakuni, 3/1821
Ōban
Signature: Yoshikuni ga
Publisher: Toshin
Theater: Kado
69-208-347
See Plate 18.

368. Nakamura Utaemon III as Izaemon, 3/1821
Ōban

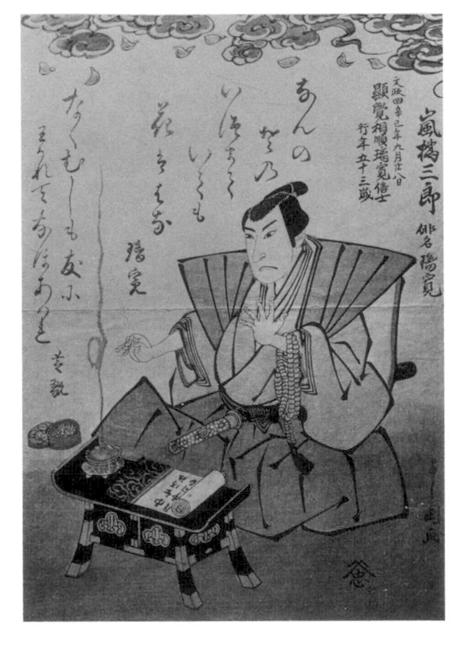

369

Signature: Yoshikuni ga
Publishers: Arichū, Toshin
Theater: Kado
Reference: Matsudaira, *Yoshikuni* 18.2
69-208-348

This is the left panel only of a diptych, the right panel of which shows Bandō Mitsugorō III as Yūgiri. The inscription reads: "The Yūgiri and Izaemon roles are switched every other day."

*369. Arashi Kichisaburō I, 9/1821
Ōban
Signature: Yoshikuni ga
Publishers: Chū, Toshin
Reference: Matsudaira, *Yoshikuni* 29
69-208-349

This is a memorial portrait. The poems are by Rikan (Kichisaburō I) and Shikan (Utaemon III).

370. Ichikawa Ebijūrō I as Heita
11/1821
Ōban
Signature: Yoshikuni ga
Publishers: Chū, Toshin
Theater: Naka
Reference: Matsudaira, *Yoshikuni* 34.2
69-208-350

This is the center panel only of a triptych, the right panel of which shows Arashi Koroku IV as Ofune; the left, Nakamura Utaemon III as Genpachi.

371. Ichikawa Danzō V as Tamaya Shinbei, 7/1822
Ōban
Signature: Yoshikuni ga, Yoshi as circular cartouche
Publishers: Honsei, Ichi
Theater: Naka
69-208-351
See Plate 26.

372. Nakamura Karoku I as Kochō, Shōkurō's wife, 1/1823
Ōban
Signature: Yoshikuni ga
Publishers: Toshin, Iden
Theater: Kado
Reference: Matsudaira, *Yoshikuni* 52.2
69-208-352

This is the center panel only of a triptych, the right panel of which is signed by Ashiyuki and shows Fujikawa Tomokichi II as Nakai Ohana; the left panel, signed by Kunihiro, shows Sawamura Kunitarō II as Shigarami.

373. *See* Cat. 358 (Tamikuni).

*374. Nakamura Tsurusuke I as Kuzunoha and Sōma Tarō, c. 1823
Ōban
Signature: Yoshikuni ga
Publishers: Toshin, Chū
69-208-353

375. *Kyūhenge no uchi*
a. Nakamura Utaemon III as a heavenly musician
b. Nakamura Utaemon III as a nine-tailed fox
1/1825
Ōban
Signature: Jukōdō Yoshikuni ga
Seal: Yoshi
Publisher: ab. Honsei; a. Tamaoki
Theater: Kado
Reference: Matsudaira, *Yoshikuni* 70.2,4
69-208-354ab
See Plate 29.

376. *Nakamura Utaemon Isse Ichidai ni tsuki.* Nakamura Tsurusuke I as Urashima, 3/1825
Ōban
Signature: Jukōdō Yoshikuni ga
Publisher: Honsei
Theater: Kado
Reference: Matsudaira, *Yoshikuni* 75
69-208-355

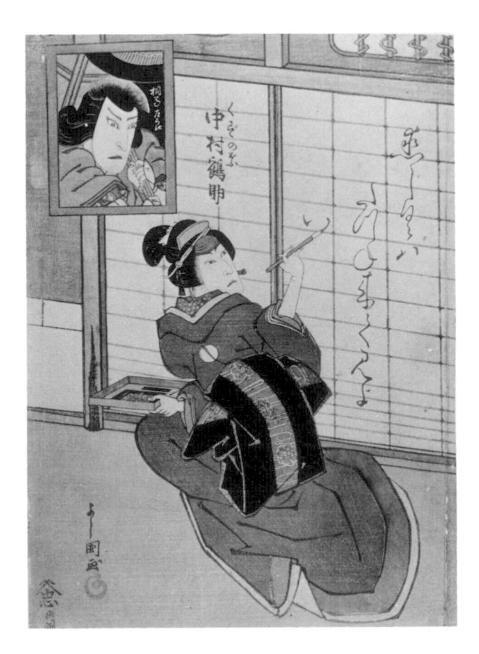

374

*377a. Asao Gakujūrō as Shiba Shōgun Ryūei
*b. Ichikawa Danzō V as Go Dōshi
*c. Fujikawa Tomokichi II as Tagoto
7/1825
Ōban triptych
Signature: Jukōdō Yoshikuni ga
Publisher: ab. Honsei;
abc. Tamaoki
Theater: Naka
Reference: Matsudaira, *Yoshikuni* 79
69-208-356abc

378. Nakamura Shikan II as Honda Naiki, 11/1825
Ōban
Signature: Jukōdō Yoshikuni ga
Publisher: Honsei
Theater: Kitagawa, Kyoto
Reference: Matsudaira, *Yoshikuni* 84
69-208-357

379. Onoe Kikugorō III as Kan Shōjō
3/1826
Ōban
Signature: Jukōdō Yoshikuni ga
Publisher: Honsei
Theater: Naka
Reference: Matsudaira, *Yoshikuni* 91
69-208-358

380a. Nakamura Shikan II as Matsuōmaru
b. Asao Gakujūrō as Takebe Genzō
3/1826

377abc

Ōban diptych
Signature: Jukōdō Yoshikuni ga
Publisher: Honsei
Theater: Naka
Reference: Matsudaira, *Yoshikuni* 93
69-208-359ab

381. Nakamura Shikan II as Iruka Daijin, 4/1826
Ōban
Signature: Yoshikuni ga
Publisher: Wataki
Theater: Kado
69-208-360

See Plate 35.

382. Nakamura Shikan II as Yokoyama Tarō, and Nakamura Matsue III as Asaka, his wife 5/1826
Ōban
Signature: Jukōdō Yoshikuni ga
Publisher: Honsei
Theater: Horie Ichinogawa
Reference: Matsudaira, *Yoshikuni* 96
69-208-361

383. Seki Sanjūrō II as Hanaregoma Chōkichi, 7/1827
Ōban
Signature: Toyokawa Yoshikuni ga
Publisher: Honsei
Theater: Kado
69-208-362

This is the left panel only of a diptych, the right panel of which shows Nakamura Shikan II as Nuregami Chōgorō.

384. *Nakamura Shikan Somen Nōryō no Zu.* Nakamura Shikan II, in summer attire, cooling himself by a river, c. mid-1827
Ōban
Signature: Toyokawa Yoshikuni ga
Publisher: Honsei
69-208-363

This right panel of a diptych is mounted with Cat. 16 (Ashiyuki).

385. *Onagori Kyōgen Shosagoto. Gomai no uchi.* Nakamura Shikan II as Daijin, 10/1827
Ōban
Signature: Toyokawa Yoshikuni ga
Publisher: Honsei
Theater: Kado
Reference: Matsudaira, *Yoshikuni* 113.2
69-208-364

This is the second panel only of a pentaptych. Other panels show Nakamura Shikan II as a babysitter, a palanquin bearer, the Kuzunoha Fox, and Fox Kanpei.

386. Ichikawa Ebijūrō II as Ki no Haseo, 1/1828
Ōban
Signature: Yoshikuni
Publishers: Tamaoki, Kichi
Theater: Kado
Reference: Matsudaira, *Yoshikuni* 114.1
69-208-365

This is the right panel only of a triptych, the center panel of which shows Fujikawa Tomokichi II as Kōbaihime; the left panel, Nakamura Utaemon III as Kujaku Saburō.

388

387. Nakamura Utaemon III as Ishikawa Goemon, 1/1830
Ōban
Signature: Jukōdō Yoshikuni ga
Publisher: Kichi
Theater: Kado
Reference: Matsudaira, *Yoshikuni* 117.1
69-208-366

This is the right panel only of a triptych, the center panel of which shows Arashi Rikan II as Kobuna Gengorō; the left, Ichikawa Takijūrō as Katata Kosuzume.

*388. Courtesan Hinasakudayū of Nishi-Ōgiya as *eboshigimi* (a *shirabyōshi* dancer), c. 1830
Ōban
Signature: Jukōdō Yoshikuni ga
69-208-367

This is the left panel only of a diptych, the right panel of which shows courtesan Agemakidayū of Naka-Kineya as Dengaku Bōzu.

389a. Geisha Misaki of Naka-Ōgiya as *tsuemochi* (a baton bearer)
b. Geisha Rikino of Wataya as *morokoshi kanjo* (a Chinese court lady)
c. Geisha Hinadori of Naka-Ōgiya as *tatarazuri* (a musician)
c. 1830
Ōban triptych
Signature: Jukōdō Yoshikuni ga
Seals unread
69-208-368abc

390. *Naniwa Shimanouchi Nerimono*
a. Geisha Kiju of Kyōya as Yūgao (a flower)
b. Geisha Emika of Kyōkiya as Shizuka at Yoshino (snow)
Early 1830s
Ōban
Unsigned
Seal: Kō uji zuga
69-708-369ab

These are two panels only of a triptych, the third panel of which portrays a geisha representing the moon.

c. Geisha Emi of Kyōki as Shizuka, another version of 390b
Publisher unidentified
69-208-369c

In this state the face of the geisha has been re-engraved. The cartouche and titles have been altered, and a publisher's mark added for republication in the series described in Cat. 232 (Kunihiro).

391ab

Yoshimine (active 1856–1858 or later)

Yoshimine was a pupil of Yoshiume. Very little is known about his life; even his names are obscure.

391. *Mitate Buyūden*
*a. [Kataoka Gadō II] as Tawara Tōda
*b. [Arashi Rikaku II] as Otohime
c. 1857
Chūban diptych
Signature: Yoshimine
Printer: Suri Gen
69-208-370ab

Yoshitaki (1841–1899; active 1854–1880)

Yoshitaki was the son of a paste merchant. His earliest prints were published when he had barely entered his teens. By the time he was twenty, he had firmly established himself as the leading theatrical portraitist in Osaka, a position that he held for at least twenty years. His son, Kawasaki Kyosen, wrote an interesting article on his father's practice as an artist. It shows the tremendous pressure Yoshitaki and his contemporaries worked under, and enables us to understand the conditions that led to the decline of actor-print design in the second half of the nineteenth century. The article is translated as Appendix XXIII.

*392. *Setsugekka*, Act 3, *Kiri*. Jitsukawa Ensaburō as Gengorō, Arashi Kichisaburō III as Kuranosuke, Onoe Tamizō II as Goemon, Ichikawa Ebijūrō IV as Masaemon, Bandō Hikosaburō V as Shirojirō, 1/1858
Chūban
Signature: Ichiyōsai Yoshitaki ga
Theater: Naka
69-208-371

392

409ab

393. *Jin Gi Rei Chi Shin no uchi: Rei.*
[Arashi Rikaku II] as Terakoya Hyōsuke, and an unidentified actor as Fudematsu, his son
5/1861
Chūban
Signature: Yoshitaki ga
Theater: Horie
69-208-372

This is one panel only of a series of five virtues.

394. *Adakurabe Kokonoe Nishiki*
a. [Nakamura Jakuemon I] as Sarusuberi no Iwamatsu
b. [Arashi Rikaku II] as Soma Yasaku
7/1861
Chūban diptych
Signature: Yoshitaki ga
Theater: Kado
69-208-373ab

395a. [Ichikawa Takijūrō] as Hata no Kurando, and [Arashi Rikan III] as Oryū, spirit of the willow tree
b. [Arashi Rikaku II] as Soma Yasaku
7/1861
Chūban diptych
Signature: Yoshitaki ga
Seal: Atari
Theater: Kado
69-208-374ab

396. *Nazoraebana Yuki no Kikusui*
a. [Jitsukawa Ensaburō] as Hosokawa Kizunokami
b. [Arashi Kichisaburō III] as Harubashi Shūya
8/1861
Chūban diptych
Signature: Yoshitaki
Seal: Atari
Theater: Naka
69-208-375ab

397. *Nazoraebana Yuki no Kikusui*
a. [Jitsukawa Ensaburō] as Yumishi Tōzaburō
b. [Kataoka Ainosuke] as Koume no Omatsu
8/1861
Chūban diptych
Signature: Yoshitaki ga
Theater: Naka
69-208-376ab

398. *Godairiki Koi no Fūjime*
a. [Kataoka Ainosuke] as Kikuno
b. [Jitsukawa Ensaburō] as Gengobei
c. [Arashi Kichisaburō III] as Sangobei
8/1861
Chūban triptych
Signature: Yoshitaki ga
Theater: Naka
69-208-377abc

399a. Nakamura Nakasuke as Tetsugatake Dazaemon
b. Arashi Kichisaburō III as Inagawa Jirokichi
10/1861
Chūban
Signature: Yoshitaki
Theater: Horie Ichinogawa
69-208-378ab

These are the center and left panels only of a triptych, the right panel of which shows Kataoka Ainosuke as Otowa.

400. *Honchō Nijūshiko*
a. Onoe Tamizō II as Yokozō
b. Arashi Rikaku II as Jihizō
10/1861
Chūban diptych
Signature: Yoshitaki ga
Theater: Kado
69-208-379ab
See Plate 78.

401. *Honchō Nijūshikō*
a. Arashi Rikan III as Yaegakihime
b. Arashi Rikaku II as Katsuyori
c. Nakamura Sennosuke as Nureginu
10/1861
Chūban triptych
Signature: ac. Ichiyōtei Yoshitaki sha/ga; b. Yoshitaki ga
Seal: ac. Satonoya
Theater: Kado
69-208-380abc

402. *Daikyōji Mukashi Goyomi*
a. Arashi Rikaku II as Utsuke no Sanshirō
b. Ichikawa Takijūrō as Daikyōji Ishun, and Kameju Saidayū as Fujiwara Koito
c. Arashi Rikan III as Zubora no Denkichi
10/1861
Chūban triptych
Signatures: ab. Yoshitaki ga; c. Yoshitaki
Printer: a. Horikame (on lantern)
Theater: Kado
69-208-381abc

403. *Keisei Ōmonguchi*
a. Jitsukawa Shachizō as Sadō Junsai, and Jitsukawa Ensaburō as Imagawa Otokonosuke
b. Fujikawa Tomokichi III as Sakurahime, and Arashi Kikusaburō as Mayoiji
1/1862
Chūban diptych
Signatures: a. Yoshitaki ga; b. Yoshitaki
Publisher: ab. Junshi Suri Shin (?)
Theater: Naka
69-208-382ab

418abc

404. *Keisei Ōmonguchi*
   a. Jitsukawa Ensaburō as Uekiya Bunzō
   b. Fujikawa Tomokichi III as Oshizu, a geisha, and Jitsukawa Shachizō as Bansuke
   1/1862
   Chūban diptych
   Signatures: a. Ichiyōtei Yoshitaki sha; b. Yoshitaki
   Theater: Naka
   69-208-383ab

405. *Keisei Ōmonguchi*
   a. Arashi Kichisaburō III as Gantetsu, an outcast
   b. Onoe Tamizō II as Mino no Shōkurō
   1/1862
   Chūban diptych
   Signature: Yoshitaki ga
   Publisher: b. Kinoyasu
   Theater: Naka
   69-208-384ab

406. *Keisei Ōmonguchi*
   a. Onoe Tamizō II as Mino no Shōkurō
   b. Arashi Kichisaburō III as Gantetsu, an outcast
   1/1862
   Chūban diptych
   Signature: Yoshitaki ga
   Publisher: b. Junshi Suri Shin (?)
   Theater: Naka
   69-208-385ab

407. *Keisei Ōmonguchi*
   a. Mimasu Gennosuke III as a mask seller
   b. Onoe Tamizō II as Wankyū
   c. Fujikawa Tomokichi III as Matsuyama
   1/1862
   Chūban triptych
   Signatures: ac. Ōju Yoshitaki ga; b. Ichiyōtei Yoshitaki ga
   Seals: a. paulownia; bc. Yoshitaki
   Theater: Naka
   69-208-386abc

408. *Mitate Jūnikagetsu no uchi: Sangatsu.* Onoe Tamizō II as Wankyū, Fujikawa Tomokichi III as Matsuyama, and Mimasu Gennosuke III as a mask seller
   1/1862
   Chūban
   Signature: Ōju Ichiyōtei Yoshitaki
   Publisher: Kinoyasu
   Theater: Naka
   69-208-387

This panel is for March, from a series of twelve months.

409. *Hanafubuki Hakone no Akebono*
   *a. Arashi Kichisaburō III as Satō Imasuke
   *b. Onoe Tamizō II as Fudesuke, a *yakko*
   3/1862
   Chūban diptych
   Signature: a. Yoshitaki ga; b. Yoshitaki
   Theater: Naka
   69-208-388ab

410. *Hanafubuki Hakone no Akebono*
   a. Fujikawa Tomokichi III as Hatsuhana
   b. Jitsukawa Ensaburō as Michisuke
   3/1862
   Chūban diptych
   Signature: Yoshitaki sha
   Theater: Naka
   69-208-389ab

411. *Hanafubuki Hakone no Akebono*
   a. Fujikawa Tomokichi III as Hatsuhana
   b. Jitsukawa Ensaburō as Katsugorō
   c. Nakamura Jakuemon I as Shōya Tokuemon
   3/1862
   Chūban triptych
   Signature: Yoshitaki ga
   Printer: a. Horikame
   Theater: Naka
   69-208-390abc

412. *Dōjima Sukui no Tatehiki*
   a. Arashi Kichisaburō III as Gokumon no Shōbei
   b. Jitsukawa Ensaburō as Hanjimono no Kihei
   c. Mimasu Gennosuke III as Kamakuraya Gorohachi
   d. Onoe Tamizō II as Kurofune Chūemon
   3/1862

428

Chūban tetraptych
Signatures: ac. Yoshitaki ga;
bd. Yoshitaki
Theater: Naka
69-208-391a–d

413. *Dōjima Sukui no Tatehiki*
   a. Mimasu Gennosuke III as Kamakuraya Gorohachi
   b. Jitsukawa Ensaburō as Hanjimono no Kihei
   3/1862
   Chūban diptych
   Signature: Yoshitaki ga
   Seal: ab. Atari
   Publisher: b. Junshi Suri Shin (?)
   Theater: Naka
   69-208-392ab

414. *Dōjima Sukui no Tatehiki*
   a. Arashi Kichisaburō III as Gokumon no Shōbei
   b. Onoe Tamizō II as Kurofune Chūemon
   3/1862
   Chūban diptych
   Signature: Yoshitaki
   Theater: Naka
   69-208-393ab

415. *Keisei Ama no Hagoromo*
   a. Nakamura Jakuemon I as Kariya Saemon
   b. Arashi Kichisaburō III as Noriwakamaru
   8/1862
   Chūban diptych
   Signatures: a. Ōju Yoshitaki hitsu;
   b. Yoshitaki hitsu
   Theater: Naka
   69-208-394ab

416. *Keisei Ama no Hagoromo*
   a. Nakamura Nakasuke as Ginbei, and Arashi Kichisaburō III as Otsuma
   b. Fujikawa Tomokichi III as Okoma
   c. Nakamura Jakuemon I as Kōjō, a painter, and Jitsukawa Ensaburō as Saizaburō
   8/1862
   Chūban triptych
   Signatures: a. Satonoya Yoshitaki hitsu; bc. Yoshitaki hitsu
   Theater: Naka
   69-208-395abc

417. *Keisei Ama no Hagoromo*
   a. Jitsukawa Ensaburō as Saizaburō
   b. Fujikawa Tomokichi III as Okoma
   8/1862
   Chūban diptych
   Signatures: a. Ōju Yoshitaki hitsu;
   b. Yoshitaki
   Theater: Naka
   69-208-396ab

418. *Keisei Ama no Hagoromo*
   *a. Arashi Kichisaburō III as Akamatsu Shirō
   *b. Onoe Tamizō II as Kitagawa Sōemon
   *c. Jitsukawa Ensaburō as Hosokawa Katsumoto
   8/1862
   Chūban triptych
   Signatures: ab. Yoshitaki hitsu;
   c. Yoshitaki ga
   Theater: Naka
   69-208-397abc

419. *Ichinotani Futaba Gunki*
   a. Arashi Rinshi as Atsumori
   b. Arashi Kichisaburō III as Kumagai Naozane
   10/1863
   Chūban diptych
   Signatures: a. Yoshitaki ga;
   b. Yoshitaki hitsu
   Publisher: Kinoyasu
   Theater: Naka
   69-208-398ab

420. *Kanadehon Chūshingura,* Act 5
   a. Mimasu Gennosuke III as Senzaki Yagorō
   b. Ichikawa Udanji I as Hayano Kanpei
   c. 1863

430

Chūban diptych
Signature: Yoshitaki ga
69-208-399ab

421. *Inazuma Zōshi. Mitate Shiki no uchi: Haru.* Jitsukawa Enjaku I as Banzaemon and Ichikawa Udanji I as Sanzaburō, c. 1863
   Horizontal *ōban*
   Signature: Ōju Yoshitaki ga
   Publisher: Fujimasa
   69-208-400

The subject is spring, from a set of four seasons.

422. *Mitate Iroha Datoe: Ro.* Mimasu Daigorō V as Musashibō Benkei
   c. 1865
   Chūban
   Signature: Yoshitaki ga
   69-208-401

This is the second panel only of a series numbered with *kana* syllables.

423. *Kamakura Sandaiki.* Ōtani Tomoemon V as Miuranosuke
   c. 1865
   Ōban
   Signature: Ichiyōtei Yoshitaki hitsu
   Publisher: Ishiwa
   Engraver: Horikō Heizō
   69-208-402

424. *Yukigeshiki Haru no Nigiwai*
   a. Arashi Rikan IV as Toranosuke
   b. Onoe Tamizō II as Sarunosuke
   c. Ichikawa Udanji I as Ichimatsu
   4/1874

Chūban triptych
Signature: Yoshitaki hitsu
Publisher: Yaozen
Theater: Kado
69-208-403abc

See Plate 80.

425a. Onoe Tamizō II as Kan'u
b. Arashi Rikan IV as Gentoku
c. Ichikawa Udanji V as Chōhi
c. 1874

Chūban triptych
Signature: Yoshitaki hitsu
Publisher: Hon'yasu
69-208-404abc

426. *Tori no Hachigatsu Itsuka: Mokushō no Hito Uke ni Iru* ("August 5 of the year of the rooster: lucky dates for people of wooden natures"), 5/1861

Ōban
Signature: Ittensai Yoshitaki ga
Seal: paulownia
Publisher: Shimizuya (Edo)
Censor seal: aratame with date, *tori* 5
69-208-405

This is an almanac print that was published in Edo while Yoshitaki was active in Osaka. It may be by an unrecorded pupil of Kuniyoshi's by the same name. The central figure, a Fukusuke, is a rebus of the letter *Fu*.

427. Advertisement for a Kyoto seal carver, Seikodō, c. 1860s

Horizontal *ōban*
Signature: Yoshitaki ga
Seal: Hōsai
69-208-406

Yoshitoyo I (active 1854–1857 in Osaka; died 1866)

The Yoshitoyo who designed actor prints in Osaka in the early 1850s is probably the same as the Yoshitoyo who was a pupil of Kuniyoshi, designed portraits of foreigners and a series of prints on the Indian elephant that was exhibited near Ryōgoku Bridge in Edo in 1863, and died in 1866. His Osaka prints display a sense of humor that sets them quite apart from the usually straight-faced productions of the rest of the Osaka school.

*428. Unidentified actor as Tayori, a *kamuro*; c. 1854
Chūban
Signature: Yoshitoyo
69-208-407

429. *Katakiuchi Ukiki no Kameyama*
a. [Jitsukawa Ensaburō] as Ishii Hyōsuke
b. [Arashi Rikaku II] as Ishii Genzō
8/1855
Chūban diptych
Signature: Yoshitoyo
Theater: Kado
69-208-408ab

See Plate 74.

Yoshitsugu (active 1839)

Yoshitsugu was a pupil of Sadayoshi who apparently designed one print.

*430. Jitsukawa Ensaburō as Inukawa Sōsuke, c. late 1830s
Chūban
Signature: Utagawa Sadayoshi monjin Yoshitsugu ga
69-208-409

Yoshiyuki (1835–1879; active 1856–1872)

A pupil of Yoshiume, Yoshiyuki visited Edo in 1872 and designed an architectural print published there. He is not the same as Ichireisai Yoshiyuki, the pupil of Kuniyoshi who died earlier.

431. *Sankatsu Gushi Akane no Irozashi*
*a. Jitsukawa Ensaburō as Hanshichi
*b. Fujikawa Tomokichi III as Sankatsu
10/1863
Chūban diptych
Signature: Yoshiyuki
Theater: Naka
69-208-410ab

Anonymous

432. *Shibai Ebanzuke Edoban*
Illustrated theater programs in four pamphlets bound as one, with dark blue cover and handwritten title slip; 8⅞ x 6⅜″.
69-208-411a–d
a. *Hanayagura Kikugaki Taiheiki*
11/1765
Theater: Anegawa Kikuhachi Za at Wakadayū
7 pages numbered 2-8
b. *Edo Kanoko Musubu no Iroage*
12/1765
Theater: Anegawa Kikuhachi Za at Wakadayū
7 pages numbered 2-8
c. *Ōmonguchi Yoroi Gasane*
12/1743
Theater: Nakamura Jūzō Za at Ōnishi
6 pages numbered 2-7

See Plate 1.

431ab

d. *Natsumatsuri Naniwa Kagami*
7/1767
Theater: Arashi Hinasuke Za at Kado
8 pages numbered 2-9

433. Untitled
Illustrated theater programs in two pamphlets bound as one, with embroidered cover; 8 x 6″
69-208-412
a. *Kinmon Gosan no Kiri*, 12/1790
Theater: Asao Sennosuke Za at Naka
Four sheets numbered 1-3, but 1-4 in manuscript; stenciled frontispiece
b. Unidentified play, lacking title sheet, c. 1790s
Four sheets numbered 3-6, lacking frontispiece

434. *Keisei Chigogafuchi*
An illustrated theater program of four pages, two numbered 4–5; stenciled frontispiece and list of actors and roles; 8 x 5⅜″
c. 1830s
Publisher: Honsei
Theater: Wakadayū
69-208-413

435. *Yakusha Ezōshi*. Frontispiece for an album of portraits of actors
1820s or early 1830s
Ōban
Publisher: Naniwa Shorin Jihon Don'ya
69-208-414
See Plate 23.

436. [Nakamura Daikichi III] as Gentō's wife, 10/1852
Chūban
Publisher undecipherable, trimmed
Theater: Kado
69-208-415

*437. Ichikawa Yonezō as the ghost of Oiwa, c. 1864
Chūban
69-208-416

438. *Irokurabe Nishikie*
An album of drawings depicting scenes from plays, with brown striped cover and manuscript title slip centered on panel with printed pine needles; 8⅛ x 6⅛″
69-208-417 (1-28)

437

Sheet 1a
Blank inside cover

Sheet 1b
Shirabyōshi dancer in *Dōjōji*

Sheets 2ab-3ab
Unidentified

Sheets 4ab
Otomi and Yosaburō in *Gen'yadana*

Sheets 5ab
Omiwa and Tachibanahime in *Imoseyama*

Sheets 6ab
Tokiwa Gozen with Ushiwaka and his two brothers in *Gikeiki*

Sheets 7ab
Hinadori and Sadaka in *Imoseyama*

Sheets 8ab
Onoe and Iwafuji in *Kagamiyama*

Sheets 9ab
Yamauba and Kintoki in *Komochi Yamauba*

Sheets 10ab
Yakko no Koman in *Kurofune*

Sheets 11ab
Kuzunoha with her child in *Kuzunoha*

Sheets 12ab
Unidentified

Sheets 13ab
Kyō Ningyō doll and Hidari Jingorō in *Kyō Ningyō*

Sheets 14ab
Okiku (?) in *Sarayashiki* (?)

Sheets 15ab
Osono in *Hikosan Gongen*

Sheets 16ab
Unidentified

Sheets 17ab
Umegae in *Hiragana Seisuiki*

Sheets 18ab
Umegawa and Chūbei in *Meido no Hikyaku*

Sheets 19ab
Osome and Hisamatsu in *Osome Hisamatsu*

Sheets 20ab
Seigen-ni in *Onna Seigen*

Sheets 21ab
Unidentified

Sheets 22ab
Unidentified

Sheets 23ab
Kamuro and two palanquin bearers in *Modorikago*

Sheets 24ab
Musashi and Kohagi in *Miyamoto Musashi*

Sheets 25ab
Unidentified

Sheets 26ab
Tonase and Konami in *Chūshingura*

Sheets 27ab
Oyumi and Otsū in *Awa no Naruto*

Sheet 28a
Nine-tailed fox in *Tamamo no Mae*

Sheet 28b
Blank inside cover

List of Artists

The Japanese characters used in this list for artist's names appear as in their signatures whenever possible.

Dates and names in brackets are included on the authority of other writers. Asterisks denote Kamigata artists and book illustrators for whom no single-sheet Osaka woodblock prints are known.

芦陽 — ASHIAKI
Active 1823 [1824]; possibly pronounced Ashiharu.

芦舟 — ASHIFUNE
Active 1814–1816 [1813–1825]; the *haigō* of the actor Asao Okuyama III if pronounced Roshū.

芦陽 — ASHIHARU
See Ashiaki.

芦廣 蘆廣 あし廣 — ASHIHIRO
Active 1816–1824, 1836 [1817–1836]; there were possibly two artists of this name.
春川 — Surname: Harukawa (1836)

芦尚 あし尚 — ASHIHISA
Active 1817; possibly pronounced Ashitaka or Ashinao.

芦清 — ASHIKIYO
Active 1816–1817.

芦喜津 — ASHIKIZU*
Period of activity unknown.

芦國 蘆國 あし國 — ASHIKUNI
Lived c. 1775–9/1818; active c. 1807–1818 [1804–1818].
Lived c. 1775–9/1818; active c. 1807–1818 [1804–1818].
淺山 — Surname: Asayama
狂画堂 — *Gō*: Kyōgadō
青陽齋 — Seiyōsai
蘭齋 — Ransai
蘭英齋 — Ran'eisai
布屋忠三郎 — Personal name: Nunoya Chūzaburō
Seal: Naniwa
Naniwa Kuni (?)
See Cat. 1-3.

芦麿 あし麿 — ASHIMARO
See Yoshikuni.

芦丸 — ASHIMARU
See Yoshikuni.

芦尚 — ASHINAO
See Ashihisa.

芦貫 — ASHINUKI
Active 1818 [1817–1831]; possibly pronounced Ashitsura. Mentioned as a portraitist (*see* Appendix XI). Osaka address: Shinsaibashi Kitazume

芦郷 — ASHISATO
Active 1800, 1816 [1813–1816]; listed as a copyist in the colophon of *Naniwa no Ume* (1800).
風竹館 — *Gō*: Fūchikukan (1800)

芦尚 — ASHITAKA
See Ashihisa.

芦友 — ASHITOMO
Active 1814–1816 [1817].

芦貫 — ASHITSURA
See Ashinuki.

ASHIYUKI
芦幸 — (1814–1818)
蘆幸 — (1814–1819)
あし幸 — (1814–1817)
芦由起 — (1821–1823)
芦雪 — (1823)
(as seal)
Active c. 1814–1833. Recorded on a print dated c. 1814 as a pupil of Ashikuni; recorded name change from Nagakuni to Ashiyuki on a print dated 1/1814. Prints signed Nagakuni between 1814 and 1821 may be by a second artist of this name.
長國 — Early names: Nagakuni (1814–1821; concurrently used with Ashiyuki from 1814)
楮 — Surname: Kōzo (?) (1823)
戯画堂 — *Gō*: Gigadō (1818–1832)
ニトロ — Seal: Ni To Ro (1814)
芦行 — Ashiyuki
Osaka address: Doshōmachi Goryōsuji
See Cat. 4-18.

芦雪 — ASHIYUKI
Active [1868]; probably a misreading of Rokkaen Yoshiyuki
六花園 — *Gō*: Rokkaen
Osaka address: Shimanouchi Sankyūbashisuji Shimizumachi Minami

馬圓 — BAEN*
[Active 1790s–1800s]; died c. 1810. An Edo pupil of Hokusai who

moved to Osaka and was adopted by the map-maker Ōoka Kitōji. He was chiefly an illustrator.
馬遠 Early name: Baen
大岡 Surname: Ōoka
一峯齋 *Gō*: Ippōsai
Personal names:
由平 Yoshihei
藤二 Tōji
Osaka address: Kameyamamachi Gotōyashiki

楳莚 **Baien**
Active 1819.

梅花 **Baika**
Active c. 1819 [1830s]; possibly the *haigō* of the actor Nakamura Tomijūrō II.

梅溪 **Baikei**
Active 1816.
年古樓 *Gō*: Nenkorō

梅國 **Baikoku**
Possible alternate pronunciation of Umekuni. *See* Shiken.

梅好齋 **Baikōsai**
Active 1805; possibly a *gō* of the poet Kageyama Hakuensai Baikō, who was also the publisher Shioya Saburobei around 1800.
See Shunkei.

梅雪堂 **Baisetsudō***
Active 1743 [1720s]; a designer of hand-colored prints published in Kyoto.
貞道 Personal name: Sadamichi (as seal)

朴仙 **Bokusen**
See Shiken.

茶樂齋 **Charakusai**
See Seikoku.

千歌國 千哥國 **Chikakuni**
Active 1821–1823; recorded on an undated print as a pupil of Ashikuni; recorded on a print dated c. 1823 as a pupil of Yoshikuni.
壽寶堂 *Gō*: Juhōdō

竹溪 **Chikukei***
Active c. 1835; mentioned as an ukiyoe artist (*see* Appendix XIII).
菊川 Surname: Kikukawa

長秀齋 **Chōshūsai**
See Nagahide.

海老兼 **Ebikane**
Active 1827–1828.
See Cat. 19.

英壽 **Eiju**
[Active 1830s–1850s].
泉壽 Early name: Senju
酒井 Surname: Sakai
英齋 *Gō*: Eisai
景齋 Keisai
一筆庵 Ippitsuan
伊三郎 Personal name: Isaburō

英泉 **Eisen**
Active 1823.
See Kuninao.

永春 **Eishun**
See Mitsunobu.

猿雀 **Enjaku**
Active 1858–1865.
See Cat. 20-22.

不韻齋 **Fuinsai***
[Active c. 1770s]; designed a few perspective landscapes published in Kyoto.

ふじ國 **Fujikuni**
Active 1826.
壽松堂 *Gō*: Jushōdō

岳亭 **Gakutei**
Active 1815–1830s; Gakutei was an Edo artist who visited Osaka in the late 1820s to mid-1830s and designed surimono and landscapes, which were published there.
Early names:
春信 Harunobu
定岡 Sadaoka
八島 Surname: Yashima
五岳 *Gō*: Gogaku
丘山 Kyūzan
一老 Ichirō
南山 Nanzan
陽亭 Yōtei
陽齋 Yōsai
黄園 Kōen
神歌堂 Shinkadō
神岳堂 Shingakudō
堀川多樓 Horikawa Tarō
梁左 Ryōsa
Personal names:
丸屋斧吉 Maruya Onokichi
鳳卿 Hōkyō

源三 **Genzō***
Active c. 1831; mentioned as a block-copyist (*see* Appendix XI).
三木 Surname: Miki

五長 **Gochō**
Active c. 1826.
See Hirosada.

五七 GOSHICHI
Lived 1776–c. 1831; active 1810s–1820s. Goshichi was an Edo writer and engraver who lived in Kyoto from the late 1810s and designed a few prints and erotica.
Early names:
神屋蓬洲 Kamiya Hōshū
はる川 Harukawa (1810s)
Surnames:
春川 Harukawa
青木 Aoki
蓬萊山人亀遊 *Gō*: Hōraisanjin Kiyū
亀助 Personal name: Kamesuke

玉江 GYOKKŌ*
[Active 1790s].
Surname: Tamaki

玉安齋 GYOKUANSAI*
Active 1778; illustrator of a book on hair ornament.

玉園 GYOKUEN
Active c. 1860; chiefly a Kyoto artist.

玉峰 GYOKUHŌ
See Gyokuzan II.

玉泉 GYOKUSEN*
Active c. mid-1830s; known only by a drawing of an actor in the Victoria and Albert Museum, London.

玉洲 GYOKUSHŪ
Active 1834.
See Tamakuni.

玉藻 GYOKUSŌ*
Active 1830s; an Utagawa-style Osaka illustrator.
水原 Surname: Mizuhara

初代 玉山 GYOKUZAN I
Lived 1737–1812 [active 1770s–1810s]; an Osaka illustrator.
岡田 Surname: Okada
金陵齋 *Gō*: Kinryōsai
Personal names:
尚友 Naotomo
子徳 Shitoku
Osaka address: Kita Watanabemachi

二代 玉山 GYOKUZAN II*
Active 1810s; an Osaka painter who moved to Edo in the mid-1810s. Two artists may have used the name Gyokuhō.
蓼華齋玉峰 Early name: Ryōkasai Gyokuhō (to 1812)
石田 Surname: Ishida
揚輝齋 *Gō*: Yōkisai
Personal names:
修徳 Shūtoku
子秀 Shishū
Edo address: Kanda Kon'ya-chō 1-chōme

白藤 HAKUTŌ
Period of activity unknown.

半兵衛 HANBEI*
Active 1660s–1700s; a Kyoto illustrator.
吉田 Surname: Yoshida
定吉 Personal name: Sadayoshi

半山 HANZAN*
[Active 1850s–1870s]; died c. 1880. An Osaka illustrator.
松川 Surname: Matsukawa
翠栄堂 *Gō*: Suieidō
霞居 Kakyo
直水 Chokusui
Personal names:
高二 Takaji
安信 Yasunobu
義卿 Gikyō

はる川 HARUKAWA
See Goshichi.

春子 HARUKO
Died 1860; a female artist, possibly the same person as Shun'yōsai Shunshi.
春婦 *Gō*: Shunpu

晴國 HARUKUNI*
Active c. 1822; mentioned as a poet on a Yoshikuni surimono (*see* Appendix VI).

春貞 HARUSADA
See Shuntei and Shunki.

春友 HARUTOMO
Possible alternate pronunciation of Shun'yū.

はし國 橋國 HASHIKUNI
Active mid-1820s.

はつ國 HATSUKUNI
Active 1826–1828.
芳國堂 *Gō*: Hōkokudō
芳花堂 [Hōkadō]

英國 HIDEKUNI
Active mid-1820s.
豊川 Surname: Toyokawa

秀麿 HIDEMARO
Active 1823; a Kyoto artist.

英信 HIDENOBU*
[Active 1760s–1770s]; an Osaka painter and illustrator.
雲鯨齋 *Gō*: Ungeisai
Osaka address: Tennōji Watayamachi

秀信 HIDENOBU*
Active 1800s; an Osaka painter.
巨勢 Surname: Kose

鞁啓 HIKEI*
Active c. 1831; mentioned as a block-copyist (*see* Appendix XI).
Osaka address: Uemachi

ひこ國 彦國 HIKOKUNI
Active 1821–1824.
Surnames:
あし川 Ashikawa
豊川 Toyokawa (used as signature in 1827)
あら川 [Arakawa]
See Cat. 23-25.

廣兼 HIROKANE
See Sadahiro II.

廣國 HIROKUNI
See Hirosada and Hironobu II.

初代 廣信 HIRONOBU I
Active 1851–1870.
木下 Surname: Kinoshita
白水 *Gō*: Hakusui
白水齋 Hakusuisai
五葉亭 Goyōtei
五蒲亭 Gohotei
東林 Tōrin
芦野家 Ashinoya
See Cat. 26-31.

二代 廣信 HIRONOBU II
Born 1844; active 1870s–1880s.
二代 廣國 Early name: Hirokuni II
木下 Surname: Kinoshita
白峰 *Gō*: Hakuhō
日峰 [Nippō] (probably a misreading of Hakuhō)
柳塘 Ryūtō
芦水 Rosui

廣貞 HIROSADA
Active 1819(?)–1863; died c. 1865. Recorded name change from Hirokuni to Hirosada on a print dated 5/1847; recorded on a print dated 8/1852, published in Edo, as a pupil of Kunimasu.
Early names:
登美國 Tomikuni (?) (1821)
多美國 Tamikuni (?) (1823–1826)
五長 Gochō (?) (1826)
貞廣 Sadahiro (?) (1830–1846; apparently used concurrently with Hirosada until 1851)
初代 廣國 Hirokuni I (1847)
Surnames:
鈴木 [Suzuki]
小西 Konishi
石井 [Ishii]
歌川 Utagawa
五粽亭 *Gō*: Gosōtei
五樂亭 Gorakutei
Seals: The following seals appear after Hirosada's signatures between 1849 and 1852, often linked with particular publishers, whose names appear here in parentheses.
小西五長（金花堂） Konishi Gochō (Kinkadō)
蘭畦（川音） Rankei (?) (Kawaoto)
貞板（伊勢吉） Sada han (Isekichi)
貞（錦鯱堂） Sada (Kinkodō)
金石堂（池吉） Kinsekidō (Ikekichi)
子（名皐堂） Ko (Meikōdō)
板貞（大甚） Han Sada (Daijin)
五長（天喜） Gochō (Tenki)
長 Chō
貞廣 Sadahiro
五粽亭 Gosōtei
In addition, there are seven undecipherable seals associated with four other publishers and on unmarked prints.
See Cat. 32-137.

北海 HOKKAI
Active 1832; recorded name change from Hokusei to Shunshisai Hokkai on a print dated 8/1832.
東方南北西 Early name: Tōhōnan Hokusei (1832)
春始齋 *Gō*: Shunshisai

[HOKKAKU]
Misreading of Hokugan.

北敬 HOKKEI
Active 1818–1820s; listed as a copyist-pupil (*see* Appendix V).
Early names:
謹多樓春陽 Kintarō Shun'yō (1813–1818) [1824]
春陽齋 Shun'yōsai
春陽齋 *Gō*: Shun'yōsai
山東閣 Seal: Santōkaku

北慶 HOKKEI
Active 1830s.
嵐陽齋 *Gō*: Ran'yōsai

北廣 HOKKŌ
[Active 1820s].
葛飾 Surname: Katsushika
畫狂人 *Gō*: Gakyōjin

北恒 HOKKŌ
[Active 1810s–1830s]; a pupil of Hokusai.

北項 [Hokkō]
Misreading of Hokuchō.

北木 Hokuboku
Period of activity unknown.

北項 Hokuchō
Active 1822–1830. As Hokuchō, recorded on prints dated 11/1825 and 5/1826 as a pupil of Shunkō (Hokushū); as Shunsho, recorded on a print dated 9/1822 as a pupil of Shunkōsai (Hokushū).
春曙 Early name: Shunsho (1822)
井上 Surname: Inoue
春曙齋 *Gō*: Shunshosai
See Cat. 138-48.

北長 Hokuchō
[Active 1850s].
春曉齋 *Gō*: Shungyōsai
春潮齋 Shunchōsai

北英 Hokuei
Active 1824 (?)–1837; died 1837. Recorded on prints dated 1/1828, 9/1828, and 5/1829 as a pupil of Shunkōsai (Hokushū).
春江 Early name: Shunkō (1824 [?]–1829)
春江齋 *Gō*: Shunkōsai (1829–1833)
春梅齋 Shunbaisai (1833–1837)
雪花(華)樓 Sekkarō (1836)
雪華 Sekka
春陽齋 [Shun'yōsai]
ふもとのゆき Seals: Fumoto no yuki
ふもとのむめ Fumoto no ume
こしぢのむめ Koshiji no ume
Osaka address: Itachibori 1-chōme
See Cat. 149-84.

北雅 Hokuga
Active 1821–1826.
南陽齋 *Gō*: Nan'yōsai (1821; as signature 1825–1826)
南陽 Nan'yō (as signature)

北鴈 Hokugan
Active 1816 (?)–1832. As Toshikuni, recorded on a print dated 7/1817 as a pupil of Ashikuni, and on a print dated 2/1824 as a pupil of Yoshikuni. Recorded name change from Toshikuni to Hokugan on a print dated 9/1832.
とし國 年國 歲國 Early names: Toshikuni (1816 [?]–1832)
豐川 Toyokawa
Early *gō*:
蘆堂 Rodō
壽陽堂 Juyōdō
春陽堂 Shun'yōdō (1826)
春帰齋 *Gō*: Shunkisai (1832)
まがり Seal: Magari
Osaka address: Karamonomachi
See Cat. 185-87.

北壽 Hokuju
Active 1828 (?)–1836 [1859]; recorded on a print dated 11/1835 as a pupil of Hokuei.
春壽 Early name: Shunju(?) (1828–1829)
春松齋 *Gō*: Shunshōsai
春英齋 Shun'eisai (1836)
五龍軒 Goryūken
See Cat. 188.

北順 [Hokujun]
Probably a misreading of Hokuchō.

北明 Hokumei
Active c. 1830; recorded on a print dated c. 1830 as a pupil of Shunkōsai (Hokushū). Probably not Hokumeijo, a female pupil of Hokusai.
春旭齋 *Gō*: Shunkyokusai

北溟 Hokumei
Active c. 1830. Recorded on a print dated 11/1830 (?) as a pupil of Shunkōsai (Hokuei).
Surnames:
生田 [Ikuta]
手塚 [Tezuka]
橘生堂兎月 *Gō*: [Kisseidō Togetsu]

北妙 Hokumyō
Active 1830–1837. Perhaps a later name of Shun'yōsai Shunshi and possibly a female artist. Mentioned as a portraitist (*see* Appendix XI).
春婦齋 *Gō*: Shunpusai (1830–1833)
雪江亭 Sekkōtei (1837)
Osaka address: Dōjima

北來 Hokurai
[Active 1810s–1820s].

北鹿 Hokuroku
Period of activity unknown.
春陽齋 *Gō*: Shun'yōsai

北齋 Hokusai*
Lived 1760–1849; active 1779–1849. The famous Edo artist who visited Osaka in 1812 and 1817, and published work there as early as 1808.
Surnames:
中島 Nakajima
葛飾 Katsushika
Gō: omitted here
Personal names:
時太郎 Tokitarō
鐵蔵 Tetsuzō

北晴 HOKUSEI
Active 1826 [1827]; recorded on an undated print as a pupil of Shunkōsai (Hokushū).
春曉齋 *Gō*: Shungyōsai

北西 HOKUSEI
See Hokkai.

北雪 HOKUSETSU
[Active 1830s]; possibly a misreading of Hokuun.
春勇齋 *Gō*: Shun'yūsai

北信 HOKUSHIN
[Active 1830s]; recorded on an undated print as a pupil of Hokuei.
春完亭 *Gō*: Shunkantei
春光齋 [Shunkōsai]

北松 HOKUSHŌ
Active 1822–1832; possibly the same artist as the Hokushō below.
春頂 Early name: Shunchō (1822–1823)
春頂齋 *Gō*: Shunchōsai (1823)
Osaka address: Bakuromachi
See Cat. 189.

北升 HOKUSHŌ
Active 1815 (?)–1830s; possibly the same artist as the Hokushō above.
春蝶 Early name: [Shunchō] (1815–1821)
Surnames:
松本 Matsumoto
竹原 Takehara
春朝齋 *Gō*: Shunchōsai
Personal names:
信繁 Nobushige
門次 Monji
See Shunchō.

北洲 HOKUSHŪ
Active 1810–1832; recorded name change from Shunkō to Shōkōsai on a print dated 9/1811.
Early names:
春好 Shunkō (1810–1818; as a poet from 1806)
春好齋 Shunkōsai
松好齋 Shōkōsai (1811)
春好齋 *Gō*: Shunkōsai (1818–1832)
雪花亭 Sekkatei (1819)
よしのやま Seal: Yoshinoyama
——— Personal name: [Shima Jinsen]
Osaka address: Ishiyabashi Higashizume
See Cat. 190-220.

北水 HOKUSUI
Active c. 1860; collaborated with Tōkyo on *Miyako Hyakkei*.

北醉 HOKUSUI
See Yoshitoyo I.

北倒 HOKUTŌ
Active 1835.
松好齋 *Gō*: Shōkōsai
春好齋 [Shunkōsai]

北雲 HOKUUN
Active c. 1828. Recorded on a print dated c. 1828 as a pupil of Shunkōsai (Hokuei); probably not Hokusai's pupil Katsushika Tōnansai Hokuun.
春勇齋 *Gō*: Shun'yūsai

北洋 HOKUYŌ
Active 1819–1830s.
葛飾 Surname: Katsushika
丹青堂 *Gō*: Tanseidō
千鶴亭 Senkakutei (1819)
扇鶴堂 Senkakudō
Osaka address: Shinsaibashisuji Shiomachi
See Cat. 221.

北山 HOKUZAN*
[Active 1810s]; a designer of actor and figure prints published in Kyoto.
叶 Surname: Kanō

芳水 HŌSUI*
Active c. 1850s; a designer of stenciled actor prints published in Kyoto.
宮川 Surname: Miyagawa

百喜 HYAKKI
Active 1813; mentioned in *Kabuki Nenpyō* as having designed a surimono of Nakamura Utamaro III as a red *Shōki*.

一丸 ICHIMARU
Active c. 1820s.
十方舍 *Gō*: Jippōsha

伊八 IHACHI*
Active 1824; mentioned as a Kyoto ukiyoe artist resident in Osaka in *Naniwa Shōnin Kaimono Hitori Annai* (*see* Inoue, p. 4).
ならや Personal name: Naraya
Osaka address: Tazaemonbashi Kitazume Kitairu
See Nagahide.

一舩 ISSEN
Period of activity unknown; chiefly an illustrator.
浦川 Surname: Urakawa

一醉齋 Issuisai*
Active 1822 [1830s]; a designer of stenciled actor prints published in Kyoto.

耳鳥齋 Jichōsai*
A popular pronunciation of Nichōsai.

如圭 Jokei
See Ryūkōsai.

壽景 Jukei
See Toshikage.

壽好 壽公 Jukō
See Yoshikuni.

景明 Kageaki
See Sadanobu I.

景秀 Kagehide
See Kagematsu.

景松 Kagematsu
Active 1840–1841. Signed Ukiyoeshi Ippōsai Kagehide on a print dated 1841. Probably the same person as the Edo artist Utagawa Kagematsu (1830s–1840s).
歌川 Surname: Utagawa
一峯齋 *Gō*: Ippōsai
五流亭 Goryūtei

景年 Kagetoshi
Period of activity unknown; a pupil of Sadakage, possibly an Edo artist.

鐘成 Kanenari
Lived 1793–1860; active 1810s–1850s. Author and illustrator; listed as a block-copyist (*see* Appendix XI).
木村 Surname: Kimura
曉鐘成 *Gō*: Akatsuki no Kanenari
鶏鳴舍 Keimeisha
晴翁 Seiō
(and others)
Personal names:
和泉屋彌四郎 Izumiya Yashirō
明啓 Akihiro (?)
Osaka address: Shinsaibashi Bakuromachi

鐘成 Kanenaru
See Kanenari.

關月 Kangetsu*
Lived 1747–1797; an Osaka painter and illustrator, and the proprietor of the Chigusaya bookshop through the mid-1770s. He was Ryūkōsai's teacher.
蔀 Surname: Shitomi
菁莪堂 *Gō*: Seigadō
Personal names:
徳基 Tokki
子温 Shion
源二郎（原次郎） Genjirō
原二 Genji
Osaka addresses:
Kyōmachibori 2-chōme
Dōjima Naka 2-chōme

關牛 Kangyū*
Active 1820s; died 1833. An Osaka illustrator and block-copyist for calligraphic text.
蔀 Surname: Shitomi
蒵楊軒 *Gō*: Teiyōken
Personal names:
徳風 Tokufū
子假 Shien
Osaka address: Itachibori 1-chōme

何司 Kashi
[Active 1830].

可笑 Kashō*
Active c. 1826; a designer of stenciled actor prints published in Kyoto.
南筆 *Gō*: Nanpitsu

括嚢 Katsunō*
[Active c. 1805]; a designer of stenciled figure prints published in Kyoto.

桂齋 Keisai*
Active 1785; a designer of Osaka theater programs.
月岡 Surname: Tsukioka

慶子 Keishi*
Lived 1719–1786 [active 1760s–1780s]. An Osaka painter and illustrator. Keishi was the *haigō* of the actor Nakamura Tomijūrō I.
英 Surname: Hanabusa
嶺琴舍 *Gō*: Reikinsha

其計 Kikei*
Active 1770s; designer of Kyoto theater programs and said to be the designer of new actor portraits included in the Kyoto edition of *Ehon Butai Ōgi*, 1778.
高橋 Surname: Takahashi

杵井 Kinei*
Active c. 1800; a designer of an actor print, probably provincial.

きし國 Kishikuni
Active 1821–mid 1820s.
芳雅堂 *Gō*: Hōgadō

喜多樓 **Kitarō***
Active c. 1810s; a designer of stenciled figure prints, published in Kyoto.

清春 清晴 **Kiyoharu**
Active 1820s–1830s.
Surname:
藤原 Fujiwara
五代 菱川 Hishikawa V
春陽齋 *Gō*: Shun'yōsai
青陽齋 [Seiyōsai]
蕙泉齋 Keisensai
雪艇 Settei
曄齋 Yōsai
Personal names:
吉左衛門 Kichizaemon
小野度隆 Ono [Noritaka]
廣隆 [Hirotaka]
Osaka address: Uemachi
See Cat. 222.

清秀 **Kiyohide***
See Shunsensai.

清國 **Kiyokuni**
Active 1827.
豐川 Surname: Toyokawa
壽曙堂 *Gō*: Jushodō

清雅 **Kiyomasa**
See Shigeharu.

清貞 **Kiyosada**
Active 1848; a follower of Hirosada. The signature is written deliberately to resemble that of Hirosada.

清安 **Kiyoyasu**
Active 1826; probably a Kyoto artist.

皷圓 **Koen***
[Active 1810s]; an Osaka illustrator.
一瀧齋 *Gō*: Ichirōsai

國花堂 **Kokkadō***
[Active c. 1770s]; a designer of stenciled perspective prints published in Kyoto.

耕好 **Kōkō***
Active c. 1770; designer of a few provincial actor *hosoban* possibly printed in Kamigata or Ise, including a portrait of Nakamura Kiyosaburō as Osai.
並岡 Surname: Namioka
芳子 Seal: Hōshi or Yoshiko

小信 **Konobu**
See Sadanobu II.

國春 **Kuniharu**
Lived 1803–1839 [active 1820s–1830s]. Kuniharu was also known as the actor Arashi Tokusaburō (active 1824–1828) who retired from the stage due to bad health. He studied under Toyokuni II and seems to have worked mainly in Edo.
玉陽亭 *Gō*: Gyokuyōtei
山風亭 Sanpūtei
具足屋佐兵衛 Personal name: Gusokuya Sahei
あらし Seal: Arashi

國晴 **Kuniharu**
Active early 1840s (?). Known from one print mentioned in Kuroda.

國晴 **Kuniharu**
Active 1853–1854; possibly a pupil of Yoshimori who became Yoshimori II.
二代 兒雷也 *Gō*: Jiraiya II
一光齋 Ikkōsai (?)

國平 **Kunihira**
Active 1816; recorded on a print dated 1/1816 as a pupil of Kunihiro.

國廣 **Kunihiro**
Active 1816–1841 (?).
Surnames:
瀧川 Takigawa (1823–1826)
歌川 Utagawa (1830)
天満屋 Tenmaya (1835)
丸丈齋 *Gō*: Ganjōsai (1821–1835)
江南亭 Kōnantei (1823)
三昇亭 Sanshōtei (1829)
Osaka address: Ebisubashi Itchō Kita
See Cat. 223-34.

國景 **Kunikage**
Active 1831.
歌川 Surname: Utagawa
英齋 *Gō*: Eisai (1831)
錦葩樓 Kinharō
錦葩齋 Kinhasai
一英齋 Ichieisai
一櫻齋 Ichiōsai
Osaka address: Edobori
See Cat. 235.

國員 **Kunikazu**
Active 1849–1867.
歌川 Surname: Utagawa
一珠齋 *Gō*: Isshusai or Ichijusai
See Cat. 236–43.

國計 **Kunikazu**
Active 1856–1858.

國升 **Kunimasu**
Active 1834–1852. Recorded on a print dated 3/1834 as a pupil of Tōto Kunisada, and on a print dated 12/1852 published in Edo as a pupil of Toyokuni III; recorded name change from Sadamasu to Kunimasu on prints dated 1/1848, 5/1848, and on a print dated 8/1852 published in Edo.
初代貞升 Early name: Sadamasu I (1834–1848)
歌川 Surname: Utagawa
一樹園 *Gō*: Ichijuen
一樹亭 Ichijutei
五蝶亭 Gochōtei
五蝶齋 Gochōsai
金屋和三郎 Personal name: Kanaya Wasaburō
Osaka address: Nōninbashi Matsuyamachi, Senba
See Cat. 244–49.

——— [**Kunimichi**]
Period of activity unknown; probably one of three Edo artists of this name, or a misreading.

國直 **Kuninao**
Active 1823; not the Edo pupil of Toyokuni I.
英泉 Early name: Eisen (?) (1823)
柳川 Surname: Yanagawa
英泉齋 *Gō*: Eisensai (1823)

國貞 **Kunisada***
Lived 1786–1864; active 1807–1864
歌川 Surname: Utagawa
一雄齋 *Gō*: Ichiyūsai
五渡亭 Gototei
琴雷舎 Kinraisha
香蝶樓 Kōchōrō
See Cat. 250.

——— [**Kunisaki**]
Period of activity unknown; probably a misreading.

國重 **Kunishige**
See Shigeharu.

國重 **Kunishige**
Active 1847–1851; possibly a reversion to his early name by the artist Shigeharu.
See Cat. 251-59.

國忠 **Kunitada**
Active 1850s; not the Edo pupil of Toyokuni I.
歌川 Surname: Utagawa

[**Kunitomo**]
Period of activity unknown; probably an Edo artist or a misreading.

國鶴 **Kunitsuru**
Active 1835; an Edo pupil of Toyokuni II who visited Osaka.
歌川 Surname: Utagawa
一壽齋 *Gō*: Ichijusai

國美 **Kuniyoshi***
[Active c. 1850s]; a designer of stenciled actor prints published in Kyoto.

昌房 **Masafusa**
Active 1771–1783; an illustrator and designer of a few stenciled prints that were forerunners of the Osaka style.
岡本 Surname: Okamoto
雪圭齋 *Gō*: Sekkeisai
Osaka address: Matsuemachi

政國 **Masakuni**
Active 1823; recorded on an undated print as a pupil of Yoshikuni.
壽鶴堂 *Gō*: Jukakudō

正信 **Masanobu**
[Active 1820s–1850s].
一楊齋 *Gō*: Ichiyōsai

昌次 **Masatsugu**
[Active 1760s–1780s]; an illustrator and designer of erotica and a few actor portraits.
寺沢 Surname: Terasawa
Osaka address: Tennōji

升春 **Masuharu**
Active 1850s; recorded on an undated print as a pupil of Kunimasu.
See Cat. 260.

升直 **Masunao**
Active 1847.

升信 **Masunobu**
Active 1849–1853; recorded on an undated print as a pupil of Kunimasu.
一刀齋 *Gō*: Ittōsai
See Cat. 261-62.

升貞 **Masusada**
Active c. 1850.

升鶴 **Masutsuru**
Active 1852.
宇田川 Surname: Utagawa

峯國 **Minekuni**
Active 1820s.

三津國 **Mitsukuni**
Active 1820s.

光信 MITSUNOBU*
[Active 1730s–1760s]; an Osaka illustrator.
永春 Early name: Eishun
長谷川 Surname: Hasegawa
梅翁軒 *Gō*: Baiōken
梅峯軒 [Baihōken]
松翠軒 Shōsuiken

——— [MITSUNOBU]
[Active c. 1850]; probably a misreading.

基春 MOTOHARU*
Lived 1858–1903 [active 1880s–1890s]; an Osaka painter.
林 Surname: Hayashi
公齋 *Gō*: Kōsai
捨蔵 Personal name: Sutezō

む免國 MUMEKUNI
See Umekuni.

宗廣 MUNEHIRO
Active 1848–1867.
長谷川 Surname: Hasegawa
See Cat. 263-64.

宗信 MUNENOBU*
[Active 1780s]; died c. 1790. An Osaka illustrator.
桂 Surname: Katsura
眉山 *Gō*: Bizan
通神道人 Tsūjindōjin
源吾 Personal name: Gengo

長秀 NAGAHIDE
Active c. 1805–1842 (?).
中邑（村） Surname: Nakamura
長秀齋 *Gō*: Chōshūsai (as signature)
有樂齋 Yūrakusai (as signature)
Personal names:
有恒 [Aritsune]
有愼 [Arichika]
See Cat. 265-67.

長國 NAGAKUNI
See Ashiyuki.

長國 NAGAKUNI
Active 1814–c. 1820s. As Shūei, recorded on a print dated 1/1814 as a pupil of Nagahide; recorded name change from Shūei to Nagakuni on another print dated 1/1814. This is possibly the same Nagakuni who became Ashiyuki, but is more likely a second artist of this name.
秀榮 Early name: Shūei (1814)

長丸 NAGAMARU*
[Active 1790s–1810s]; an Osaka illustrator.
桂向山人 *Gō*: Keikōsanjin
桂向亭 Keikōtei

南陽 NANYŌ
See Hokuga.

南陽齋 NANYŌSAI
See Hokuga.

尚國 NAOKUNI*
[Active 1750s–1760s]; an Osaka illustrator.
森 Surname: Mori

耳鳥齋 NICHŌSAI*
Active 1780s; died c. 1802. An Osaka brewer, antique dealer, author, and illustrator. He designed a volume of theatrical caricatures in 1780.
Personal names:
松屋平三郎 Matsuya [Heizaburō]
半三郎 [Hanzaburō]
Osaka address Kyōmachibori 3-chōme

日本齋 NIHONSAI*
Active 1807; a designer of a stenciled actor print published in Kyoto.

信春 NOBUHARU
Active 1832.
西川 Surname: Nishikawa

信廣 NOBUHIRO
Active 1839.
Surnames:
長谷川 Hasegawa
南々川 Nanakawa
照皇亭 *Gō*: Shōkōtei
仙助 Personal name: [Sensuke]

信勝 NOBUKATSU
Active 1824–1841. As Shigenao, recorded on a print dated 8/1829 as a pupil of Shigeharu; as Nobukatsu, recorded on prints dated 1/1832 and 1/1833 as a pupil of Sadamasu. Recorded name change from Shigenao to Nobukatsu on a print dated 9/1829.
柳狂亭重直 Early name: Ryūkyōtei Shigenao (1829)
Surnames:
柳川 Yanagawa (1831)
歌川 Utagawa
哲齋 *Gō*: Tessai (1824; as signature in 1837)
五狂亭 Gokyōtei (1829)
See Cat. 268-70.

——— [NOBUKAZU]
Probably a misreading of Nobusada.

信政　信叟　NOBUMASA
Active 1832–1848; listed as a portraitist (*see* Appendix XI).
柳川　Surname: Yanagawa
Osaka address: Senba

信光　NOBUMITSU
Active 1850s.
Gō unread

信貞　NOBUSADA
Active 1823–1832 (?); recorded on a print dated 1823 as a pupil of Shigenobu with recorded name change from Yukinobu to Nobusada.
雪信　Early name: Yukinobu (1823)
柳川　Surname: Yanagawa
See Cat. 271.

信貞　NOBUSADA
See Shunki.

應擧　ŌKYO*
Lived 1733–1795; active 1750s–1790s. The founder of the Shijō school of painting, and the supposed designer of hand-colored perspective prints published in Kyoto.
圓山　Surname: Maruyama
夏雲　*Gō*: Kaun
僊嶺　Senrei
(and others)

樂齋　RAKUSAI*
Active 1813; a designer of an actor print published in Kyoto. Possibly a *gō* of Yūrakusai Nagahide.

蘭好齋　RANKŌSAI
Active 1805.
See Cat. 272.

禮山　REIZAN
Active 1871.

連山　RENZAN
See Yukinaga.

李江　RIKŌ
Active mid-1820s.
溪中庵　*Gō*: Keichūan

里席　RISEKI
See Yukinaga.

蘆溪　ROKEI*
[Active 1800s]; an Osaka artist, possibly Ashikuni's father.
淺山　Surname: Asayama

露好　露好齋　ROKŌ or ROKŌSAI
Active 1812–1813.

芦舟　ROSHŪ
See Ashifune.

流光齋　RYŪKŌSAI
Active 1770s–1809.
多賀　Surname: Taga
流光齋　*Gō*: Ryūkōsai (as signature)
Personal names:
如圭　Jokei
慈平　Jihei
Osaka addresses:
Horie Kameibashi or Kita-Horie 4-chōme
Nanba Shinchi Kyōbashimachi (later)
See Cat. 273-74.

貞房　SADAFUSA
[Active 1830s–1840s]; recorded on a print dated 3/1830 as a pupil of Shigeharu. An Edo artist who later moved to Osaka.
Surname:
大澤　Ōsawa
歌川　Utagawa
五龜亭　*Gō*: Gokitei
五楓亭　[Gofūtei]
五飄亭　[Gohyōtei]
桶蝶樓　Tōchōrō
震齋　Shinsai

貞春　SADAHARU
Active late 1830s.
長谷川　Surname: Hasegawa
五柳亭　*Gō*: Goryūtei
五蕉亭　Goshōtei

初代 貞廣　SADAHIRO I
Active 1830–1851; possibly the same as Hirosada.
多美國　Early name: Tamikuni (?) (1823–1826)
Surnames:
南々川　Nanakawa
歌川　Utagawa
三谷　Mitani
好画堂　*Gō*: Kōgadō (?)
浮世　Ukiyo
五蝶亭　Gochōtei
五樂亭　Gorakutei
五粽亭　[Gosōtei]
五輝亭　Gokitei
Seals:
多三國　Tamikuni (1830)
廣　Hiro (1834)
貞　Sada (1836)
Personal name: Kyōmaruya Seijirō
Osaka addresses:
Tatamiyamachi Mitsuderasuji
Nanba Shinchi
See Cat. 275-79.

二代貞廣 **Sadahiro II**

Lived 1840–1910; active 1864–1876. A student of Maruyama-style painting who assumed the name Sadahiro II on the death of his teacher Hirosada.

廣兼 Early name: [Hirokane]

三谷 Surname: [Mitani]

照星亭 *Gō*: Shōkōtei

又三郎 Personal name: Matasaburō

貞景 **Sadakage**

Active in Osaka c. 1830; an Edo artist who designed actor prints and surimono in the 1820s and 1830s.

Surnames:

小島 Kojima

歌川 Utagawa

五湖亭 *Gō*: Gokotei

庄五郎 Personal name: Shōgorō

貞勝 **Sadakatsu**

Active 1852 [1834]; the two known prints signed Sadakatsu may be by two different artists.

貞一 **Sadakazu**

Active 1826.

百濟堂 *Gō*: Kudaradō

一心齋 Isshinsai

心齋 [Shinsai]

貞麿 **Sadamaro**

See Sadamaru.

貞丸 **Sadamaru**

Active 1833.

貞麿 Early name: Sadamaro (1833)

歌川 Surname: Utagawa

貞政 **Sadamasa**

Active 1834–c. 1840. Recorded on an undated print as a pupil of Hasegawa (Sadanobu); recorded on a print dated 3/1834 as a pupil of Tōto Kunisada.

Surnames:

長谷川 Hasegawa

歌川 Utagawa

金助 Personal name: Kinsuke

初代貞升 **Sadamasu I**

See Kunimasu.

二代貞升 **Sadamasu II**

Active 1849; apparently recorded on an undated print as a pupil of Kunimasu.

See Cat. 280.

初代貞信 **Sadanobu I**

Lived 1809–1879; active 1834–1879.

Early names:

有長 Yūchō

貞宣 [Sadanobu]

Surnames:

長谷川 Hasegawa

小西 Konishi (1843)

五雙亭 *Gō*: Gosōtei

南窓 Nansō

南窓樓 Nansōrō

雪花園 Sekkaen

信翁 Shin'ō

信天翁 Shinten'ō

楢園 [Yūen]

緑一齋 [Ryokuitsusai]

金花堂 Kinkadō (1843)

蘭孝 Rankō (as *jōruri* singer)

奈良屋文吉 Early personal name: Naraya Bunkichi

Personal names:

奈良屋徳兵衛 Naraya Tokubei

徳兵衛 Tokubei (as signature in 1841)

景明 Kageaki (?) (as signature in 1840s)

専蔵 Senzō (as adopted son of Tenki in 1843)

Seals:

ふじのやま Fujinoyama

信天翁 Shinten'ō

Osaka addresses:

Andōjimachi Naniwabashisuji

Horie Ichinogawa (later)

See Cat. 281-95.

二代貞信 **Sadanobu II**

Lived 1848–1886; active 1867–1880s. The son of Sadanobu I and the second of five generations of Hasegawa artists continuing to the present. Konobu II became Sadanobu III in 1910.

初代小信 Early name: Konobu I (1867–1879)

長谷川 Surname: Hasegawa

徳太郎 Personal name: Tokutarō

貞信 **Sadanobu**

Active 1823; an artist known by a single print and not included in the Hasegawa genealogy. Possibly an early work by Sadanobu I.

貞孝 **Sadataka**

Active 1839; probably the Edo artist of this name who worked in the 1830s.

貞次 **Sadatsugu**

Active 1835–1839 [1842]; recorded on an undated print and on a print dated 2/1835 as a pupil of Kunisada.

五蝶亭 *Gō*: Gochōtei

定好 SADAYOSHI
[Active 1760s]; a designer of single-sheet prints and *fukie* published in Osaka.
吉川 Surname: Yoshikawa

貞芳 SADAYOSHI
Active 1837–1853.
歌川 Surname: Utagawa
梅窓園 *Gō*: Baisōen
五飄亭 [Gofūtei]
五瓢亭 [Gohyōtei]
魁春亭 Kaishuntei
國瓢亭 [Kokuhyōtei]
梅窓園琴金 Baisōen Kinkin (as author)
肥後屋貞七郎 Personal name: Higoya Sadashichirō
Osaka address: Shimanouchi
See Cat. 296.

貞美 SADAYOSHI
[Active c. 1850].
歌川 Surname: Utagawa

貞雪 SADAYUKI
Active 1839–1840; recorded on prints dated 1/1839 and 7/1840 as a pupil of Sadamasu.

茶樂齋 SARAKUSAI
See Seikoku.

左祐 SAYŪ*
[Active 1760s]; an Osaka painter and illustrator.
桂 Surname: Katsura

清好 SEIKŌ
Active c. 1810s–1820s; a designer, engraver, and perhaps a commissioner of surimono and illustrated books published in Osaka.
谷 Surname: Tani

清谷 SEIKOKU*
Active c. late 1810s; designer of a stenciled actor print published in Kyoto.
茶樂齋 *Gō*: Charakusai (also as signature)

青柳 SEIRYŪ*
Active 1815; designer of stenciled actor prints published in Kyoto.

星齋 SEISAI
Active 1829 (?) [1851]; designer of one print of the actor Ichikawa Hakuen, cited by Kuroda.

井特 SEITOKU*
Active 1820s; a Kyoto painter and illustrator.
祇園井特 *Gō*: Gion Seitoku
井筒屋特右衛門 Personal name: [Izutsuya Tokuemon]
Kyoto address: Gionmachi Minamigawa

雪好 SEKKŌ
[Active 1814].

雪江 SEKKŌ
[Active 1830s].

千万 SENBAN
Possible alternate pronunciation of Senman.

泉壽 SENJU
See Eiju.

千万 SENMAN
Active 1820s.

迁齋 遷齋 SENSAI
Active 1820s. Possibly an Ise artist; one print of a theater performance in Ise is known.

雪鼎 SETTEI*
Lived 1710–1786 [active 1750s–1780s].
Surnames:
月岡 Tsukioka
木田 Kida
錦童 *Gō*: Kindō
桃漪 Tōi
露仁齋 Rojinsai
Personal names:
昌信 Masanobu
大溪 Daikei
丹下 Tange
信天翁 Shinten'ō
Osaka address: Shiomachi Shinsaibashisuji

芝國 しば國 志葉國 SHIBAKUNI
Active 1821–1826.
西光亭 *Gō*: Saikōtei
Osaka address: Ryōgokubashi
See Cat. 297-99.

重房 SHIGEFUSA*
[Active 1740s–1760s]; an Osaka illustrator.
寺井 Surname: Terai
雪蕉齋 *Gō*: Sesshōsai
尚房 Personal name: Naofusa
Osaka address: Andōjimachi 5-chōme

重房 SHIGEFUSA
Active 1829–1830.
秀丸齋 *Gō*: Shūgansai

二代重房 SHIGEFUSA II (?)
[Active 1850].
吉野 Surname: [Yoshino]
勝之助 Personal name: [Katsunosuke]

重春 SHIGEHARU
Lived 1803–1853; active 1821–1841 or later. Recorded name change from Kunishige to Ryūsai Shigeharu on a print dated 7/1826.
國重 Early name: Kunishige (1821–1826)
瀧川 Early surname: Takigawa (1825)
Early *gō*:
長崎 Nagasaki (1821)
崎陽齋 Kiyōsai
崎陽亭 [Kiyōtei]
梅丸齋 Baigansai
山口 Surname: Yamaguchi
柳齋 *Gō*: Ryūsai (1827–1829, 1833–1835)
玉柳亭 Gyokuryūtei (1830–1832)
玉柳齋 [Gyokuryūsai]
Personal names:
安秀 Yasuhide
甚治郎 Jinjirō
Osaka address: Mitsuderamachi
See Cat. 300-38.

重彦 SHIGEHIKO
[Active c. 1850s].
一立齋 *Gō*: [Ichiryūsai]

重廣 茂廣 志げ廣 SHIGEHIRO
Active 1865–1878 [1850s].
菊水 Surname: [Kikusui]
秀丸齋 *Gō*: Shūgansai
秀丸 Shūgan
秀峰 Shūhō
See Cat. 339.

重勝 SHIGEKATSU
Active 1826; not the Edo pupil of Hiroshige I.
山口 Surname: [Yamaguchi]
浮世 *Gō*: Ukiyo

重麿 SHIGEMARO
Active 1816.

重直 SHIGENAO
See Nobukatsu.

重信 SHIGENOBU
Lived 1787–1832; active in Osaka 1822–1825.
Surnames:
鈴木 Suzuki
柳川 Yanagawa
雷斗 *Gō*: Raito
琴齋 Kinsai
鈴齋 Reisai
雨蕉齋 Ushōsai
Edo address: Honjo Yanagawachō
See Cat. 340–46.

重貞 SHIGESADA*
[Active 1830s]; a designer of theater programs published in Osaka.

重芳 SHIGEYOSHI
[Active c. 1830s].

芝翫 SHIKAN
Lived 1778–1838; active 1817. The *haigō* of the actor Nakamura Utaemon III. He was primarily a sketcher, but designed some prints.
See Cat. 1.

子健 SHIKEN*
Active 1810–1816; the son of Ryūkōsai, and said to have died at an early age. He was primarily a painter. Since Baikoku, Shiken's *gō*, may be pronounced Umekuni, he may be the print designer of this name.
多賀 Surname: Taga
梅國 *Gō*: Baikoku (Umekuni) (as signature in 1816)
朴仙 Bokusen (as signature)
流光齋 Ryūkōsai (1810)
指瀍山人 [Shiōsanjin]
See Umekuni.

嶋丸 SHIMAMARU
Active 1830.
See Cat. 347.

眞好 SHINKŌ
[Active 1815].

眞平 SHINPEI
Active 1813. A portrait designer for a reissue of a print by Ryūkōsai; possibly a Kyoto artist.
See Yukinaga.

松峰 SHŌHŌ*
Active 1810s; an Osaka illustrator.
菅 Surname: Suga

昌次 SHŌJI
Possible alternate pronunciation of Masatsugu.

升鶴 SHŌKAKU
Possible alternate pronunciation of Masutsuru.

正好 SHŌKŌ
Active 1816.

松好 松好齋 SHŌKŌ or SHŌKŌSAI
Active 1795–1809; recorded on a print dated 1798 as a pupil of Ryūkōsai.
半兵衛 Personal name: Hanbei
Osaka address: Shimanouchi Shimizumachi
See Cat. 348-51.

松好齋 SHŌKŌSAI
See Hokushū.

松樂 SHŌRAKU
Active 1819.

松樂齋　松洛齋 SHŌRAKUSAI*
Active 1800s (?); mentioned as a contemporary of Ryūkōsai and Shōkōsai (*see* Appendix XVII). Perhaps identical to Shōraku.
松壽 *Gō*: Shōju
以悳 Personal name: [Itoku] (?)

松濤 SHŌTO
Period of activity unknown.

秀榮 SHŪEI
See Nagakuni.

周月 SHŪGETSU*
[Active 1820s].
北川 Surname: Kitagawa

春蝶 SHUNCHŌ
Active 1815–1823. Recorded on a print dated 3/1823 as a pupil of Shunkōsai (Hokushū); possibly an early name of Hokushō.
See Cat. 352 and Hokushō.

春頂 SHUNCHŌ
See Hokushō.

春朝 SHUNCHŌ
Active mid-1820s.
画壽軒 *Gō*: Gajuken

春鳥 SHUNCHŌ
[Active 1815–1821]; chiefly a Kyoto artist.
Surnames:
堀田 Hotta
春川 Harukawa

春榮 SHUN'EI
Active 1816 [1830s]; a name by which two prints are signed, perhaps by different artists.
春曉齋 *Gō*: Shungyōsai

初代 春曉齋 SHUNGYŌSAI I
Lived c. 1760–1823; active 1790s–1820s. Chiefly an illustrator, but designed a few single-sheet prints in the late 1810s.
速水 Surname: Hayami
春曉齋 *Gō*: Shungyōsai (as signature)
恒章 Personal name: Tsuneaki

二代 春曉齋 SHUNGYŌSAI II
[Active 1820s–1860s]; died 1867. The son of Shungyōsai I.
曉雲齋春眠 Early name: Gyōunsai Shunmin
速水 Surname: Hayami
春曉齋 *Gō*: Shungyōsai (as signature)
Personal names:
恒茂 Tsuneshige
民之助 Taminosuke

春常 SHUNJŌ
Active 1832; recorded on a print dated 3/1832 as a pupil of Gatōken Shunshi.

春壽 SHUNJU
Active 1828–1829. Recorded on a print dated 3/1829 as a pupil of Shunkō (Hokuei); recorded on a print dated 3/1829 as a pupil of Shunkōsai (Hokuei). Perhaps an early name of Hokuju.
See Hokuju.

春花 SHUNKA
Active mid-1820s [1830s]; apparently known only by collaborations with Gajuken Shunchō, Shunsei, and Gatōken Shunshi.

春敬 SHUNKEI
Active 1820 [1830s].
梅好齋 *Gō*: Baikōsai

春暉 SHUNKI
Lived 1830–1887; active c. 1849 [1880s]. A Kyoto artist. As Nobusada he designed a few *chūban* portraits.
Early names:
信貞 Nobusada (c. 1849)
二代 春貞 Harusada II (1849–1867)
Surnames:
岡本 Okamoto
歌川 Utagawa
正太郎 Personal name: Shōtarō

春錦 SHUNKIN
Active 1816.

春湖 SHUNKO
Active 1794.

春江 SHUNKŌ
See Hokuei.

春好 SHUNKŌ
See Hokushū.

春紅 SHUNKŌ
Active 1824; possibly an early signature of Hokuei. Probably not the Edo artist of this name.

春江齋 SHUNKŌSAI
See Hokuei.

春好齋 SHUNKŌSAI
See Hokushū.

春郷 SHUNKYŌ
Active 1814 [1813].

春王 SHUN'Ō
画遊軒 *Gō*: Gayūken

春峯 SHUNPŌ
Active mid-1820s.
画照軒 *Gō*: Gashōken

春勢 **Shunsei**
Active mid-1820s.
画遊軒 *Gō*: Gayūken
See Cat. 353.

春泉齋 **Shunsensai***
[Active 1790s–1810s]; an Osaka illustrator who also used the name Kiyohide.
竹原 Surname: Takehara

春子 **Shunshi**
Active 1826–1828; perhaps an early name of Hokumyō.
春陽齋 *Gō*: Shun'yōsai
青陽齋 Seiyōsai
青陽堂 Seiyōdō (1826)
春婦 Shunpu (?)
See Cat. 354-55.

春芝 **Shunshi**
Active mid-1820s.
画登軒 *Gō*: Gatōken
登龍軒 Tōryūken
登龍齋 [Tōryūsai]
Osaka address: Futatsuido

春枝 **Shunshi**
Active mid-1820s [1830s]; recorded on a print of the mid-1820s as a pupil of [Gatōken] Shunshi.
画好軒 *Gō*: Gakōken
See Cat. 356.

春始 **Shunshi**
[Active 1830s]; recorded on an undated print as a pupil of [Gatōken] Shunshi.

春信 **Shunshin**
Active c. 1820s; recorded on an undated print as a pupil of Hokushū.

春曙 **Shunsho**
See Hokuchō.

春渚 **Shunsho**
See Shun'yō

春松 **Shunshō**
Period of activity unknown.

春翠 **Shunsui***
[Active 1880s]; a Kyoto etcher.
四方 Surname: Yomo
平野屋茂兵衛 (茂平) Personal name: Hiranoya Mohei
Osaka address: Rokkakudōri Yanaginobanba Higashiiru

春貞 **Shuntei**
Active 1816 [1822]; possibly the same as the Kyoto rice merchant and ukiyoe painter Yasukawa Harusada (1798–1849).

春定 **Shuntei**
Active mid-1820s [1830s–1840s]; apparently known by only one print, a portrait of Onoe Tamizō.
画蝶軒 *Gō*: Gachōken

春陽 **Shun'yō**
See Hokkei.

春要 **Shun'yō**
[Active 1822]; recorded name change from Shunsho to Shun'yō on a print dated 5/1822.
春渚 Early name: Shunsho [1822]

春陽齋 **Shun'yōsai**
See Hokkei.

春友 **Shun'yū**
Active 1817–1822.

春山 **Shunzan**
Active 1827–1829; recorded on a print dated 1/1829 as a pupil of Shunkōsai (Hokushū).
北心齋 *Gō*: Hokushinsai

秀隣 **Shūrin***
[Active 1786]; an Osaka illustrator.
鈴木 Surname: Suzuki

集升 **Shūshō**
Active 1847–1848; a follower of Sadamasu. The signature is written deliberately to resemble that of Sadamasu.

秋亭 **Shūtei***
Active 1821; a designer of stenciled actor prints published in Kyoto. Mentioned as a pupil of Ueda Kōchō (*see* Appendix XIX).
田中 Surname: Tanaka

翠釜亭 **Suifutei***
Active 1782.
See Cat. 357.

祐信 **Sukenobu***
Lived 1671–1751; active 1700s–1740s. A Kyoto illustrator and painter who may have designed one set of twelve single-sheet prints in 1711.
西川 Surname: Nishikawa
自得齋 *Gō*: Jitokusai
自得叟 Jitokusō
文華堂 Bunkadō
Personal names:
祐助 Yūsuke
孫右衛門 Magoemon
右京 Ukyō

二代 戴斗 **Taito II**
[Active 1810s–1850s]; an Edo pupil of Hokusai who designed prints and books published in Osaka in the 1840s.
斗圓樓北泉 Early name: Toenrō Hokusen (to 1819)
Surnames:
藤原 Fujiwara
近藤 Kondō
葛飾 Katsushika (1819)
洞庭舎 *Gō*: Dōteisha
昇山 Shōzan
玄龍齋 Genryūsai
米華道人 Beikadōjin
米華齋 Beikasai
Personal names:
文雄 Fumio
伴右衛門 Ban'emon

玉國 **Tamakuni**
Active 1823; mentioned as a portraitist (*see* Appendix XI).
春松堂 *Gō*: Shunshōdō

玉洲 **Tamakuni**
Active 1834; probably pronounced Gyokushū.

多美國 民國 多三國(?) **Tamikuni**
Active 1823–1826.
豊川 Surname: Toyokawa
好画堂 *Gō*: Kōgadō
兒龍齋 Jiryūsai
See Cat. 358-59.

探月 **Tangetsu**
See Tangetsusai.

探月齋 **Tangetsusai**
[Active 1800s–1820s]; an Osaka illustrator. Some Meiji landscape prints are also signed Tangetsusai.

照國 **Terukuni***
Active c. 1820s; a pupil of Yoshikuni mentioned on surimono.

哲齋 **Tessai**
See Nobukatsu.

辰宣 **Tokinobu***
Active 1740s–1750s; a painter and designer of books, theater programs, and perhaps an occasional print, published in Osaka.
北尾 Surname: Kitao
雪抗齋 *Gō*: Sekkōsai
仁翁 Jin'ō
Osaka address: Suōmachi

徳兵衛 **Tokubei**
See Sadanobu I.

東居 **Tōkyo**
Active 1860s; a Kyoto artist chiefly of landscape and figure prints.
梅川 Surname: Umekawa

登美國 **Tomikuni**
Active c. 1821–1822.
香雅堂 *Gō*: Kōgadō
See Cat. 360.

富雪 **Tomiyuki**
Active 1850s; chiefly an illustrator.
六花亭 緑華亭 *Gō*: Rokkatei
千錦亭 Senkintei

友國 **Tomokuni**
Active late 1810s.

友岡 **Tomooka***
Active c. 1831; mentioned as a block-copyist (*see* Appendix XI).
Osaka address: Uemachi

壽景 **Toshikage**
Active 1850s; possibly pronounced Jukei.

とし國 年國 歳國 **Toshikuni**
See Hokugan.

年基 **Toshimoto**
Active 1870s; known from several single-sheet prints, some of which are dated 1877.
鈴木 Surname: Suzuki
雷(蕾)齋 *Gō*: Raisai
雷之助 Personal name: Rainosuke
Address: Andōjibashidōri 3-chōme 23

東雲 **Tōun***
Active c. 1800.
山 *Gō*: San
See Cat. 361.

豊秀 **Toyohide**
Active 1839–1841.
北川 Surname: Kitagawa
一流亭 *Gō*: Ichiryūtei
一信亭 Isshintei

豊秀 **Toyohide**
Active 1863; possibly the same artist as above. Another Utagawa Toyohide is mentioned as an Osaka illustrator c. 1806–1811.
歌川 Surname: Utagawa

豊川 **Toyokawa**
See Hikokuni.

初代 豊國 **Toyokuni I***
Lived 1769–1825; active 1786–1825.
Surnames:
倉橋 Kurahashi
歌川 Utagawa
一陽齋 *Gō*: Ichiyōsai

熊吉 熊右衛門
Personal names:
Kumakichi
Kumaemon
See Cat. 362.

豊國 TOYOKUNI*
Active 1810s [1830s]. A designer of stencil prints published in Kyoto; no relation to the Edo artist of the same name.
長谷川 Surname: Hasegawa
稲香 *Gō*: Tōka

常丸 TSUNEMARU
[Active 1849 (?)]
花齋 *Gō*: Kasai

梅春 UMEHARU
Active mid-1820s.

梅英 UMEHIDE
[Active c. 1870s].

梅國 む免國 UMEKUNI
Active 1823–1826; also written Mumekuni. Recorded on a print dated 4/1823 as a pupil of Yoshikuni.
豐川 Surname: Toyokawa
四季亭 *Gō*: Shikitei
壽曉堂 Jugyōdō
兼珊 Kensan (?)
See Cat. 363-64.

梅貞 UMESADA
[Active 1830s].

梅雪 UMEYUKI
[Active c. 1870s]; later opened a restaurant in Uwajima.
岩井 Surname: Iwai
梅次郎 Personal name: Umejirō

歌國 哥國 UTAKUNI
Lived 1777–1827; active 1814–1816. An author, illustrator, and kabuki playwright who designed a few prints.
Surnames:
濱松 Hamamatsu
八重牆(垣) Yaegaki
——— *Gō*: Shikitei (1816)
颯々亭南水 Fūfūtei Nansui (as author)
Personal names:
布屋氏助 Nunoya Ujisuke
清兵衛 Seibei
Osaka address: Shimanouchi Aburamachi 2-chōme

雨多國(?) UTAKUNI (?)
Active 1824; designer of one print with an undeciphered signature.

歌好 UTAYOSHI*
Active c. 1831; a *kyōka* poet, who designed at least one square actor surimono. Mentioned as a block-copyist (*see* Appendix XI).
浮世 *Gō*: Ukiyo
Osaka address: Uemachi

保一 YASUKAZU*
Active 1827–1828; a designer of stenciled actor prints published in Kyoto. Recorded on prints dated 11/1827 and 8/1828 as a pupil of Yasuyuki.

保之 YASUYUKI*
[Active 1820s–1830s]; a Kyoto illustrator.
森川 Surname: Morikawa

より國 YORIKUNI*
Active c. 1827; mentioned on a Yoshikuni print (*see* Appendix VIII).

——— [YOSHICHIKA]
[Active c. 1850]; the name is probably a misreading.

芳英 YOSHIFUSA
[Active 1830s–1850s].
歌川 Surname: Utagawa
一櫻齋 *Gō*: Ichiōsai
一春齋 Isshunsai

芳春 YOSHIHARU
[Active 1870s].
Surnames:
藤井 Fujii
歌川 Utagawa
喜三郎 Personal name: Kisaburō

好廣 YOSHIHIRO
Active 1865.

芳景 YOSHIKAGE
Active 1874–c. 1878.
後藤 Surname: Gotō
豊齋 *Gō*: Hōsai
徳次郎 Personal name: Tokujirō

義清 YOSHIKIYO*
[Active 1700s–1710s]; a Kyoto illustrator.
大森 Surname: Ōmori

芳琴 YOSHIKOTO
Active 1852–1856.
一樋齋 *Gō*: Ittōsai

よし國 芳國 芳洲 YOSHIKUNI
Active 1800 (?), 1813–1830 [1831]; recorded name change from Ashimaru to Yoshikuni on a print dated 3/1816.

Early names:
壽公 Jukō (1800 [?])
壽好 Jukō (1813)
芦(あし)麿 Ashimaro (1813–1814)
芦丸 Ashimaru (1816)
高城(木) Surnames: Takagi or Takaki
高 Kō (or Takagi, Takaki) (1822)
豊川 Toyokawa
壽好堂 壽公堂 *Gō*: Jukōdō
岡丈堂 Kōjōdō (?)
Osaka address: Bakuromachi
See Cat. 365-90.

芳國 芳洲 Yoshikuni
Lived 1856–1904; active 1850s–1880s. A Kyoto landscape artist, mentioned as a pupil of Yoshiume.
野村 Surname: Nomura
一陽亭 *Gō*: Ichiyōtei
笑翁 Shōō
Kyoto address: Teramachidōri Nishikikōji agaru

芳京 [Yoshikyō]
Apparently a misreading of Yoshikage.

芳升 Yoshimasu
[Active 1850s–1870s]; possibly the same artist as Ichiensai Yoshimasu who worked in Edo in the 1830s.
歌川 Surname: Utagawa

芳峯 Yoshimine
Active 1856–1858 or later.
Surnames:
武部 Takebe
歌川 Utagawa
一梅齋 *Gō*: Ichibaisai
胡蝶樓 Kochōrō
旭亭 Kyokutei
玉亭 Gyokutei
安兵衛 Personal name: Yasubei
See Cat. 391.

芳光 Yoshimitsu
Lived 1850–1891; active 1873–1880; younger brother of the artist Yoshitaki.
Surnames:
笹木 [Sasaki]
笹本 [Sasamoto]
嘉造 Personal name: Yoshizō

よし直 Yoshinao*
Active c. 1822; mentioned as a poet (*see* Appendix VI); this is probably not the Edo pupil of Kuniyoshi active in the 1840s and 1850s.

芳信 Yoshinobu
Active 1842.
歌川 Surname: [Utagawa]
一瓢亭 *Gō*: [Ippyōtei]
一瓢齋 [Ippyōsai]

芳重 Yoshishige
Active 1847; possibly the Edo pupil of Kuniyoshi active from the 1830s to the 1850s.
歌川 Surname: [Utagawa]
一要齋 *Gō*: [Ichiyōsai]
——— [Nan'yūsai]

芳瀧 Yoshitaki
Lived 1841–1899; active 1854–1880s.
Surnames:
中井 Nakai
笹木 Sasaki
一養齋 *Gō*: Ichiyōsai
一養亭 Ichiyōtei
一点齋 Ittensai (1861)
壽榮堂 Jueidō
糊家 Noriya
里の家 Satonoya
養水 Yōsui
豐玉 [Hōgyoku]
阪田舎居 [Handenshakyo]
Seals:
(paulownia crest) paulownia
里のや Satonoya
豐齋 Hōsai
當 Atari
恒次郎 Personal name: Tsunejirō (or Kōjirō)
Osaka address: Minami Honmachi 2-chōme (later moved to Sakai)
See Cat. 392-427.

初代 芳豐 Yoshitoyo I
Active 1854–1857 in Osaka; died 1866.
Surnames:
上原 Uehara
歌川 Utagawa
含粋亭 *Gō*: Gansuitei
北粋(酔, 翠, 水) Hokusui
北碎 [Hokusai]
北碎舎 [Hokusaisha]
兵三 Personal name: Hyōzō
See Cat. 428-29.

二代 芳豐 Yoshitoyo II*
Born 1868 [active 1890s–1900s]; he was the son of Yoshimine.
武部 Surname: Takebe
豐次郎 Personal name: Toyojirō

芳次 Yoshitsugu
Active 1839; recorded on a print dated late 1830s as a pupil of Utagawa Sadayoshi.
歌川 Surname: Utagawa
See Cat. 430.

芳梅 YOSHIUME
Lived 1819–1879; active 1841–1848 [1840]. Chiefly an illustrator.
中島 Surname: Nakajima
一鶯齋 *Gō*: Ichiōsai
夜梅樓 Yabairō
藤助 Personal name: Tōsuke
Osaka address: Horie

芳幸 よし幸 YOSHIYUKI
Active 1822 [1821].
高 Surname: Kō (or Takagi, Takaki)

芳雪 YOSHIYUKI
Lived 1835–1879; active 1856–1872.
森 Surname: Mori
南粋 *Gō*: Nansui
六花園 Rokkaen
六花軒 Rokkaken
Personal names:
米次郎 [Yonejirō]
半次郎 [Hanjirō]
See Cat. 431.

有長 YŪCHŌ
See Sadanobu.

幸國 YUKIKUNI
Active 1816.

雪國 YUKIKUNI
[Active 1820s]. Possibly the same artist as above.
柳川 Surname: Yanagawa

行長 YUKINAGA*
Active 1804 [1800s–1810s]; a designer of actor and genre prints published in Kyoto, possibly the same artist as Shinpei.
堀田 Surname: Hotta
里席 *Gō*: Riseki (also as signature)
連山 Renzan (also as signature)
眞平 Personal name: Shinpei

雪信 YUKINOBU
See Nobusada.

有樂齋 YŪRAKUSAI
See Nagahide.

Signature Facsimiles

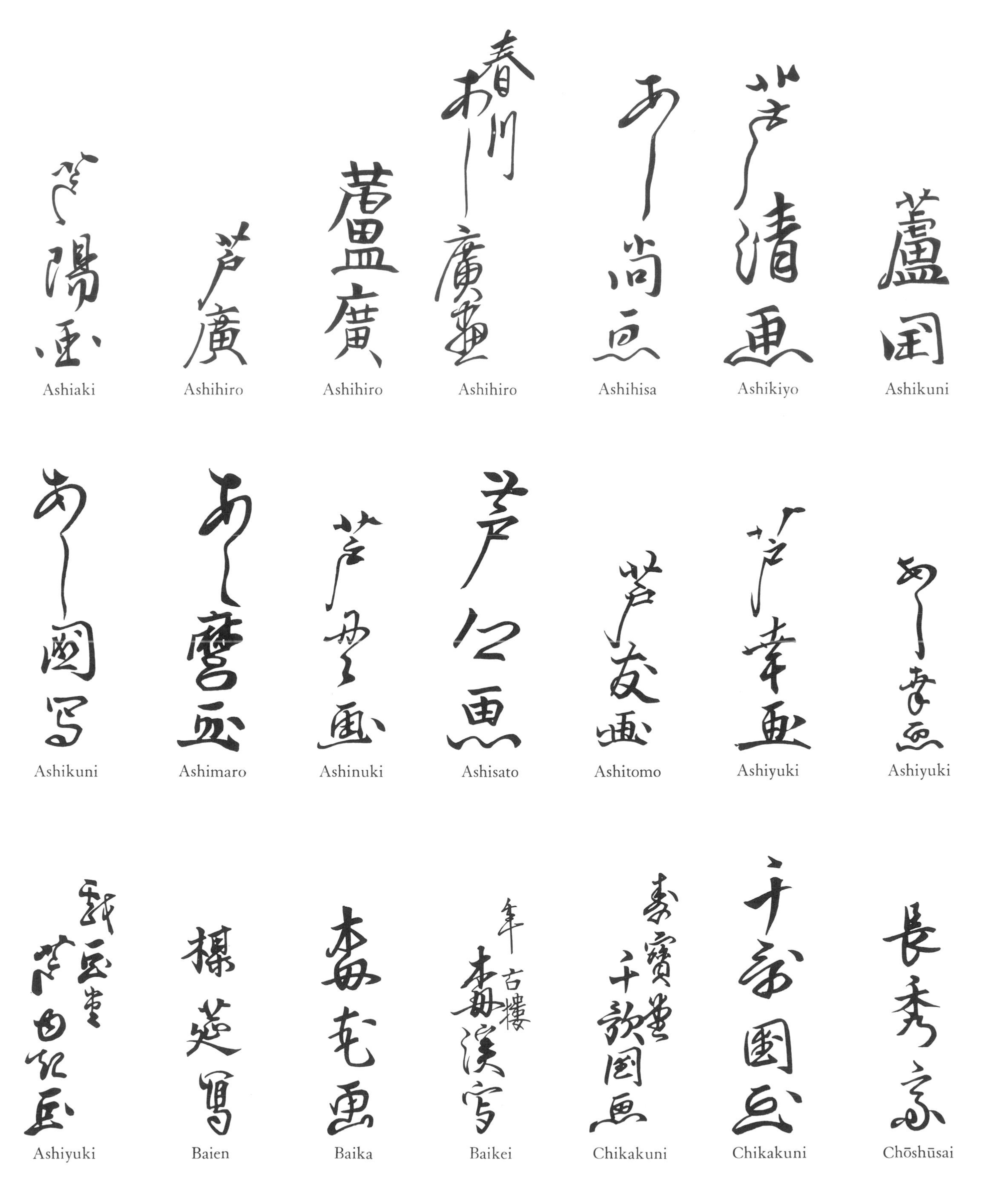

Ebikane

Enjaku

Fujikuni

Gakutei

Goshichi

Gyokuhō

Gyokusen

Gyokushū

Hatsukuni

Hidekuni

Hikokuni

Hikokuni

Hirokuni (Hirosada)

Hironobu I

Hirosada

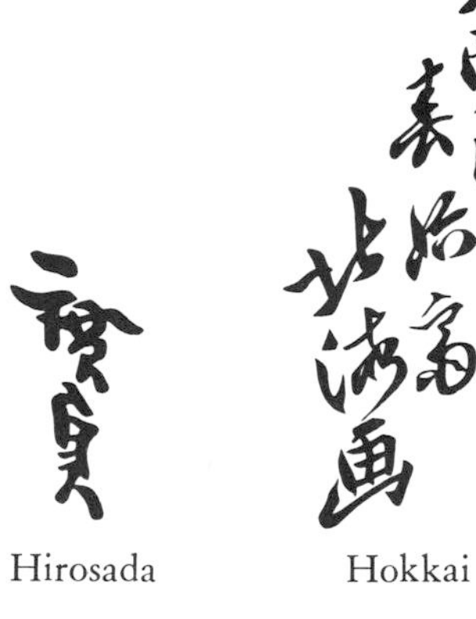

Hirosada

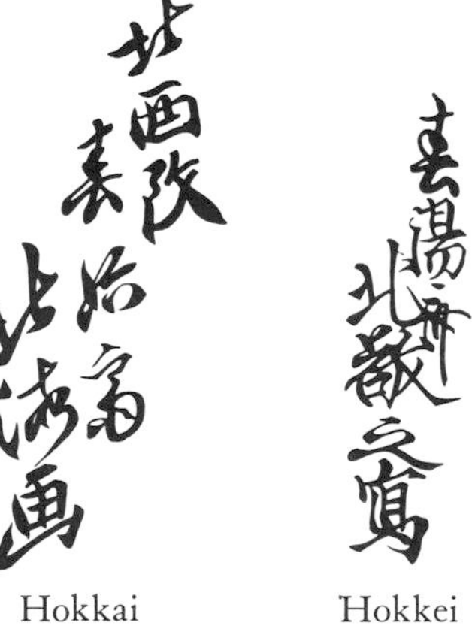

Hokkai

Hokkei

Hokuchō

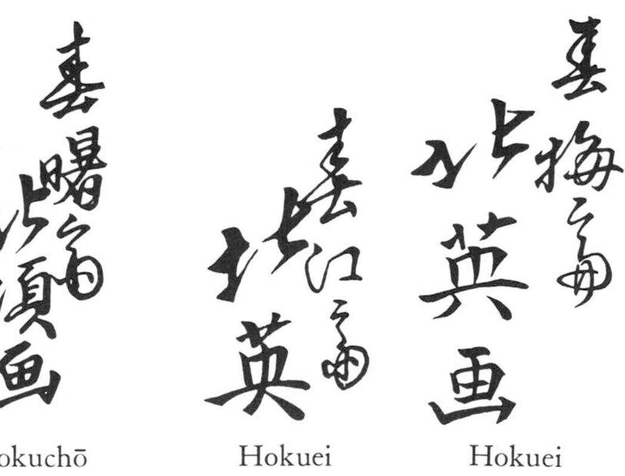

Hokuei

Hokuei

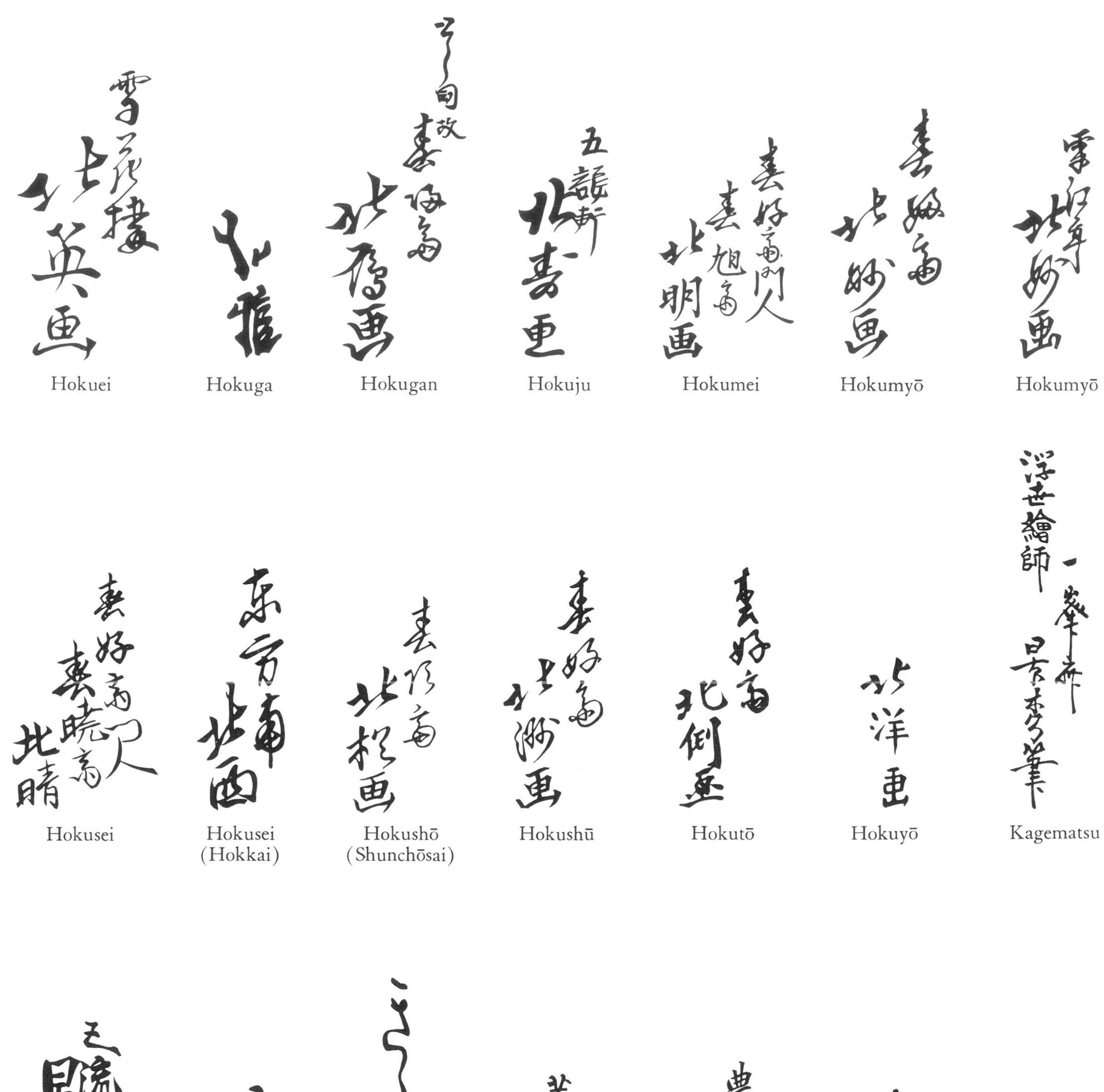

Hokuei · Hokuga · Hokugan · Hokuju · Hokumei · Hokumyō · Hokumyō

Hokusei · Hokusei (Hokkai) · Hokushō (Shunchōsai) · Hokushū · Hokutō · Hokuyō · Kagematsu

Kagematsu

Kagetoshi

Kishikuni

Kiyoharu

Kiyokuni

Kiyosada

Konobu

Kuniharu

Kuniharu

Kunihiro

Kunihiro

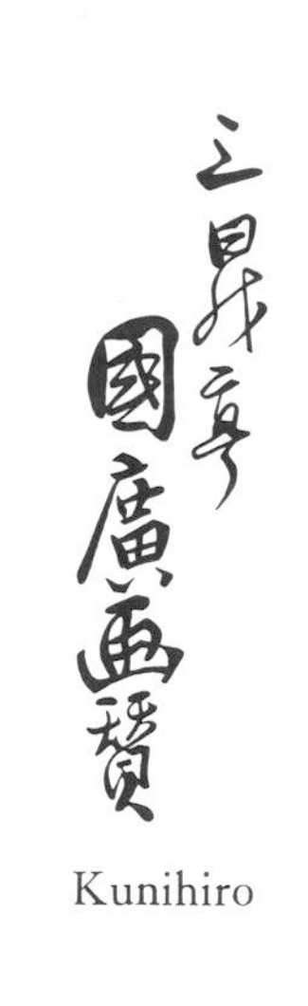
Kunihiro

Kunihiro

Kunikage

Kunikazu

Kunimasu

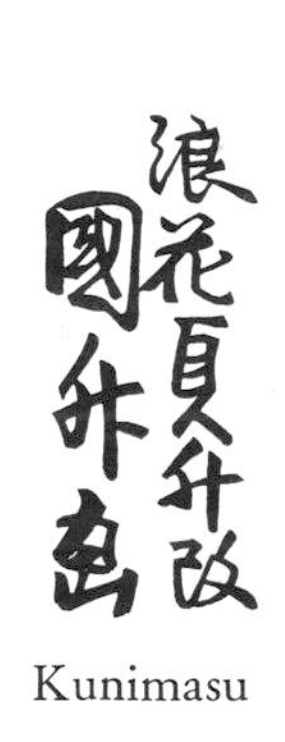
Kunimasu

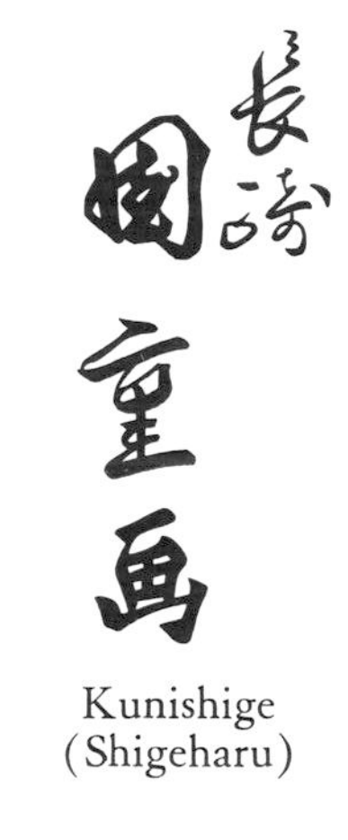
Kunishige (Shigeharu)

Kunishige (Shigeharu)

Kunishige (active 1847–1851)

Kunitsuru

Masakuni

Masuharu

Masunobu

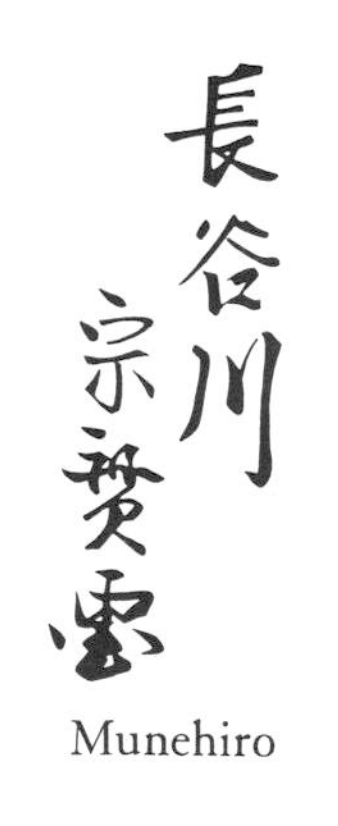
Munehiro

Nagahide

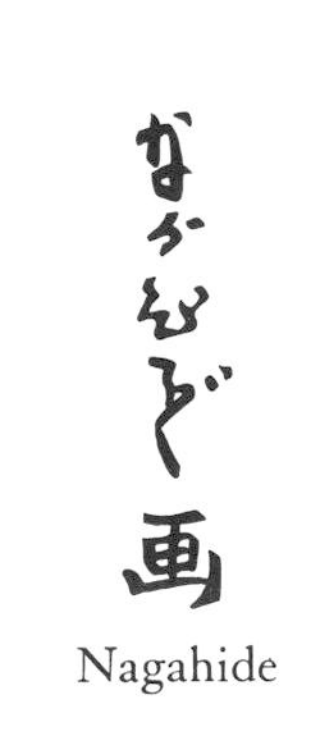
Nagahide

Nagakuni

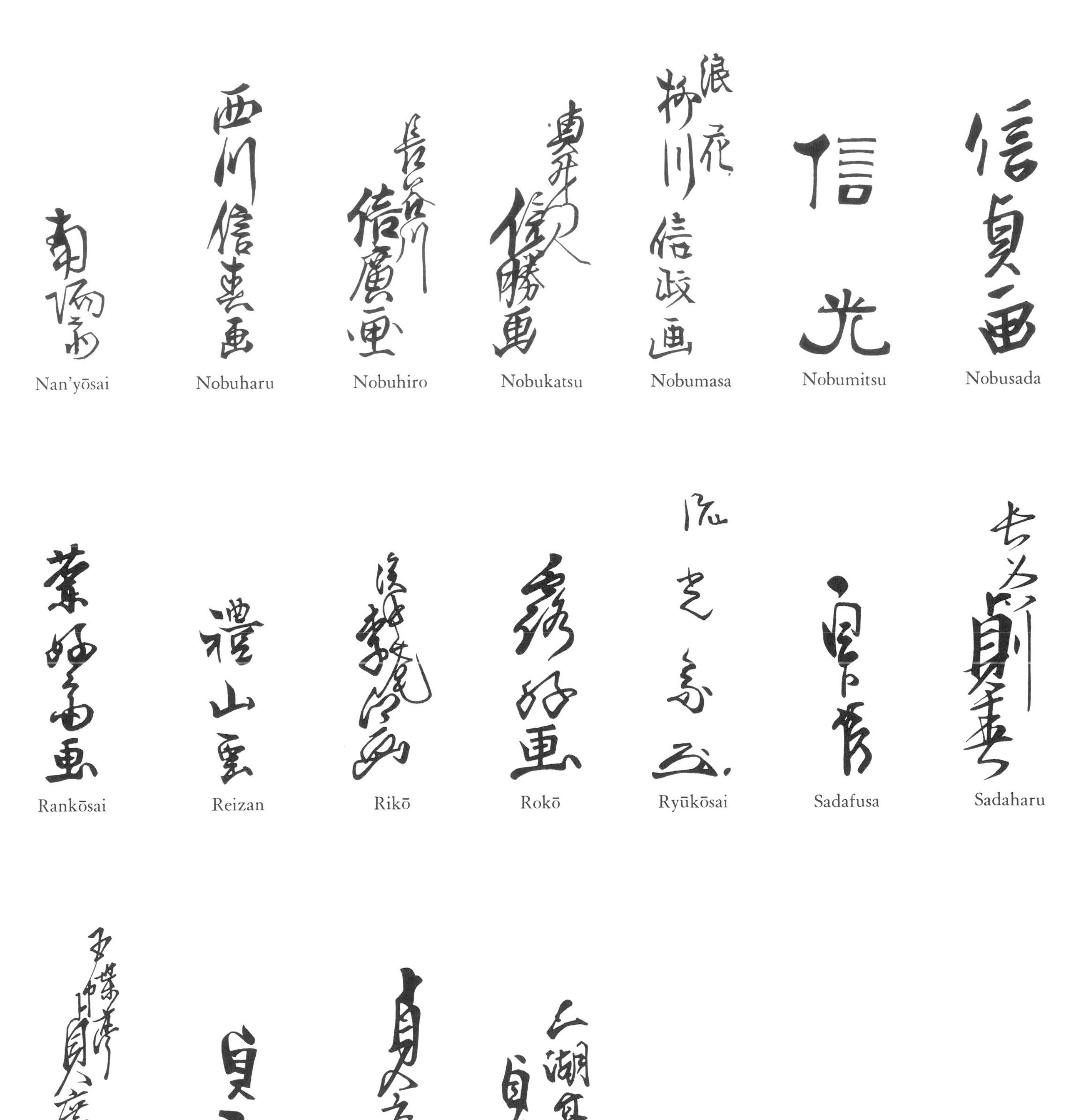

Sadahiro I Sadahiro II Sadahiro II Sadakage Sadakazu

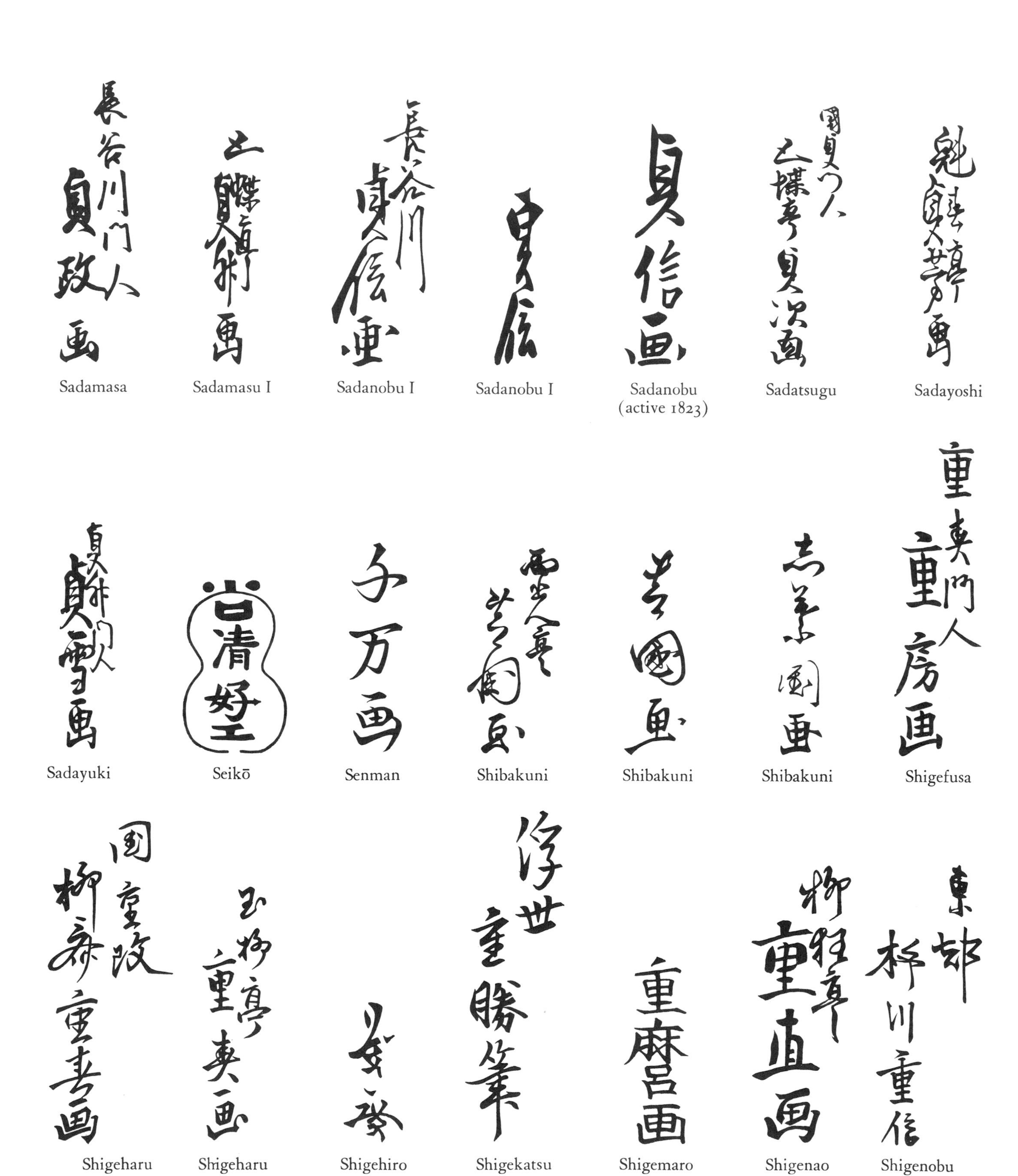
Sadamasa
Sadamasu I
Sadanobu I
Sadanobu I
Sadanobu
(active 1823)
Sadatsugu
Sadayoshi
Sadayuki
Seikō
Senman
Shibakuni
Shibakuni
Shibakuni
Shigefusa
Shigeharu
Shigeharu
Shigehiro
Shigekatsu
Shigemaro
Shigenao
Shigenobu

Shikan

Shimamaru

Shōkō
(active 1816)

Shōkō
(Shōkōsai)

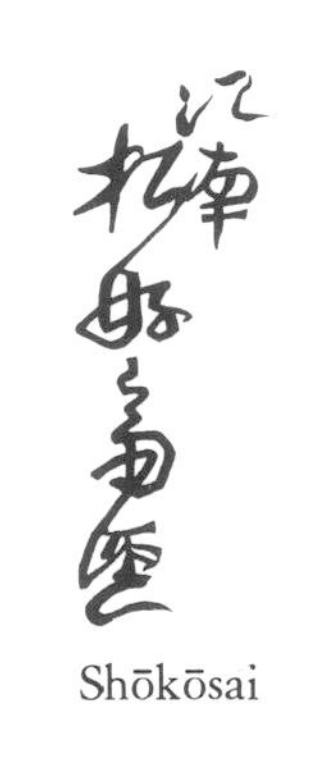

Shōkōsai

Shōraku

Shunchō
(active 1815–1823)

Shunchō
(Gajuken)

Shunchō
(Hokushō)

Shun'ei

Shunju

Shunkei

Shunkin

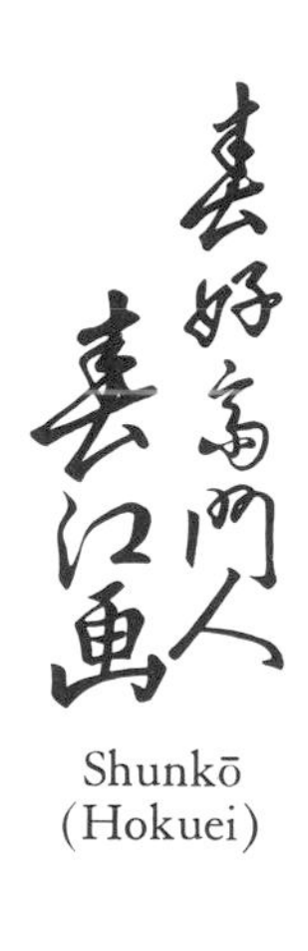

Shunkō
(Hokuei)

Shunkō
(Hokushū)

Shunkyō

Shun'ō

Shunpō

Shunsei

Shunshi
(Gakōken)

Shunshi
(Gatōken)

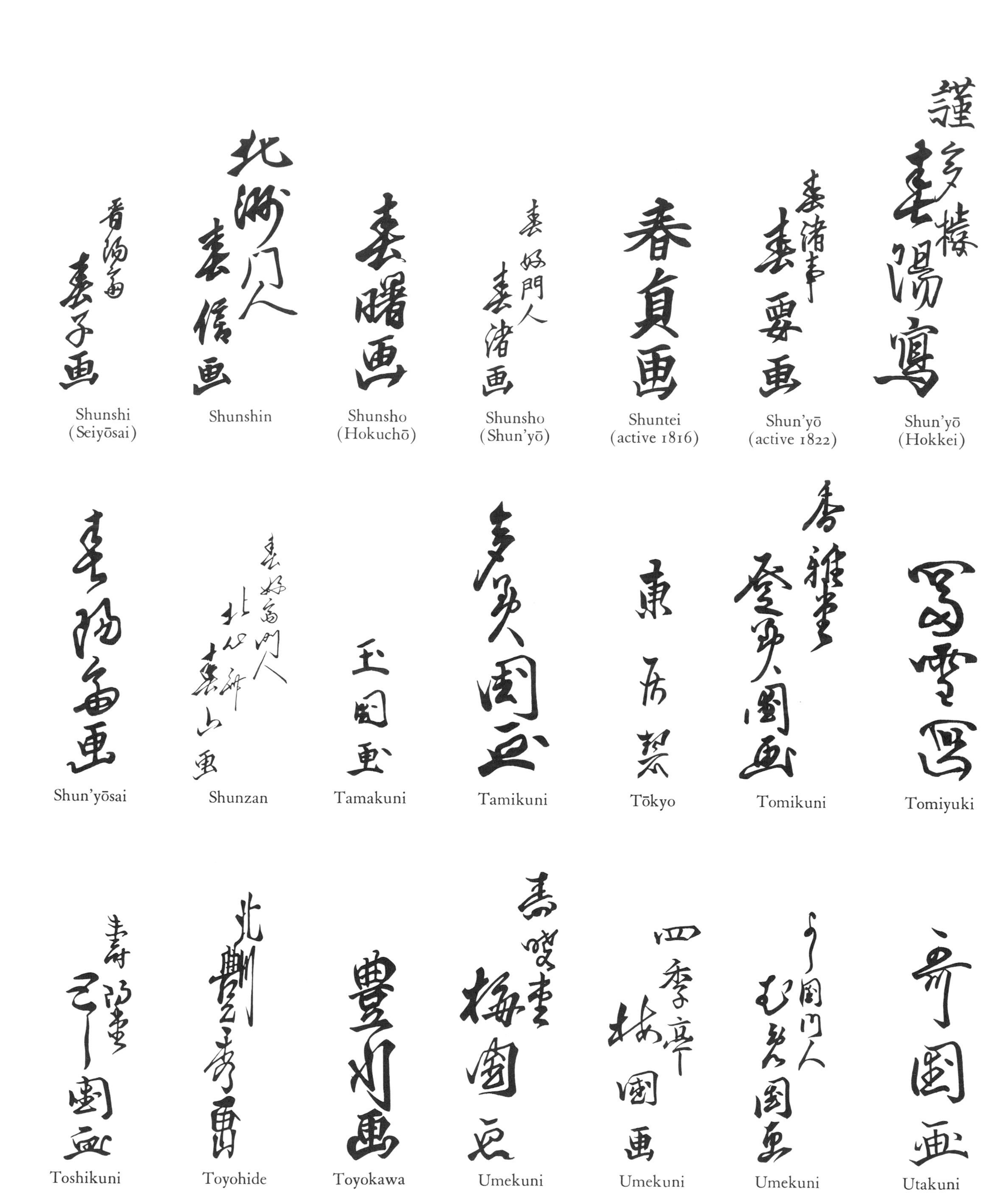

Shunshi (Seiyōsai) · Shunshin · Shunsho (Hokuchō) · Shunsho (Shun'yō) · Shuntei (active 1816) · Shun'yō (active 1822) · Shun'yō (Hokkei)

Shun'yōsai · Shunzan · Tamakuni · Tamikuni · Tōkyo · Tomikuni · Tomiyuki

Toshikuni · Toyohide · Toyokawa · Umekuni · Umekuni · Umekuni · Utakuni

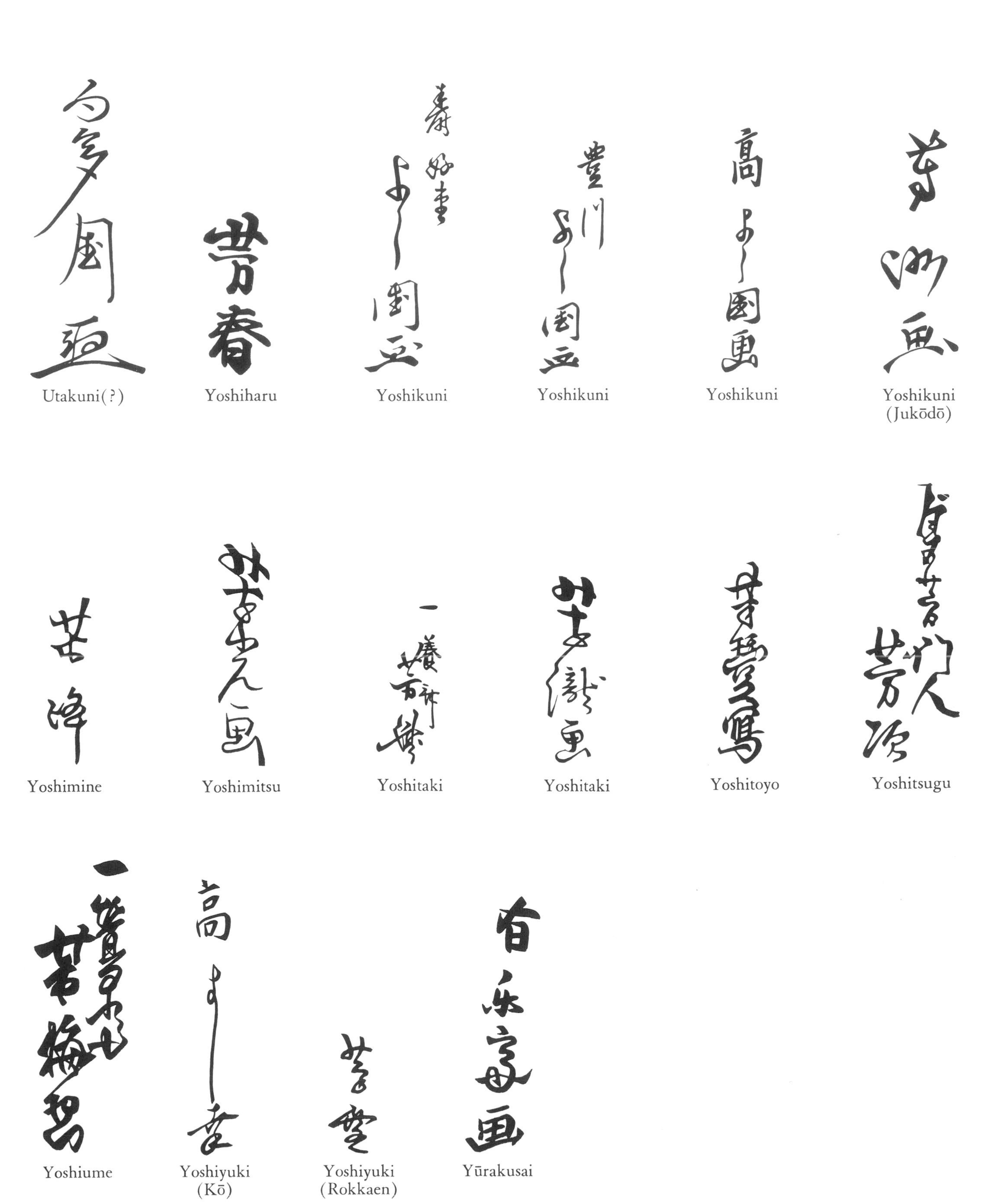

Utakuni(?) Yoshiharu Yoshikuni Yoshikuni Yoshikuni Yoshikuni (Jukōdō)

Yoshimine Yoshimitsu Yoshitaki Yoshitaki Yoshitoyo Yoshitsugu

Yoshiume Yoshiyuki (Kō) Yoshiyuki (Rokkaen) Yūrakusai

List of Actors

初世 嵐猪三郎 三笠屋 環子 — **Arashi Isaburō I** (1766–5/1825)
Yagō: Mikasaya
Haigō: Kanshi
Acted as: Isaburō I (?–5/1825)
Apparently acted in Kamigata only.

二世 嵐吉三郎 岡島屋 璃寛 — **Arashi Kichisaburō II** (1769–9/1821)
Yagō: Okajimaya
Haigō: Rikan
Other names:
大璃寛 Ō-Rikan
初世 璃寛 Rikan I
Acted as:
Kichisaburō II (1787–3/1821)
Kitsusaburō I (3/1821–9/1821)
Acted in Kamigata only.

三世 嵐吉三郎 岡島屋 鱗昇 — **Arashi Kichisaburō III** (1810–9/1864)
Yagō: Okajimaya
Haigō: Rinshō
Acted as: Kichisaburō III (3/1821–9/1864)
Acted in Kamigata to 1839; 1/1846–1849; 1856–9/1864.

初世 嵐橘三郎 — **Arashi Kitsusaburō I** (active 1821)
See Arashi Kichisaburō II.

二世 嵐橘三郎 — **Arashi Kitsusaburō II** (active 1822–1828)
See Arashi Rikan II.

四世 嵐小六 吉田屋 — **Arashi Koroku IV** (1783–11/1826)
Yagō: Yoshidaya
Haigō:
紫朝 Shichō
珉子 Minshi
湖鹿 Koroku
Acted as:
Kanō Minshi I (1801–11/1817)
Arashi Koroku IV (11/1817–11/1826)
Acted in Kamigata only.

嵐来芝 — **Arashi Raishi** (active 1823–1838)
See Arashi Sangorō III.

二世 嵐璃珏 豊島屋 璃玉 — **Arashi Rikaku II** (1812–7/1864)
Yagō: Teshimaya
Haigō: Rigyoku
Acted as:
Yoshisaburō II (to 11/1831)
Rikaku II (11/1831–7/1864)
Acted in Kamigata to 1852; 1/1854–7/1864.

初世 嵐璃寛 — **Arashi Rikan I** (active to 1821)
(*Haigō* only.) See Arashi Kichisaburō II.

二世 嵐璃寛 伊丹屋 璃鶴 — **Arashi Rikan II** (1788–6/1837)
Yagō: Itamiya
Haigō: Rikaku
Acted as:
Tokusaburō I (to 9/1822)
Kitsusaburō II (9/1822–11/1828)
Rikan II (11/1828–6/1837)
Acted in Kamigata 9/1822–6/1837.

三世 嵐璃寛 葉村屋 巌獅 — **Arashi Rikan III** (1812–4/1863)
Yagō: Hamuraya
Haigō: Ganshi
Acted as:
Tokusaburō II (1/1831–1834)
Kitchō (1834–1835)
Tokusaburō II (1835–9/1843)
Rikan III (9/1843–4/1863)
Acted in Kamigata to 11/1851; 12/1855–4/1863.

四世 嵐璃寛 — **Arashi Rikan IV** (1837–6/1894)
Acted as:
Tokusaburō III (1861–8/1867)
Rikan IV (8/1867–6/1894)
Apparently acted in Kamigata only.

嵐璃光 伏見屋 — **Arashi Rikō** (1784–9/1839)
Yagō: Fushimiya
Acted in Kamigata to 1835; summer 1836–9/1839.

三世 嵐三五郎 京屋 雷子 — **Arashi Sangorō III** (died in 1838)
Yagō: Kyōya
Haigō: Raishi
Acted as:
Sangorō III (to 1823)
Raishi (1823–1838)
Often on provincial tours from about 1823.

初世 嵐徳三郎 — **Arashi Tokusaburō I** (active to 9/1822)
See Arashi Rikan II.

二世 嵐徳三郎 — **Arashi Tokusaburō II** (active 1/1831–1834)
See Arashi Rikan III.

三世 嵐徳三郎 — **Arashi Tokusaburō III** (active 1861–8/1867)
See Arashi Rikan IV.

嵐富三郎 — **Arashi Tomisaburō** (active c. 1790–8/1830)
Acted in Kamigata to 11/1811; 8/1812–8/1830.

浅尾額十郎 — **Asao Gakujūrō** (active 1822–1833)
See Jitsukawa Gakujūrō I.

浅尾工左衛門
金田屋
鬼丸

Asao Kuzaemon I (1758–8/1824)
Yagō: Kanedaya
Haigō: Kigan
Acted as: Kuzaemon I (11/1794–8/1824)
Acted in Kamigata 11/1808–1816; 1/1817–8/1824.

二世 浅尾工左衛門
金田屋
鬼丸

Asao Kuzaemon II (1786–9/1845)
Yagō: Kanedaya
Haigō: Kigan
Acted as:
Shibazaki Rinzaemon III (1/1832–8/1832)
Asao Kuzaemon II (8/1832–9/1845)
Acted in Kamigata to 9/1843 (died in Edo).

二世 浅尾奥山

Asao Okuyama II (active 1807–1831)
See Asao Tamejūrō III.

三世 浅尾為十郎

Asao Tamejūrō III (1780–spring 1836)
Yagō:
銭屋 Zeniya
河内屋 Kawachiya
奥山 *Haigō*: Okuyama
Acted as:
Okuyama II (1807–1831)
Tamejūrō III (1831–1836)
Apparently acted as Tamejūrō in Edo, 1818–1820 and 1829–1830.
Acted in Kamigata to 5/1818; 12/1820–1828; 11/1830–spring 1836.

初世 浅尾与六
浅田屋
一甫

Asao Yoroku I (1798–12/1851)
Yagō: Asadaya
Haigō: Ippo
Acted as: Yoroku I (11/1830–12/1851)
山村内匠 Temporary acting name: Yamamura Takumi (1847)
Apparently acted in Kamigata only.

浅尾勇次郎

Asao Yūjirō (active 1809–1822)
See Jitsukawa Gakujūrō I.

三世 坂東彦三郎

Bandō Hikosaburō III (1754–2/1828)
Yagō:
万屋 Yorozuya
音羽屋 Otowaya
薪水 *Haigō*: Shinsui
Other names:
半草庵 Hansōan
楽善坊 Rakuzenbō
Acted as: Hikosaburō III (1771–2/1828)
Acted in Kamigata 11/1803–1805; 11/1812–1813.

四世 坂東彦三郎
音羽屋

Bandō Hikosaburō IV (1800–11/1873)
Yagō: Otowaya
Haigō:
薪水 Shinsui
楽善 Rakuzen
Acted as:
Hikosaburō IV (11/1816–3/1856)
Kamezō (3/1856–11/1873)
Acted in Kamigata 1/1830–1/1835; 1/1858–1/1861.

五世 坂東彦三郎
音羽屋
薪水

Bandō Hikosaburō V (1832–10/1877)
Yagō: Otowaya
Haigō: Shinsui
Acted as: Hikosaburō V (1/1856–10/1877)
Acted in Kamigata 1/1858–11/1860; 1/1869–11/1869.

初世 坂東寿太郎

Bandō Jutarō I (active 1825–1840)
See Bandō Jūtarō I.

二世 坂東寿太郎

Bandō Jutarō II (active 1847–1849)
See Ichikawa Ebijūrō IV.

初世 坂東重太郎
鳴田屋
岩子，巖獅

Bandō Jūtarō I (1769–12/1840)
Yagō: Narutaya
Haigō: Ganshi
Acted as:
Jūtarō I (to 11/1825)
Jutarō I (11/1825–12/1840)
Acted in Kamigata to 4/1812; 6/1812–3/1817; autumn 1817–12/1840.

二世 坂東簑助

Bandō Minosuke II (active to 1832)
See Bandō Mitsugorō IV.

三世 坂東三津五郎
大和屋
秀歌，秀佳

Bandō Mitsugorō III (1773–12/1831)
Yagō: Yamatoya
Haigō: Shūka
Acted as:
Minosuke I (to 1799)
Mitsugorō III (1799–12/1831)
Acted in Kamigata 12/1820–2/1822.

四世 坂東三津五郎
大和屋
秀朝

Bandō Mitsugorō IV (1800–11/1863)
Yagō: Yamatoya
Haigō: Shūchō
Acted as:
Minosuke II (to 3/1832)
Mitsugorō IV (3/1832–11/1850)
Morita Kanya XI (11/1850–11/1863)
Acted in Kamigata 1/1821; c. 1822–11/1827; 11/1838–1/1839.

二世 藤川友吉
江戸屋
花友

Fujikawa Tomokichi II (died c. 1834)
Yagō: Edoya
Haigō: Kayū
Acted as:
Tomokichi II (1/1810–1815)
Kayū (1815–1819)
Tomokichi II (1819–c. 1834)
Acted in Kamigata to 1809; 1815–1819; winter 1820–7/1833.

三世 藤川友吉
江戸屋
花友
仙女

Fujikawa Tomokichi III (died c. 1872)
Yagō: Edoya
Haigō:
Kayū
Senjo
Acted as:
Kayū (1838–1/1852)
Tomokichi III (1/1852–1/1864)
Ogino Senjo (1/1864–1872)
Acted in Kamigata to 11/1845; 1851–c. 1872.

七世 市川団十郎
成田屋
三升
白猿
夜雨庵
寿海老人
子福長者
二九亭
成田屋七左衛門
白猿
幡谷十蔵
松本幸四郎

Ichikawa Danjūrō VII (1791–4/1859)
Yagō: Naritaya
Haigō:
Sanshō
Hakuen
Other names:
Yauan
Jukai Rōjin
Kobuku Chōja
Nikutei
Naritaya Shichizaemon
Acted as:
Danjūrō VII (1799–3/1832)
Ebizō V (3/1832–4/1859)
Temporary acting names:
Hakuen (1829–1830, Kamigata)
Hataya Jūzō (autumn 1843, Ise)
Matsumoto Kōshirō (1854, Kamigata)
Acted in Kamigata 5/1829–4/1830; 3/1834–5/1834; 11/1843–2/1850; 1/1853–3/1858.

八世 市川団十郎
成田屋
三升

Ichikawa Danjūrō VIII (1823–8/1854)
Yagō: Naritaya
Haigō: Sanshō
Acted as:
Ebizō VI (to 3/1832)
Danjūrō VIII (3/1832–8/1854)
Visited Osaka 1/1850; committed suicide in Osaka 8/1854.

五世 市川団蔵
三河屋
市紅

Ichikawa Danzō V (1788–4/1845)
Yagō: Mikawaya
Haigō: Shikō
Acted as:
Shikō (1/1815–4/1819)
Danzō V (4/1819–4/1845)
Acted in Kamigata to 1822; 11/1839–4/1845.

六世 市川団蔵
三河屋
団猿

Ichikawa Danzō VI (1800–10/1871)
Yagō: Mikawaya
Haigō: Dan'en
Acted as:
Kuzō II (to 10/1852)
Danzō VI (10/1852–10/1871)
Acted in Kamigata autumn 1846; 10/1852–6/1856; 1870–10/1871.

初世 市川鰕十郎
幡磨屋
新升

Ichikawa Ebijūrō I (1777–7/1827)
Yagō: Harimaya
Haigō: Shinshō
Acted as:
Ichizō I (to 9/1815)
Ebijūrō I (9/1815–7/1827)
Acted in Kamigata 11/1815–1819; 1/1822–7/1827.

二世 市川鰕十郎
幡磨屋
新升

Ichikawa Ebijūrō II (1806–11/1829)
Yagō: Harimaya
Haigō: Shinshō
Acted as:
Ichizō II (to 11/1828)
Ebijūrō II (11/1828–11/1829)
Acted in Kamigata only.

三世 市川鰕十郎
幡磨屋
新升

Ichikawa Ebijūrō III (1787–9/1836)
Yagō: Harimaya
Haigō: Shinshō
Acted as:
Takijūrō (to 1/1830)
Ebijūrō III (1/1830–9/1836)
Apparently acted in Kamigata only.

四世 市川鰕十郎
小紅屋
眼玉

Ichikawa Ebijūrō IV (1809–10/1858)
Yagō: Kobeniya
Haigō: Gangyoku
Acted as:
Ebijūrō IV (1844–1847)
Bandō Jutarō II (1847–4/1849)
Ichikawa Gangyoku (4/1849–1/1850)
Ebijūrō IV (1/1850–10/1858)
Acted in Kamigata to 1/1849; 1/1851–10/1858.

五世 市川海老蔵

Ichikawa Ebizō V (active 1843–1859)
See Ichikawa Danjūrō VII.

市川白猿

Ichikawa Hakuen (active 1829–1830)
See Ichikawa Danjūrō VII.

二世 市川市蔵

Ichikawa Ichizō II (active to 1828)
See Ichikawa Ebijūrō II.

市川森之助 **Ichikawa Morinosuke** (active to c. 1847)
See Ichikawa Shikō.

市川市紅 **Ichikawa Shikō** (active mid-1830s–1850s)
三河屋（？） *Yagō*: Mikawaya (?)
市紅（？） *Haigō*: Shikō (?)
Acted as:
Morinosuke (to c. 1847)
Shikō (c. 1847–8/1850)
Tōshō (8/1850–1850s)
Apparently acted in Kamigata only.

市川助寿郎 **Ichikawa Sukejurō** (1783–9/1860)
大和屋 *Yagō*: Yamatoya
素桐 *Haigō*: Sotō
Acted as: Sukejurō (1823–9/1860)
Acted in Kamigata only.

初世 市川右団次 **Ichikawa Udanji I** (1843–3/1916)
Yagō:
鶴屋 Tsuruya
高島屋 Takashimaya
家升 *Haigō*: Kashō
Acted as:
Udanji I (8/1862–1909)
Sainyū (1909–3/1916)
Acted in Kamigata 8/1862–early Meiji.

五世 岩井半四郎 **Iwai Hanshirō V** (1776–4/1847)
大和屋 *Yagō*: Yamatoya
杜若 *Haigō*: Tojaku
Acted as:
Hanshirō V (11/1804–11/1832)
Tojaku (11/1832–mid-1840s)
Acted in Kamigata 10/1820–1/1822.

二世 岩井粂三郎 **Iwai Kumesaburō II** (1799–4/1836)
大和屋 *Yagō*: Yamatoya
梅我 *Haigō*: Baiga
Acted as:
Kumesaburō II (to 11/1832)
Hanshirō VI (11/1832–4/1836)
Acted in Kamigata 11/1829.

初世 岩井紫若 **Iwai Shijaku I** (1804–4/1845)
大和屋 *Yagō*: Yamatoya
紫若 *Haigō*: Shijaku
Acted as:
Matsunosuke (to 11/1822)
Shijaku I (11/1822–3/1844)
Hanshirō VII (3/1844–4/1845)
Acted in Kamigata 1820–1822; 11/1831–3/1835.

初世 実川延若 **Jitsukawa Enjaku I** (1830–9/1885)
河内屋 *Yagō*: Kawachiya
正鴈 *Haigō*: Seigan
Acted as:
Nakamura Enjaku (to 3/1859)
Onoe Baikō (3/1859–11/1861)
Jitsukawa Enjirō (11/1861–3/1862)
Enjaku I (3/1862–9/1885)
Acted in Kamigata to 10/1856; 1860–8/1862; 11(?)/1862.

実川延三郎 **Jitsukawa Ensaburō** (1813–2/1867)
井筒屋 *Yagō*: Izutsuya
延若 *Haigō*: Enjaku
Acted as:
Asao Ensaburō (to 1/1833)
Jitsukawa Ensaburō (1/1833–1/1865)
Jitsukawa Gakujūrō II (1/1865–2/1867)
Acted in Kamigata only.

初世 実川額十郎 **Jitsukawa Gakujūrō I** (1782–11/1835)
井筒屋 *Yagō*: Izutsuya
延若 *Haigō*: Enjaku
Acted as:
Asao Yūjirō (1/1809–1822)
Asao Gakujūrō (1822–1/1833)
Jitsukawa Gakujūrō I 1/1833–11/1835)
Acted in Kamigata to 1809; 11/1818–11/1835.

二世 実川額十郎 **Jitsukawa Gakujūrō II** (active 1865–1867)
See Jitsukawa Ensaburō.

初世 叶珉子 **Kanō Minshi I** (active 1801–1817)
See Arashi Koroku IV.

初世 片岡我童 **Kataoka Gadō I** (active to 1837)
(*Haigō* only.) *See* Kataoka Nizaemon VII.

二世 片岡我童 **Kataoka Gadō II** (1810–2/1863)
松島屋 *Yagō*: Matsushimaya
我童 *Haigō*: Gadō
Acted as:
Gatō I (to 1837)
Gadō II (1837–1/1857)
Nizaemon VIII (1/1857–2/1863)
Acted in Kamigata to 1853; 10/1862–2/1863.

二世 片岡我当
松島屋
我童

Kataoka Gatō II (1839–11/1871)
Yagō: Matsushimaya
Haigō: Gadō
Acted as: Gatō II (4/1856–11/1871)
Posthumously (in 1907) named Nizaemon IX.
Acted in Kamigata to 1853; 1862–11/1871.

初世 片岡市蔵
松島屋
我升
片市
竹川市蔵

Kataoka Ichizō I (1792–7/1862)
Yagō: Matsushimaya
Haigō: Gashō
Other name: Kata Ichi
Acted as: Ichizō I (1810–7/1862)
Temporary acting name:
Takekawa Ichizō (10/1858)
Acted in Kamigata to 1829; 5/1834–7/1862.

七世 片岡仁左衛門
松島屋
我童

Kataoka Nizaemon VII (1755–3/1837)
Yagō: Matsushimaya
Haigō: Gadō
Acted as: Nizaemon VII (1787–3/1837)
Acted in Kamigata to 1816; 11/1817–5/1825; 11/1828–3/1837.

八世 片岡仁左衛門

Kataoka Nizaemon VIII (active 1857–1863)
See Kataoka Gadō II.

五世 松本幸四郎
高麗屋
錦升

Matsumoto Kōshirō V (1764–5/1838)
Yagō: Kōraiya
Haigō: Kinshō
Acted as:
Ichikawa Komazō III (to 11/1801)
Matsumoto Kōshirō V (11/1801–5/1838)
Acted in Kamigata 10/1820–11/1821; 11/1829–3/1830.

四世 三桝大五郎
京桝屋
梅桝

Mimasu Daigorō IV (1798–5/1859)
Yagō: Kyōmasuya
Haigō: Baishō
Acted as:
Gennosuke I (1822–1/1846)
Daigorō IV (1/1846–5/1859)
Acted in Kamigata to 8/1820; 2/1833–5/1859.

五世 三桝大五郎
京桝屋
梅升

Mimasu Daigorō V (1807–10/1873)
Yagō: Kyōmasuya
Haigō: Baishō
Acted as:
Baisha (to 1865)
Daigorō V (1865–10/1873)
Acted in Kamigata 7/1850–10/1873.

三世 三桝源之助
末広屋
霞仙

Mimasu Gennosuke III (1835–10/1889)
Yagō: Suehiroya
Haigō: Kasen
Acted as:
Gennosuke III (8/1860–1/1865)
Nakamura Sōjūrō (1/1865–10/1889)
Acted in Kamigata to 1878.

三世 中村大吉
八幡屋
巴丈

Nakamura Daikichi III (1815–11/1857)
Yagō: Yawataya
Haigō: Hajō
Acted as:
Daikichi III (5/1840–1846)
Matsue V (1846–11/1848)
Daikichi III (11/1848–11/1857)
Acted in Kamigata autumn 1848–5/1855; 7/1856–11/1857.

中村儀左衛門

Nakamura Gizaemon (active to 1851)
See Nakamura Jakuemon.

初世 中村雀右衛門
江戸屋
芝斗

Nakamura Jakuemon I (1806–8/1871)
Yagō: Edoya
Haigō: Shitō
Acted as:
Gizaemon (to 11/1851)
Jakuemon (11/1851–8/1871)
Acted in Kamigata 1834–8/1871.

初世 中村歌六
幡磨屋
梅枝

Nakamura Karoku I (1779–7/1859)
Yagō: Harimaya
Haigō: Baishi
Acted as:
Moshio (to 1804)
Karoku I (1804–7/1859)
Acted in Kamigata to 3/1818; 4/1819–9/1827; 8/1832–1851; 1854–7/1859.

三世 中村松江

Nakamura Matsue III (active 1813–1833)
See Nakamura Tomijūrō II.

中村三光

Nakamura Sankō (active 1812–1813)
See Nakamura Tomijūrō II.

初世 中村芝翫

Nakamura Shikan I (active 1818–1819)
See Nakamura Utaemon III.

二世 中村芝翫

Nakamura Shikan II (active 1825–1835)
See Nakamura Utaemon IV.

三世 中村芝翫
加賀屋
眼玉

Nakamura Shikan III (1810–11/1847)
Yagō: Kagaya
Haigō: Gangyoku
Acted as:
Tsurusuke II (to 1/1836)
Shikan III (1/1836–11/1847)
Acted in Kamigata only.

中村宗十郎 NAKAMURA SŌJŪRŌ (active 1865–1889)
See Mimasu Gennosuke III.

中村玉七 NAKAMURA TAMASHICHI (1836–4/1860)
加賀屋 *Yagō*: Kagaya
加玉 *Haigō*: Kagyoku
Acted in Kamigata only.

初世 中村玉助 NAKAMURA TAMASUKE I (active 1835–1838)
See Nakamura Utaemon III.

二世 中村富十郎 NAKAMURA TOMIJŪRŌ II (1786–2/1855)
八幡屋 *Yagō*: Yawataya
Haigō:
梅花 Baika
三光 Sankō
慶子 Keishi
Acted as:
Sankō (11/1812–11/1813)
Matsue III (11/1813–11/1833)
Tomijūrō II (11/1833–2/1855)
Temporary acting name: apparently used Sankō (1822, Edo; and 1824, Kamigata) 三光
Acted in Kamigata to 1813; 11/1816–autumn 1822; 11/1823–9/1853; 1855. Forbidden to perform in Osaka from 1843 on, but acted in Kyoto, Sakai, etc.

四世 中村友蔵 NAKAMURA TOMOZŌ IV (1795–3/1861)
京屋 *Yagō*: Kyōya
丸幸 *Haigō*: Gankō
Apparently acted in Kamigata only.

初世 中村鶴助 NAKAMURA TSURUSUKE I (active 1813–1825)
See Nakamura Utaemon IV.

三世 中村歌右衛門 NAKAMURA UTAEMON III (1778–7/1838)
加賀屋 *Yagō*: Kagaya
Haigō:
芝翫 Shikan (to 11/1825)
梅玉 Baigyoku (11/1825–7/1838)
Other names:
初世 芝翫 Shikan I
百戯園 Hyakugien
初世 金沢竜玉 Kanazawa Ryūgyoku I (as a playwright from 1820)
Acted as:
Fukunosuke (to 11/1791)
Utaemon III (11/1791–7/1838)
Tamasuke I (11/1835–7/1838)
Temporary acting name: Shikan (1818–1819, Edo) 芝翫
Acted in Kamigata to 1808; 9/1812–3/1814; 11/1815–5/1817; 11/1819–7/1838.
Retirement performances: 1816 (?), 4/1825, but without actually retiring.

四世 中村歌右衛門 NAKAMURA UTAEMON IV (1798–2/1852)
成駒屋 *Yagō*: Narikomaya
翫雀 *Haigō*: Kanjaku
魁香舎 Other name: Kaikōsha
Acted as:
Fujima Kamesaburō (to 1808)
Nakamura Tōtarō (1808–3/1813)
Tsurusuke I (3/1813–11/1825)
Shikan II (11/1825–1/1836)
Utaemon IV (1/1836–2/1852)
Acted in Kamigata to 10/1827; 11/1833–1/1838; 1/1850–2/1852.

三世 中山文七 NAKAYAMA BUNSHICHI III (1764–2/1853)
紅屋 *Yagō*: Beniya
百花 *Haigō*: Hyakka
Acted as:
Bunshichi III (11/1804–5/1809)
Hyakka (5/1809–2/1815)
Bunshichi III (2/1815–1850)
Hyakka (1850–2/1853)
Acted in Kamigata to 11/1804; 6/1806–2/1853.

二世 中山南枝 NAKAYAMA NANSHI II (1790–7/1858)
大黒屋 *Yagō*: Daikokuya
Haigō:
一枝 Isshi
由男 Yoshio
Acted as:
Nanshi II (11/1831–1/1838)
Yoshio III (1/1838–1845)
Nanshi II (1845–7/1858)
Acted in Kamigata only.

三世 中山新九郎 NAKAYAMA SHINKURŌ III (1761–10/1827)
折屋 *Yagō*: Oriya
Haigō:
一蝶 Itchō
喜楽 Kiraku
Acted as:
Shinkurō III (11/1802–1/1826)
Kiraku (1/1826–10/1827)
Acted in Kamigata only.

四世 中山新九郎 NAKAYAMA SHINKURŌ IV (active in Kamigata mid-1820s–1832)
和泉屋 *Yagō*: Izumiya
一蝶 *Haigō*: Itchō
Acted as:
Itchō (to 1/1826)
Shinkurō IV (1/1826–[?])
Acted in Kamigata to 1832 (mainly in provinces thereafter).

初世 中山富三郎
近江屋
錦車

Nakayama Tomisaburō I (1760–9/1819)
Yagō: Ōmiya
Haigō: Kinsha
Acted in Kamigata to 9/1810; 8/1814–1819 (?).

三世 中山由男

Nakayama Yoshio III (active 1838–1845)
See Nakayama Nanshi II.

三世 小川吉太郎
加賀屋
英子

Ogawa Kitchitarō III (1785–1851)
Yagō: Kagaya
Haigō: Eishi
Acted as: Kitchitarō III (3/1805–1851)
Acted in Kamigata 1807–1825; summer 1826–11/1839.

荻野仙女

Ogino Senjo (active 1864–c. 1872)
See Fujikawa Tomokichi III.

大川橋蔵

Ōkawa Hashizō (1848–1849)
See Onoe Kikugorō III.

四世 尾上梅幸
音羽屋
梅幸

Onoe Baikō IV (1808–6/1860)
Yagō: Otowaya
Haigō: Baikō
Acted as:
Eisaburō (to 1/1846)
Baikō IV (1/1846–9/1855)
Kikugorō IV (9/1855–6/1860)
Acted in Kamigata 1845–1/1855.

三世 尾上芙雀
南部屋
青蛾

Onoe Fujaku III (1793–1/1831)
Yagō: Nanbuya
Haigō: Seiga
Apparently acted in Kamigata only.

三世 尾上菊五郎
音羽屋
梅幸
菊屋万平

Onoe Kikugorō III (1784–4/1849)
Yagō: Otowaya
Haigō: Baikō
Other name: Kikuya Manpei (during temporary retirement, 10/1847–1848)
Acted as:
Eisaburō (to 11/1809)
Matsusuke II (11/1809–11/1814)
Baikō III (11/1814–11/1815)
Kikugorō III (11/1815–5/1848)
Ōkawa Hashizō (5/1848–4/1849)
Acted in Kamigata 7/1820; 11/1825–4/1826; 1/1841–9/1841; 4/1848–1/1849.

二世 尾上多見蔵
音羽屋
松玉

Onoe Tamizō II (1799–3/1886)
Yagō: Otowaya
Haigō: Shōgyoku
Acted as:
Nakamura Waichi (to 11/1820)
Onoe Tamizō II (11/1820–3/1886)
Temporary acting name:

大川八蔵

Ōkawa Hachizō (1848, Nagoya)
Acted in Kamigata to 1820; 1823–1840; 1842–1845; 1848 on.

二世 大谷友右衛門
明石屋
此友

Ōtani Tomoemon II (1769–3/1830)
Yagō: Akashiya
Haigō: Shiyū
Acted as: Tomoemon II (11/1795–3/1830)
Acted in Kamigata 11/1808–4/1812; autumn 1812–3/1830 (?)

五世 大谷友右衛門
明石屋
紫道

Ōtani Tomoemon V (1833–2/1873)
Yagō: Akashiya
Haigō: Shidō
Acted as:
Tomomatsu (to 1/1865)
Tomoemon V (1/1865–8/1869)
(later names omitted)
Acted in Kamigata 7/1857–summer 1865.

二世 沢村源之助
紀伊国屋
訥升

Sawamura Gennosuke II (1802–11/1853)
Yagō: Kinokuniya
Haigō: Tosshō
Acted as:
Gennosuke II (to 11/1831)
Tosshō (11/1831–7/1844)
Sōjūrō V (7/1844–1848)
(later names omitted)
Acted in Kamigata 11/1820–11/1828; 1835.

沢村其答
荻野屋（？）
其答（？）

Sawamura Kitō (died 9/1849)
Yagō: Oginoya (?)
Haigō: Kitō (?)
Acted in Kamigata to 9/1849.

二世 沢村国太郎
荻野屋
錦子
其答

Sawamura Kunitarō II (died spring 1836)
Yagō: Oginoya
Haigō:
Kinshi
Kitō
Acted as:
Ogino Kinshi (to 11/1819)
Sawamura Kunitarō II (11/1819–1836)
Apparently acted in Kamigata only.

二世 沢村田之助
紀伊国屋
曙山

Sawamura Tanosuke II (1788–1/1817)
Yagō: Kinokuniya
Haigō: Shozan
Acted as: Tanosuke II (1802–1/1817)
Acted in Kamigata 11/1813–3/1815.

二世関三十郎 尾張屋 歌山	SEKI SANJŪRŌ II (1786–9/1839) *Yagō*: Owariya *Haigō*: Kazan Acted as: Sanjūrō II (11/1807–9/1839) Acted in Kamigata to 1807; 11/1826–11/1827; 8/1835–1836.
三世関三十郎 尾張屋 歌山	SEKI SANJŪRŌ III (1805–12/1870) *Yagō*: Owariya *Haigō*: Kazan Acted as: Sanjūrō III (4/1840–12/1870) Acted in Kamigata 9/1853–11/1854.
四世山下金作 天王寺屋 来芝 里虹	YAMASHITA KINSAKU IV (1791–12/1858) *Yagō*: Tennōjiya *Haigō*: Raishi Rikō Acted as: Kinsaku IV (11/1832–12/1858) Acted in Kamigata c. 1835–12/1858 Acted in Kamigata c. 1835–12/1858 (?).

Concordance of Names

油嘉 **Aburaka**
Engraver (?), active mid-1830s

あ禺 **Agū**
Publisher (?); found with Chū (1822), Toshin (1822)

明石堂 **Akashidō**
Publisher, active 1825; possibly pronounced Meisekidō

暁鐘成 **Akatsuki no Kanenari**
Gō of artist Kanenari

あき惣 **Akisō**
Publisher (?); found with Su (1821), Shima (1824)

あき藤 **Akitō**
Publisher, active 1833

アコ伊 **Akoi**
Publisher or printseller, active 1848

㊌ *aratame*
Seal found with Tenki (1833), Wataki (1833), Honsei (1833)

有忠 **Arichū**
Publisher, *see* Ariharadō

有原 **Arihara**
Publisher, *see* Ariharadō

有原堂 **Ariharadō**
Publisher, active 1821–1825; found alone (1823–1825) usually as Chū, with Toshin (1821–1822), Agū (1822), *kiwame* (1823), Wataki (1825), Goichi (1825); also appears as Arichū, Arihara, Ariharadō Kōbun, and mark of plum blossom; possibly pronounced Yūgendō

有原堂好文 **Ariharadō Kōbun**
Publisher, *see* Ariharadō

浅 **Asa**
Engraver, active c. 1855

芦野家，芦の家 **Ashinoya**
Gō of artists Hironobu I and Yoshitaki

Awa
Publisher (?); found with Honsei (1816)

阿波文，阿ハ文 **Awabun**
Publisher, active 1810s–1860s; address: Shinsaibashi Mitsuderasuji Kitairu, Juōdō Awaya Bunzō

阿波又 **Awamata**
Publisher (?); found with Kawaden (c. 1877)

アワトヨ **Awatoyo**
Printer, active 1838

阿波屋文蔵 **Awaya Bunzō**
Publisher, *see* Awabun

梅丸斎 **Baigansai**
Gō of artist Shigeharu

梅玉 **Baigyoku**
Haigō of actor Nakamura Utaemon III

梅峯軒 **Baihōken**
Gō of artist Mitsunobu

梅幸 **Baikō**
Haigō of actor Onoe Kikugorō III

梅国 **Baikoku**
Gō of artist Shiken

梅好斎 **Baikōsai**
Gō and signature of artist Baikōsai

梅翁軒 **Baiōken**
Gō of artist Mitsunobu

梅雪堂 **Baisetsudō**
Gō and signature of artist Baisetsudō Sadamichi

梅窓園 **Baisōen**
Gō of artist Sadayoshi (active 1837–1853)

米華堂人 **Beikadōjin**
Gō of artist Taito II

米華斎 **Beikasai**
Gō of artist Taito II

紅宗 **Benisō**
Printer, publisher, and printseller; found with Honsei and Tenki (1835–1837 and later); also appears as Suri Benisō, Sō; address: Shinsaibashisuji Junkeimachi Kita

尾与 **Biyo**
Publisher, *see* Oyo

眉山 **Bizan**
Gō of artist Munenobu

朴仙 **Bokusen**
Gō of artist Shiken

文華堂 **Bunkadō**
Gō of artist Sukenobu

文金堂 **Bunkindō**
Publisher, *see* Kawachiya Tasuke

茶楽斎 CHARAKUSAI
Gō of artist Seitoku

茶碗屋 CHAWANYA
Publisher, active 1821

茶碗屋吉兵衛 CHAWANYA KICHIBEI
Publisher, *see* Chawanya

直水 CHOKUSUI
Gō of artist Hanzan

長秀斎 CHŌSHŪSAI
Gō and signature of artist Nagahide

忠, 忠 CHŪ
Publisher, *see* Ariharadō

忠二 CHŪJI
Engraver, *see* Tanaka Chūji

大長 DAICHŌ
Publisher or printseller, active 1850s

大栄 DAIEI
Publisher or printseller, active mid-1860s

大甚 DAIJIN
Publisher and printseller, active late 1840s and early 1850s; address: Kyōmachibori Kinokuniyabashi Kitazume Kitairu

大亀 DAIKAME
Publisher, *see* Daiki

大亀 DAIKI
Publisher and printseller, active 1826, 1848–1850; found with Toshin (1826); address: Shinsaibashisuji Junkeimachi Minami

大吉 DAIKICHI
Publisher, active 1780s

大左 DAISA
Publisher, active 1793

大清 DAISEI
Publisher, active c. 1860; address: Tenma Tenjin Toriimae Kita

大松 DAISHŌ
Publisher, *see* Fujimasa

傳, 傳 DEN
Publisher, *see* Iden

洞庭舎 DŌTEISHA
Gō of artist Taito II

江戸岩 EDO IWA
Printer, active 1826

江戸松 EDO MATSU
Engraver, active 1838–1842

江戸斧 EDO ONO
Engraver, *see* Nakamura Onozō

栄 EI
Publisher or printseller, active 1816

永寿堂 EIJUDŌ
Publisher of surimono, active 1817

英斎 EISAI
Gō of artists Eiju and Kunikage

英泉斎 EISENSAI
Gō of artist Kuninao

風竹館 FŪCHIKUAN
Gō of artist Ashisato

諷々亭 FŪFŪTEI
Gō of artist Utakuni

富士政 FUJIMASA
Publisher, active 1863 and later; formerly called Daishō; also appears as Kinkōdō, Shimada Kinkōdō; address: Andōjimachi Shinsaibashisuji Kitairu Higashigawa

ふし太, 太 FUJITA
Publisher, active 1832–1834, 1840; *see* Honsei

福 FUKU
Engraver, *see* Kanai Fuku

伏見豊吉 FUSHIMI TOYOKICHI
Publisher, active late nineteenth century; address: Minamiku Minami Watayamachi 33

画蝶軒 GACHŌKEN
Gō of artist Shuntei (active mid-1820s)

我童 GADŌ
Haigō of actors Kataoka Nizaemon VII, Kataoka Gadō II

画寿軒 GAJUKEN
Gō of artist Shunchō (active mid-1820s)

画好軒 GAKŌKEN
Gō of artist Shunshi (active mid-1820s)

画狂人 GAKYŌJIN
Gō of artist Hokkō (active 1820s)

丸丈斎 GANJŌSAI
Gō of artist Kunihiro

含粋亭 GANSUITEI
Gō of artist Yoshitoyo

画照軒 GASHŌKEN
Gō of artist Shunpō

画登軒 GATŌKEN
Gō of artist Shunsei (active mid-1820s)

画遊軒 Gayūken
Gō of artists Shun'ō and Shunshi

源 Gen
Engraver and printer, active 1850s; possibly same as Gen, below

源 Gen
Printer and publisher or printseller, active 1852; appears as Suri Gen; possibly same as Gen above

玄龍斎 Genryūsai
Gō of artist Taito II

戯画堂 Gigadō
Gō of artist Ashiyuki

㊎ *gō*
Seal found with Honsei (1831, 1834)

五長 Gochō
Gō of artist Hirosada; publisher, *see* Tenki

五蝶斎 Gochōsai
Gō of artist Kunimasu

五蝶亭 Gochōtei
Gō of artists Kunimasu, Sadahiro I, and Sadatsugu

五楓亭 Gofūtei
Gō of artist Sadafusa

五岳 Gogaku
Gō of artist Gakutei

五蒲亭 Gohotei
Gō of artist Hironobu I

五瓢亭 Gohyōtei
Gō of artist Sadayoshi (active 1837–1853)

五飄亭 Gohyōtei
Gō of artist Sadafusa

五市 Goichi
Publisher (?); found with Chū (1825)

五亀亭 Gokitei
Gō of artist Sadafusa

五輝亭 Gokitei
Gō of artist Sadahiro I

五湖亭 Gokotei
Gō of artist Sadakage

五狂亭 Gokyōtei
Gō of artist Nobukatsu

五楽亭 Gorakutei
Gō of artists Hirosada and Sadahiro I

五龍軒 Goryūken
Gō of artist Hokuju

五流亭 Goryūtei
Gō of artist Kagematsu

五柳亭 Goryūtei
Gō of artist Sadaharu

五蕉亭 Goshōtei
Gō of artist Sadaharu

五粽亭 Gosōtei
Gō of artists Hirosada and Sadahiro I

五双亭 Gosōtei
Gō of artist Sadanobu I

五渡亭 Gototei
Gō of artist Kunisada

五葉亭 Goyōtei
Gō of artist Hironobu I

玉光軒 Gyokkōken
Publisher, *see* Hankin

玉柳斎 Gyokuryūsai
Gō of artist Shigeharu

玉柳亭 Gyokuryūtei
Gō of artist Shigeharu

玉水 Gyokusui
Publisher (?), *see* Tamamizu

玉亭 Gyokutei
Gō of artist Yoshimine

玉陽亭 Gyokuyōtei
Gō of artist Kuniharu (active 1820s–1830s)

ハジ Haji
Engraver, active c. 1821

白猿 Hakuen
Haigō of actor Ichikawa Danjūrō VII

白峰 Hakuhō
Gō of artist Hironobu II

柏宗 Hakusō
Publisher, active 1800s; also pronounced Kashiwasō; address: Teramachi Nijō sagaru, Kashiwaya Sōshichi (Kyoto)

白水 Hakusui
Gō of artist Hironobu I

白水斎 Hakusuisai
Gō of artist Hironobu I

白象 Hakuzō
Publisher or printseller (?); found with Honsei (1816)

阪田舎居 Handenshakyo
Gō of artist Yoshitaki

半治 **HANJI**
Printer, active c. 1826

判金 **HANKIN**
Publisher, active 1820s–1830s; address: Shinmachi Uwajimabashi Kitazume, Gyokkōken Hankin

板元草紙屋 *hanmoto sōshiya*
Seal found with Na (1816), Honsei (1816–1821), Hirooka (1817), Tenki (1816–1821), Wataki (c. late 1810s), Senri (1823)

判定 **HANSADA**
Engraver, active 1860s

ハタキ **HATAKI**
Publisher, *see* Wataki

ハツ **HATSU**
Engraver, active 1820s

兵善 **HEIZEN**
Publisher, *see* Hyōzen

平三 **HEIZŌ**
Engraver, active mid 1850s–1860s

秀 **HIDE**
Printer, active 1834–1835

広岡 **HIROOKA**
Publisher, active 1817–1818; found with *hanmoto sōshiya* (1817)

広三郎 **HIROSABURŌ**
Printer, *see* Kōzaburō

芳雅堂 **HŌGADŌ**
Gō of artist Kishikuni

豊玉 **HŌGYOKU**
Gō of artist Yoshitaki

芳花堂 **HŌKADŌ**
Gō of artist Hatsukuni

芳国堂 **HŌKOKUDŌ**
Gō of artist Hatsukuni

北砕 **HOKUSAI**
Gō of artist Yoshitoyo

北砬 **HOKUSAI (?)**
Publisher or retailer, active 1850s; found with Honsei (1858)

北砕舎 **HOKUSAISHA**
Gō of artist Yoshitoyo

北心斎 **HOKUSHINSAI**
Gō of artist Shunzan

北粋（酔，翠，水） **HOKUSUI**
Gō of artist Yoshitoyo

北粋舎 **HOKUSUISHA**
Gō of artist Yoshitoyo

本 **HON**
Publisher (?); found with Shiochō (1813), Honsei (late 1810s)

本亀 **HONKAME**
Publisher, *see* Honki

本亀 **HONKI**
Publisher, active 1830s

本せ，本セ **HONSE**
Publisher, *see* Honsei

本清 **HONSEI**
Publisher, active 1816–1896; also appears as Honse, Oki, Tamaoki; found with Na (1816), Hakuzō (1816), Awa (1816), *hanmoto sōshiya* (1816–1821), Hon (late 1810s), Shiochō (1820), *kiwame* (1821), Senri (1821–1824), Yamaichi (1822–1824), Ki (1822), Tenki (1823), Sumiyoshi (1823), Kichi (1823–1833), Toshin (1825), I (1826 and 1835), Wataki (1827), Oki (1828), Nakamura (1829), Kawaji (1830–1832), Man (1831), *gō* (1831, 1834), Fujita (1832–1834), Ya (date uncertain), *aratame* (1833), Tenki and Wataki (1834–1836), Benisō (1835), Fujita (1840), Hokusai (?) (1858), Torisō (c. 1861); addresses: Tamaokiuji Shōhonya Seibei, Unagidani Donburiike Nishiiru; Tamaokiuji Shōhonya Seishichi, Ōsaka Shinsaibashisuji Shiomachi Kado; Hanmoto Honsei, Shimanouchi Shinsaibashi Hachimansuji Higashiiru (1835); Minamiku Kasayamachi, Tamaoki Seishichi (1890s)

本為 **HONTAME**
Publisher, active mid-1850s on; full name, Uemura Tamesuke

本屋清兵衛 **HONYA SEIBEI**
Publisher, *see* Honsei

本屋清七 **HONYA SEISHICHI**
Publisher, *see* Honsei

本屋安兵衛 **HONYA YASUBEI**
Publisher; *see* Honyasu

本安 **HONYASU**
Publisher, active late nineteenth century; addresses: Dōtonbori Nihonbashi Minamizume Higashieiru Minamigawa; Shōeidō; Honya Yasubei; Shinsaibashisuji Suōmachi Minamiiru Higashigawa; Sueyoshibashisuji Matsuyamachi Kado

蓬来山人 HŌRAISANJIN
Gō of artist Goshichi

彫・・・ *Hori . . .*
See under individual name without the prefix

堀亀 HORIKAME
Engraver and printer, active 1849–1865; also appears as Kawa

堀川多楼 HORIKAWA TARŌ
Gō of artist Gakutei

堀尾 HORIO
Engraver, active c. 1850; address: Minami Daimaru Mukai

豊斎 HŌSAI
Gō of artist Yoshikage

百戯園 HYAKUGIEN
Pen name of actor Nakamura Utaemon III

兵善 HYŌZEN
Publisher, active 1826–1838; found alone (1826–1829), with Toshin (1826–1827, 1838), Wataki (1827–1832), Wataki and Touse (1827)

い I
Publisher, active 1822–1836; found with Toshin (1822–1823), Tenki (1824–c. 1830), Honsei (1826 and 1835)

一 ICHI
Printer, active 1831; possibly same as Yamaichi

市 ICHI
Publisher, *see* Yamaichi

一梅斎 ICHIBAISAI
Gō of artist Yoshimine

一英斎 ICHIEISAI
Gō of artist Kunikage

一樹園 ICHIJUEN
Gō of artist Kunimasu

一珠斎 ICHIJUSAI
Gō of artist Kunikazu (active 1849–1867)

一寿斎 ICHIJUSAI
Gō of artist Kunitsuru

一桜斎 ICHIŌSAI
Gō of artists Kunikage and Yoshifusa

一鴬斎 ICHIŌSAI
Gō of artist Yoshiume

一老 ICHIRŌ
Gō of artist Gakutei

一瀧斎 ICHIRŌSAI
Gō of artist Koen

一立斎 ICHIRYŪSAI
Gō of artist Shigehiko

一龍斎 ICHIRYŪSAI
Gō of artist Yoshitoyo

一流亭 ICHIRYŪTEI
Gō of artist Toyohide (active 1839–1841)

一楊斎 ICHIYŌSAI
Gō of artist Masanobu

一陽斎 ICHIYŌSAI
Gō of artists Toyokuni I and Yoshitaki

一要斎 ICHIYŌSAI
Gō of artist Yoshishige

一陽亭 ICHIYŌTEI
Gō of artists Yoshikuni (active 1850–1880s) and Yoshitaki

一雄斎 ICHIYŪSAI
Gō of artist Kunisada

井伝, 傳, 傳 IDEN
Publisher, active 1820–1835; found with Ki (1823)

田 IIDA
Printer and publisher, *see* Iida Kichi

飯田吉 IIDA KICHI
Printer and publisher, active 1849 and later; addresses: Bakuromachi Nakabashisuji Higashiiru Kitagawa; Andōjimachi Sakaisuji Kado

池田伝兵衛 IKEDA DENBEI
Publisher, *see* Kawaden

池吉 IKEKICHI
Publisher or printseller, active early 1850s

池政 IKEMASA
Printer, active c. 1861

一光斎 IKKŌSAI
Gō of artist Kuniharu (active 1853–1854)

井ノ田 INODA
Printer, active 1830s; perhaps same as Iida

一筆庵 IPPITSUAN
Gō of artist Eiju

一峯斎 IPPŌSAI
Gō of artist Baen

一瓢斎 IPPYŌSAI
Gō of artist Yoshinobu

一瓢亭 IPPYŌTEI
Gō of artist Yoshinobu

イ三，イサ ISA
Printer, active late 1840s

伊勢吉 ISEKICHI
Publisher or printseller, active 1852–1853

石川屋和助 ISHIKAWAYA WASUKE
Publisher, *see* Ishiwa

石和 ISHIWA
Publisher, active 1850–1880 or later; addresses: Hiranomachi Uonotana; Hiranomachi Shinsaibashisuji Nishi; Hiranodōri Yodoyabashi Nishiiru, Ishikawaya Wasuke Saiundō; Shinmachi Shinsaibashisuji Nishi

一心斎 ISSHINSAI
Gō of artist Sadakazu

一信亭 ISSHINTEI
Gō of artist Toyohide

一春斎 ISSHUNSAI
Gō of artist Yoshifusa

一珠斎 ISSHUSAI
Gō of artist Kunikazu (active 1849–1867)

一酔斎 ISSUISAI
Gō and signature of artist Issuisai

一点斎 ITTENSAI
Gō of artist Yoshitaki

一刀斎 ITTŌSAI
Gō of artist Masunobu

一樋斎 ITTŌSAI
Gō of artist Yoshikoto

泉 IZUMI
Publisher, active 1822

耳鳥斎 JICHŌSAI
Same as artist Nichōsai

仁翁 JIN'Ō
Gō of artist Tokinobu

十方舎 JIPPŌSHA
Gō of artist Ichimaru

二代 児雷也 JIRAIYA II
Gō of artist Kuniharu (active 1853–1854)

児龍斎 JIRYŪSAI
Gō of artist Tamikuni

自得斎 JITOKUSAI
Gō of artist Sukenobu

自得叟 JITOKUSŌ
Gō of artist Sukenobu

重 JŪ
Publisher (?); found with Shiochō (1816)

寿栄堂 JUEIDŌ
Gō of artist Yoshitaki

寿暁堂 JUGYŌDŌ
Gō of artist Umekuni

寿宝堂 JUHŌDŌ
Gō of artist Chikakuni

寿鶴堂 JUKAKUDŌ
Gō of artist Masakuni

寿好堂 JUKŌDŌ
Gō of artist Yoshikuni (active 1813–1836)

順四摺進（？） JUNSHI SURI SHIN (?)
Printer, *see* Shin (?)

寿桜堂 JUŌDŌ
Publisher, *see* Awabun

寿曙堂 JUSHODŌ
Gō of artist Kiyokuni

寿松堂 JUSHŌDŌ
Gō of artist Fujikuni

寿陽堂 JUYŌDŌ
Gō of artist Toshikuni

㋕ KA
Publisher (?), active c. 1860

分 KA
Publisher, *see* Ueda

香川 KAGAWA
Publisher or printseller, active late 1840s

加賀屋 KAGAYA
Yagō of actor Nakamura Utaemon III

カホリ，カ刀 KA HORI
Engraver, *see* Kasuke

魁香舎 KAIKŌSHA
Pen name of actor Nakamura Utaemon IV

魁春亭 KAISHUNTEI
Gō of artist Sadayoshi (active 1837–1853)

分金 KAKIN
Engraver, *see* Kin

カ小，賀こ KAKO
Engraver, active 1830–1831

鶴勢堂 KAKUSEIDŌ
Printseller (?); found with Toshin (1822–1824), Tenki (1824)

霞居 **Kakyo**
Gō of artist Hanzan

亀，[illegible] **Kame**
Printer, active 1827

亀村文助 **Kamemura Bunsuke**
Publisher, active 1865

上丁 **Kamichō**
Printer, active 1821

金井福 **Kanai Fuku**
Engraver, active 1882–1885; also appears as Fuku

金沢龍玉 **Kanazawa Ryūgyoku**
Pen name of actor Nakamura Utaemon III

神田熊次郎 **Kanda Kumajirō**
Publisher, active 1895

叶 **Kanō**
Publisher (?); found with Toshin (1822)

勘助 **Kansuke**
Engraver, active 1821–1822

から伊 **Karai**
Publisher, active early 1830s

花斎 **Kasai**
Gō of artist Tsunemaru

鹿嶋堂 **Kashimadō**
Publisher or printseller, active 1850s

柏宗 **Kashiwasō**
Publisher, *see* Hakusō

春日堂 **Kasugadō**
Publisher, active late nineteenth century; also appears as Kawasuke; possibly same as Zuiundō Sukeshichi; address: Tenma Tsunokunimachi, Kasugadō Izō

加助，加介，嘉助，カスケ **Kasuke**
Engraver, active 1821–1834; signatures: Hokushū monjin hori Kasuke (1822), Kasuke horu (1822–1824), Ka hori (1825–1828), Kasuke hori (1829–1830), Saiku Kasuke (1831–1832), surimono hangishi Kasuke (1832), surimono hori Kasuke (1832–1833), Yama saiku Kasuke (1833–1834); found with Toshin (1822–1824), Senri (1823), Chū (1825), Honsei (1825–1831), Honsei and Kawaji (1831–1832), Tenki (1827–1830), Wataki (1827–1831), Den (1827–1834), Hyōzen (1827–1828), Kichi (1828), Ya (1833), without publisher (1821–1826, 1832–1834)

嘉寿小 **Kasuko**
Engraver, active c. 1830

片岡 **Kataoka**
Publisher, active c. 1830s; address: Naniwa Shimanouchi Suōmachi Nakabashisuji Nishi

カツ **Katsu**
Printer, active 1830

^カ上田 **Ka Ueda**
Publisher, *see* Ueda

夏雲 **Kaun**
Gō of artist Ōkyo

川 **Kawa**
Engraver, *see* Horikame

河内屋太助 **Kawachiya Tasuke**
Publisher, active 1780s–late nineteenth century; surname Morimoto; also appears as Bunkindō; address: Shinsaibashisuji Bakuromachi Kitairu

川伝 **Kawaden**
Publisher, active late nineteenth century; addresses: Hachimansuji Shinsaibashisuji Nishi; Shinmachidōri Ton'yabashi Kado Ikeda Denbei

河治 **Kawaji**
Publisher, active 1830–1832, 1850s; found with Honsei (1830–1832)

川音，河音 **Kawaoto**
Publisher or printseller, active 1847–1854; found with Tenki (1854), Kinkadō, Ka Ueda

河新 **Kawashin**
Publisher or printseller, active c. 1850s

河輔 **Kawasuke**
Publisher, *see* Kasugadō

渓中庵 **Keichūan**
Gō of artist Rikō

鶏鳴舎 **Keimeisha**
Gō of artist Kanenari

景斎 **Keisai**
Gō of artist Eiju

蕙泉斎 **Keisensai**
Gō of artist Kiyoharu

慶子 **Keishi**
Haigō of actor Nakamura Tomijūrō II

兼珊（？） **Kensan (?)**
Gō of artist Umekuni

貴 — Ki
Publisher (?); found with Honsei (1822), Wataki (1823), Tenki (1823), Iden (1823)

Ki
Publisher, *see* Wataki

鬼 — Ki
Publisher, active c. 1807

吉, 吉, 吉 — Kichi
Publisher, active 1824–1833; found alone (1828–1830), with Oki (1824–1826), Honsei (1823–1833)

桔梗屋 — Kikyōya
Publisher and printseller, *see* Matsumoto

木村 — Kimura
Publisher (?), active late 1840s

金 — Kin
Engraver, active c. 1840; also appears as Kakin

錦童 — Kindō
Gō of artist Settei

錦葩楼 — Kinharō
Gō of artist Kunikage

錦葩斎 — Kinhasai
Gō of artist Kunikage

金治 — Kinji
Printer, active 1821–1822

金花堂 — Kinkadō
Publisher, *see* Tenki; *gō* of artist Sadanobu I

琴金 — Kinkin
Gō of artist Sadayoshi (active 1837–1853)

金鯱堂 — Kinkodō
Publisher or printseller, active late 1840s–1859

金光堂 — Kinkōdō
Publisher, *see* Fujimasa

紀保 — Kinoyasu
Publisher, active 1850s–1860s; address: Zamamae Honmachi Minami

琴雷舎 — Kinraisha
Gō of artist Kunisada

金陵斎 — Kinryōsai
Gō of artist Gyokuzan I

琴斎 — Kinsai
Gō of artist Shigenobu

錦升 — Kinshō
Haigō of actor Matsumoto Kōshirō V

錦松堂 — Kinshōdō
Publisher or printseller, active early 1850s

謹多楼 — Kintarō
Gō of artist Shun'yō

金随堂 — Kinzuidō
Publisher, *see* Wataki

きし本 — Kishimoto
Publisher, *see* Tenki

橘生堂兎月 — Kisseidō Togetsu
Gō of artist Hokumei

橘仙堂 — Kissendō
Publisher (?); found with Tenki (1827)

北香川 — Kitakagawa
Publisher or printseller, active late 1840s–early 1850s

北豊 — Kitatoyo
Publisher, period of activity uncertain

極 — *kiwame*
Seal found with Honsei (1821), Toshin (1822), Ariharadō (1823)

崎陽斎 — Kiyōsai
Gō of artist Shigeharu

崎陽亭 — Kiyōtei
Gō of artist Shigeharu

胡蝶楼 — Kochōrō
Gō of artist Yoshimine

香蝶楼 — Kōchōrō
Gō of artist Kunisada

黄園 — Kōen
Gō of artist Gakutei

好画堂 — Kōgadō
Gō of artist Tamikuni

香雅堂 — Kōgadō
Gō of artist Tomikuni

幸一 — Kōichi
Engraver and printer, active 1829

岡丈堂 — Kōjōdō
Gō of artist Ashimaru

国瓢亭 — Kokuhyōtei
Gō of artist Sadayoshi (active 1837–1853)

江南亭 — Kōnantei
Gō of artist Kunihiro

小西 — Konishi
Publisher, *see* Tenki

公斎 — Kōsai
Gō of artist Motoharu

紅宗 — Kōsō
Printer and publisher, *see* Benisō

広三郎 — Kōzaburō
Printer, active c. 1860

百済堂 — Kudaradō
Gō of artist Sadakazu

熊, くま, クマ — Kuma
Engraver, *see* Kumazō

熊治 — Kumaji
Printer, active 1822

クマヤ七 — Kuma Yashichi
Engraver, active 1835–1838; also appears as Suke Yashichi and Yashichi

熊造, 熊蔵, 熊象 — Kumazō
Engraver, active 1831–1838

国広 — Kunihiro
Publisher, active 1860s

黒小 — Kuroko
Publisher (?), active early 1830s

草 — *kusa*
Seal, *see sō*

狂画堂 — Kyōgadō
Gō of artist Ashikuni

京伊三 — Kyō Isa
Printer and publisher or printseller, active 1848–early 1850s

旭亭 — Kyokutei
Gō of artist Yoshimine

丘山 — Kyūzan
Gō of artist Gakutei

前田 — Maeda
Publisher, same as Wataki

万 — Man
Publisher (?); found with Honsei (1831)

万玉堂 — Mangyokudō
Publisher (?), active early 1850s

政 — Masa
Printer, active 1828

ヤ — Matsubaya (?)
Publisher (?), *see* Ya

松岩 — Matsuiwa
Printer, active 1822

松喜 — Matsuki
Publisher or printseller, active late 1840s

松本 — Matsumoto
Publisher and printseller, active late nineteenth century; also called Kikyōya; address: Hiranomachi Goryōsha Omotemonmae Higashi

松村 — Matsumura
Printer, *see* Matsumura Kinji

松村金治 — Matsumura Kinji
Printer, active 1822–1826

松弥 — Matsuya
Publisher or printseller (?); found with Isekichi, c. late 1840s

名擧(舉)堂 — Meikōdō
Publisher or printseller, active 1848–early 1850s

名楽堂 — Meirakudō
Misreading of Meikōdō

明石堂 — Meisekidō
Publisher, *see* Akashidō

珉子 — Minshi
Haigō of actor Arashi Koroku IV

木綿屋藤吉 — Momenya Tōkichi
Publisher, *see* Tenki

森本 — Morimoto
Publisher, *see* Kawachiya Tasuke

奈 — Na
Publisher (?); found with Honsei and *hanmoto sōshiya* (1816)

長尾 — Nagao
Publisher, active 1858

長崎 — Nagasaki
Gō of artist Kunishige (1821)

中忠 — Nakachū
Publisher and printseller, active late nineteenth century; address: Sennichimae Hōzenji Omotemon Kita Nishigawa

中邑 — Nakamura
Publisher, active 1826–1829; found with Honsei (1829)

中村お乃蔵 — Nakamura Onozō
Engraver, active 1838–1852; also appears as Ono

中村宗七 — Nakamura Sōshichi
Engraver, active 1861

南窓 — Nansō
Gō of artist Sadanobu I

南窓楼 — Nansōrō
Gō of artist Sadanobu I

南水 — Nansui
Gō of artist Utakuni

南粋 — Nansui
Gō of artist Yoshiyuki (active 1856–1872)

南陽斎 NAN'YŌSAI
Gō of artist Hokuga

南山 NANZAN
Gō of artist Gakutei

直 NAO
Printer, active 1831–1838

奈良亀 NARAKI
Publisher and printseller, active late nineteenth century

成駒屋 NARIKOMAYA
Yagō of actor Nakamura Utaemon IV

成田屋 NARITAYA
Yagō of actor Ichikawa Danjūrō VII

年古楼 NENKORŌ
Gō of artist Baikei

耳鳥斎 NICHŌSAI
Gō and signature of artist Nichōsai

人形 NINGYŌ
Engraver, *see* Ningyōichi

人形市 NINGYŌICHI
Engraver, active 1848–1849; also appears as Ningyō

西 NISHI
Publisher, active late 1840s; probably same as Konishi, *see* Tenki

西村，西邑 NISHIMURA
Publisher, active 1830s

西岡庄蔵 NISHIOKA SHŌZŌ
Publisher, active late nineteenth century; address: Yodoyabashi Kōraibashi Minamiiru

糊家 NORIYA
Gō of artist Yoshitaki

岡島屋 OKAJIMAYA
Yagō of actor Arashi Kichisaburō II

置，置 OKI
Publisher 1820–1828; found alone (1820–1824), with Shiochō (1820), Sumiyoshi (1823), Kichi (1824–1826), Honsei (1828); also appears as Tamaoki (*see* Honsei)

奥山 OKUYAMA
Haigō of actor Asao Tamejūrō II

斧，お拡 ONO
Engraver, *see* Nakamura Onozō

小野豊昇堂 ONO HŌSHŌDŌ
Publisher, period of activity uncertain

大璃寛 Ō-RIKAN
Popular name of actor Arashi Kichisaburō II

音 OTO
Printer, active 1827

音羽屋 OTOWAYA
Yagō of actors Onoe Kikugorō III and Onoe Tamizō II

尾与 OYO
Publisher or printseller, active c. 1850

雷斎，蕾斎 RAISAI
Gō of artist Toshimoto

雷斗 RAITO
Gō of artist Shigenobu

楽斎 RAKUSAI
Gō and signature of artist Rakusai

蘭英斎 RAN'EISAI
Gō of artist Ashikuni

蘭孝 RANKŌ
Gō of artist Sadanobu I

蘭好斎 RANKŌSAI
Gō and signature of artist Rankōsai

蘭斎 RANSAI
Gō of artist Ashikuni

嵐陽斎 RAN'YŌSAI
Gō of artist Hokkei (active 1830s)

嶺琴舎 REIKINSHA
Gō of artist Keishi

鈴斎 REISAI
Gō of artist Shigenobu

連山 RENZAN
Gō of artist Yukinaga

利 RI
Publisher, active 1821; probably same as Toshin

璃寛 RIKAN
Haigō of actor Arashi Kichisaburō II

里席 RISEKI
Gō of artist Yukinaga

利新 RISHIN
Publisher, *see* Toshin

芦堂 RODŌ
Gō of artist Toshikuni

露仁斎 ROJINSAI
Gō of artist Settei

六花園 ROKKAEN
Gō of artists Ashiyuki (active 1860s) and Yoshiyuki (active 1856–1872)

六花軒 ROKKAKEN
Gō of artist Yoshiyuki (active 1856–1872)

六花亭, 緑華亭 ROKKATEI
Gō of artist Tomiyuki

露好斎 ROKŌSAI
Gō of artist Rokō

芦水 ROSUI
Gō of artist Hironobu II

蓼華斎 RYŌKASAI
Gō of artist Gyokuhō

緑一斎 RYOKUITSUSAI
Gō of artist Sadanobu I

龍玉 RYŪGYOKU
Pen name of actor Nakamura Utaemon III

流光斎 RYŪKŌSAI
Gō and signature of artists Ryūkōsai and Shiken

柳狂亭 RYŪKYŌTEI
Gō of artist Shigenao

柳斎 RYŪSAI
Gō of artist Shigeharu

柳塘 RYŪTŌ
Gō of artist Hironobu II

[illegible] SA
Publisher (?); found with Toshin (c. 1821)

定 SADA
Engraver, active 1831

貞次郎 SADAJIRŌ
Engraver, active 1848

西光亭 SAIKŌTEI
Gō of artist Shibakuni

さいうん堂 SAIUNDŌ
Publisher, *see* Ishiwa

三改 SAN *aratame*
Seal found with Shioyama, late 1840s

サニ井 SANII
Publisher, active 1817

三光 SANKŌ
Haigō of actor Nakamura Tomijūrō II

山風亭 SANPŪTEI
Gō of artist Kuniharu (active 1820s–1830s)

三升 SANSHŌ
Haigō of actor Ichikawa Danjūrō VII

三昇亭 SANSHŌTEI
Gō of artist Kunihiro

沢田 SAWADA
Publisher, active 1847

青莪堂 SEIGADŌ
Gō of artist Kangetsu

清好 SEIKŌ
Engraver and printer, active c. 1810s–1820s; also designed prints

西光亭 SEIKŌTEI
Gō of artist Shibakuni

晴翁 SEIŌ
Gō of artist Kanenari

青陽堂 SEIYŌDŌ
Gō of artist Shunshi (active 1826–1828)

セイヤウケン SEIYŌKEN
Engraver, active 1850s

青陽斎 SEIYŌSAI
Gō of artists Ashikuni, Kiyoharu, and Shunshi (active 1826–1828)

雪華 SEKKA
Gō of artist Hokuei

雪花園 SEKKAEN
Gō of artist Sadanobu I

雪花亭 SEKKATEI
Gō of artist Hokushū

雪花楼, 雪華楼 SEKKARŌ
Gō of artist Hokuei

雪圭斎 SEKKEISAI
Gō of artist Masafusa

雪坑斎 SEKKŌSAI
Gō of artist Tokinobu

雪江亭 SEKKŌTEI
Gō of artist Hokumyō

泉 SEN
Publisher, *see* Izumi

泉市 SEN'ICHI
Publisher, active 1860s

扇鶴堂 SENKAKUDŌ
Gō of artist Hokuyō

千鶴亭 SENKAKUTEI
Gō of artist Hokuyō

千錦亭 SENKINTEI
Gō of artist Tomiyuki

僊嶺 SENREI
Gō of artist Ōkyo

泉理 SENRI
Publisher, active 1821–1824; found with Honsei (1821–1824), *hanmoto sōshiya* (1823)

千里 **Senri**
Publisher, active 1831

センヨ **Sen'yo**
Publisher, active 1860s

雪蕉斎 **Sesshōsai**
Gō of artist Shigefusa (active 1740s–1760s)

雪艇 **Settei**
Gō of artist Kiyoharu

紫朝 **Shichō**
Haigō of actor Arashi Koroku IV

紫イ **Shii**
Publisher, active 1840

紫若 **Shijaku**
Haigō of actor Iwai Hanshirō VII

四季亭 **Shikitei**
Gō of artist Umekuni

Shikitei
Gō of Utakuni

市紅 **Shikō**
Haigō of actor Ichikawa Danzō V

嶋 **Shima**
Publisher (?); found with Akisō (1824)

嶋田金光堂 **Shimada Kinkōdō**
Publisher, *see* Fujimasa

進(?) **Shin (?)**
Printer, possibly publisher or printseller, active late 1840s–early 1850s; also appears as Junshi Suri Shin (?)

神岳堂 **Shingakudō**
Gō of artist Gakutei

神歌堂 **Shinkadō**
Gō of artist Gakutei

信翁 **Shin'ō**
Gō of artist Sadanobu I

心斎 **Shinsai**
Gō of artist Sadakazu

震斎 **Shinsai**
Gō of artist Sadafusa

新升 **Shinshō**
Haigō of actor Ichikawa Ebijūrō I

薪水 **Shinsui**
Haigō of actor Bandō Hikosaburō III

新助 **Shinsuke**
Engraver, printer, possibly publisher or printseller, active 1847–1850

信天翁 **Shinten'ō**
Gō of artist Sadanobu I

塩長 **Shiochō**
Publisher, active 1792–1820; found with Hon (1813), Jū (1816), Shō (1816), Tamaoki (1820); *see* Shioya Chōbei

塩喜 **Shioki**
Publisher, active mid-1830s

塩リン **Shiorin**
Publisher, active 1793

塩三 **Shiosan**
Publisher, active 1817

指瀌山人 **Shiōsanjin**
Gō of artist Shiken

塩屋長兵衛 **Shioya Chōbei**
Publisher, *see* Shiochō

志保山 **Shioyama**
Publisher, active 1840s; found with San *aratame* (late 1840s)

此友 **Shiyū**
Haigō of actor Ōtani Tomoemon II

庄 **Shō**
Publisher (?); found with Shiochō (1816)

松栄堂 **Shōeidō**
Publisher, *see* Honyasu

正本屋 **Shōhonya**
Publisher, *see* Honsei

松寿 **Shōju**
Gō of artist Shōrakusai

松好斎 **Shōkōsai**
Gō and signature of artist Shōkōsai; *gō* of artists Hokushū and Hokutō

照皇亭 **Shōkōtei**
Gō of artists Sadahiro II and Nobuhiro

笑翁 **Shōō**
Gō of artist Yoshikuni (active 1850s–1880s)

松楽斎, 松洛斎 **Shōrakusai**
Gō and signature of artist Shōrakusai

松翠軒 **Shōsuiken**
Gō of artist Mitsunobu

曙山 **Shozan**
Haigō of actor Sawamura Tanosuke II

昇山 **Shōzan**
Gō of artist Taito II

秀丸 **Shūgan**
Gō of artist Shigehiro

秀丸斎 **Shūgansai**
Gō of artists Shigefusa (active 1829–1830) and Shigehiro

秀峰 **Shūhō**
Gō of artist Shigehiro

秀佳 **Shūka**
Haigō of actor Bandō Mitsugorō III

春梅斎 **Shunbaisai**
Gō of artist Hokuei

春潮斎 **Shunchōsai**
Gō of artist Hokuchō (active 1850s)

春頂斎 **Shunchōsai**
Gō of artist Hokushō (active 1822–1832)

春朝斎 **Shunchōsai**
Gō of artist Hokushō (active 1815–1830s)

春英斎 **Shun'eisai**
Gō of artist Hokuju

春暁斎 **Shungyōsai**
Gō and signature of artist Shungyōsai; *gō* of artists Hokuchō (active 1850s), Hokusei, and Shun'ei

春完亭 **Shunkantei**
Gō of artist Hokushin

春帰斎 **Shunkisai**
Gō of artist Hokugan

春光斎 **Shunkōsai**
Gō of artist Hokushin

春好斎 **Shunkōsai**
Gō of artist Hokushū

春江斎 **Shunkōsai**
Gō of artists Hokuei and Hokutō

春旭斎 **Shunkyokusai**
Gō of artist Hokumei

春婦 **Shunpu**
Gō of artist Shunshi (?) (active 1826–1828)

春婦斎 **Shunpusai**
Gō of artist Hokumyō

春泉斎 **Shunsensai**
Gō and signature of artist Shunsensai

春始斎 **Shunshisai**
Gō of artist Hokkai

春松堂 **Shunshōdō**
Gō of artist Tamakuni

春曙斎 **Shunshosai**
Gō of artist Hokuchō (active 1822–1830)

春松斎 **Shunshōsai**
Gō of artist Hokuju

春陽堂 **Shun'yōdō**
Gō of artist Toshikuni

春陽斎 **Shun'yōsai**
Gō of artists Hokkei (active 1818–1820s), Hokuroku, Kiyoharu (active 1820s–1830s), Shunshi (active 1826–1828), and possibly Hokuei

春勇斎 **Shun'yūsai**
Gō of artist Hokusetsu

ソ **So**
Printer, active 1824

草 *sō*
Seal found with Tenki (1819–1824)

宗 **Sō**
Publisher or printseller, active 1849; possibly same as Benisō

草改 *sō aratame*
Seal found with Tenki (c. 1820)

惣銀屋 **Sōginya**
Publisher, active late nineteenth century; address: Nakabashisuji Andōjimachi Shinsaibashi Minamizume Nishi

須 **Su**
Publisher (?); found with Akisō (1821)

末吉 **Sueyoshi**
Publisher, active 1818–1827; address: Hanmoto Ōsaka Shinmachi Nishiguchi Sunaba, Sueyoshi

翠栄堂 **Suieidō**
Gō of artist Hanzan

翠釜亭 **Suifutei**
Gō and signature of artist Suifutei

筋原屋庄右衛門 **Sujiharaya Shōemon**
Publisher, active 1820s; address: Kōraibashi Yodoyabashi Nishiiru

助祢七 **Suke Yashichi**
Engraver, *see* Kuma Yashichi

住吉 **Sumiyoshi**
Publisher (?); found with Honsei (1823), Oki (1823)

摺・・・ *Suri . . .*
See under individual name without the prefix

鈴木 SUZUKI
Publisher, active late nineteenth century; address: Sanoyabashisuji Mitsuderasuji Shinmachi Nishiguchi

鈴木 SUZUKI
Printer, period of activity uncertain

太 TA
Publisher, *see* Fujita

瀧 TAKI
Printer, active 1827

玉水 TAMAMIZU
Publisher (?); found with Tenki (1817–1824)

玉の井 TAMANOI
Printer and publisher, active late nineteenth century; address: Shimanouchi Tazaemonbashi Kitazume Higashiiru

玉置, 置 TAMAOKI
Publisher, *see* Honsei and Oki

玉屋市兵衛 TAMAYA ICHIBEI
Publisher; found with Nagasaki publisher Bunkindō (1821); address: Ōsaka Kōsho (?) Tamaya Ichibei

多見 TAMI
Printer, active 1848

民蔵 TAMIZŌ
Printer, active 1841

田中忠治 TANAKA CHŪJI
Engraver, active 1860s

探月斎 TANGETSUSAI
Gō and signature of artist Tangetsusai

谷清好 TANI SEIKŌ
Engraver and printer, *see* Seikō

タンカ TANKA
Publisher (?), period of activity uncertain

丹青堂 TANSEIDŌ
Gō of artist Hokuyō

荑楊軒 TEIYŌKEN
Gō of artist Kangyū

天 TEN
Publisher, *see* Tenki

天喜, 天キ, 天貴 TENKI
Publisher, active 1816–1850s; found with *hanmoto sōshiya* (1816–1821), *sō* and *sō aratame* (1819–1826), Ichi (1823), Ki (1823), Honsei (1823), Tamamizu (1817–1824), Kakuseidō (1824), I (1824–c. 1830), Tōmura (1827), *aratame* (1833), Wataki and Honsei (1834–1836), Benisō (1835–1837), Kawaoto (1854); addresses: Hanmoto Tenki Shinsaibashidōri Mitsuderasuji (1822); Shinsaibashidōri Kikuyamachi, Tenki (1829); Hanmoto Dōtonbori Ebisubashi Mitsuderasuji, Momenya Tōkichi (1830); Ebisubashi Mitsudera Kado, Kishimoto (1830); Ōsaka Shimanouchi Hachimansuji Shinsaibashi Nishiiru, Tenki han (1834); Ōsaka Kinkadō Tenki (1835); Naniwa Kinkadō Konishi (1835); Hanmoto Tenmaya Kihei Gochō (1848). For biographical note with death date, *see* Hirosada in Catalogue.

天摩堂 TENMADŌ
Publisher, period of activity uncertain

天満屋喜兵衛 TENMAYA KIHEI
Publisher, *see* Tenki

哲斎 TESSAI
Gō of artist Nobukatsu

鉄五郎 TETSUGORŌ
Printer, active 1835

鉄蔵 TETSUZŌ
Engraver, active c. 1850

ト TO
Printer, *see* Toyo

桶蝶楼 TOCHŌRŌ
Gō of artist Sadafusa

斗円楼 TOENRŌ
Gō of artist Taito II

東方南 TŌHŌNAN
Gō of artist Hokusei (Hokkai)

桃漪 TŌI
Gō of artist Settei

杜若 TOJAKU
Haigō of actor Iwai Hanshirō V

稲香 TŌKA
Gō of Kyoto artist Toyokuni

篤平 TOKUHEI
Printer, period of activity uncertain

利倉屋新兵衛 TOKURAYA SHINBEI
Publisher, *see* Toshin

十邑 TŌMURA
Publisher (?); found with Tenki (1827)

トラ — **Tora**
Printer, active 1830

東林 — **Tōrin**
Gō of artist Hironobu I

西草 — **Torisō**
Publisher or printseller; found with Honsei (1861)

登龍軒 — **Tōryūken**
Gō of artist Shunshi (active mid-1820s)

登龍斎 — **Tōryūsai**
Gō of artist Shunshi (active mid-1820s)

利新 — **Toshin**
Publisher, active 1815–1838; found alone (1820–1832), with Sa (1815), Tsunoji (1818), Chū (1821–1822), Iden (1822), Agū (1822), Kanō (1822), *kiwame* (1822), I (1822–1823), Kakuseidō (1822–1824), Honsei (1825), Daiki (1826), Hyōzen (1826–1827, 1838); also appears as Ri, Tokuraya Shinbei

とウセ — **Touse**
Printseller (?); found with Wataki and Hyōzen (1827), Wataki (1830), Honsei (1830), Tenki (1831–1832)

豊，トヨ — **Toyo**
Printer, active 1821–1827; probably same as Toyosaburō

豊 — **Toyo**
Engraver, active 1847

豊三郎 — **Toyosaburō**
Printer, active 1835–1838; probably same as Toyo

通神道人 — **Tsūjindōjin**
Gō of artist Munenobu

津ノ治 — **Tsunoji**
Publisher; found with Toshin (1818); address: Inarimae, Tsunoji han

蔦勘 — **Tsutakan**
Publisher or printseller, active 1852

内田寅蔵 — **Uchida Torazō**
Engraver, active 1848–1853 or later

内寅 — **Uchitora**
Engraver, *see* Uchida Torazō

上丁 — **Uechō**
Printer, *see* Kamichō

上田 — **Ueda**
Publisher or printseller, active 1840s; also appears as Ka and Ka Ueda

上村為助 — **Uemura Tamesuke**
Publisher, *see* Hontame

浮世 — **Ukiyo**
Gō of artists Sadahiro I and Shigekatsu

雲鯨斎 — **Ungeisai**
Gō of artist Hidenobu (active 1760s–1770s)

雨蕉斎 — **Ushōsai**
Gō of artist Shigenobu

綿平 — **Watahei**
Publisher, active late nineteenth century; address: Shinsaibashi, Watahei

綿喜，ワタキ，ハタキ — **Wataki**
Publisher, active 1816–1880; found with Maeda (1821–1825), Ki (1823), Chū (1825), Honsei (1827), Hyōzen (1827–1832), Touse (1832), *aratame* (1833), Tenki and Honsei (1834–1836); addresses: Horie Wataki (1827); Ōsaka Hanmoto Wataki (1830); Ōsaka Horie Ichinogawa, Nishikie Sōshi Don'ya Wataki han (1841); Shinsaibashi Shiomachi Kado, Wataya Kihei han (c. 1852)

(ヤ in diamond mark) — **Ya**
Publisher (?); found alone (1833), with Honsei (date uncertain)

夜梅楼 — **Yabairō**
Gō of artist Yoshiume

山田 — **Yamada**
Engraver, active c. 1860s

山口 — **Yamaguchi**
Publisher or printseller, active 1850s

山口 — **Yamaguchi**
Engraver, active 1896

山口音吉 — **Yamaguchi Otokichi**
Publisher, active 1877

(山一 mark)，山一 — **Yamaichi**
Engraver and publisher (?), active 1822–1824; found with Honsei (1822–1824), Tenki (1823)

山嘉 — **Yamaka**
Engraver (?), active mid-1830s; probably same as Kasuke

山キ	YAMAKI Engraver, active 1836
本 (in mark)	YAMAMOTO Publisher, *see* Hon
山中	YAMANAKA Publisher, active 1859
山崎	YAMAZAKI Engraver, *see* Yamazaki Shōkurō
山崎庄九郎	YAMAZAKI SHŌKURŌ Engraver, active 1815–1819
八尾善	YAOZEN Publisher, active late 1850s–1870s; address: Shinmachidōri Osasabeni no mukai
弥七	YASHICHI Engraver, *see* Kuma Yashichi
夜雨庵	YAUAN *Haigō* of actor Ichikawa Danjūrō VII
ヨトガワ	YODOGAWA Publisher or printseller, active 1852
揚輝斎	YŌKISAI *Gō* of artist Gyokuzan II
曄斎	YŌSAI *Gō* of artist Kiyoharu
陽斎	YŌSAI *Gō* of artist Gakutei
芳	YOSHI Printer, active c. 1840
養水	YŌSUI *Gō* of artist Yoshitaki
陽亭	YŌTEI *Gō* of artist Gakutei
楢園	YŪEN *Gō* of Sadanobu I
有原堂	YŪGENDŌ Publisher, *see* Ariharadō
有楽斎	YŪRAKUSAI *Gō* and signature of artist Nagahide
ざこば	ZAKOBA Printer, active 1822–1825
瑞雲堂	ZUIUNDŌ Publisher, *see* Kasugadō
� (mark)	Publisher, active 1800–1802
(mark)	Printer, active 1827
(mark)	Publisher, *see* Ariharadō

Appendixes

I

Ōsaka Dachin'uma. Compiled by Soketsuan Yūdōsanjin

大坂駄珍馬　鼠穴庵遊道山人

1783 (preface).

A manuscript miscellany describing events in Osaka in the late eighteenth century; original is located in the National Diet Library, Tokyo; quoted in Tsubouchi (p. 145). In the earliest recorded reference to an Osaka ukiyoe artist, the author states:

> From around last spring fans with actor's likenesses became greatly popular. The painter of these was a certain Ryūkōsai who lives near Kamei Bridge in North Horie. He is incomparably skillful in portraying actor's faces and people had him make pictures of their favorite actors.

II

Kyojitsu Satonamari, by Kōguya Sensei Rodō

虚実柳巷方言　香具屋先生魯堂

1794.

A printed guidebook to Osaka, reprinted in *Naniwa Sōsho,* vol. 14. Two contemporary artists are mentioned in a list of "Famous Adepts and Craftsmen" (p. 28): for portraits, Ryūkōsai; for paintings, Nichōsai.

III

Naniwa Namari

浪華なまり

1802.

A printed guidebook to Osaka; an original is located in Kanō Library, Tōhoku University; quoted in Tsubouchi (p. 145). In a section devoted to accomplished professionals in volume 2, the anonymous author says:

> Nowadays painting is highly fashionable. The influential painters are Buzen, Yūtoku, Ranrinsai, Rankō, Shūhō, Shūnan, Sosen, Tsukioka, Tachibana, Gyokuzan, Tōkei, Mikijo, and Shunsen. . . . Nichōsai's caricatures outdo Toba Sōjō's and Ryūkōsai and Shōkō are as good in portraiture as Kudara no Kawanari.

IV

Shibai Annai Ryōmen Kagami. Compiled by Shōkōsai

戯場案内両面鑑　松好斎

1803.

A single-sheet printed broadside with paired lists of men associated with the Osaka theater; original is in the Deguchi collection, Wakayama (Deguchi catalogue no. 464); reprinted in Kuroda, *Kamigatae Ichiran* (p. 167). Shōkōsai, a print designer and portraitist himself, lists the theater billboard painters as: Mokubei of Shimanouchi, Shinsaibashi (Kado Theater); and Rihachi of Andōjimachi (Naka Theater). He also lists two actor portraitists: Ryūkōsai Jokei of Horie Kameibashi, and "Myself (if I may be so bold) of Shimanouchi Shimizumachi."

V

Hokusai Gashiki. Katsushika Hokusai, (possibly Hokuun)

北斎画式　葛飾北斎（北雲?）

1819.

An illustrated book published in Nagoya; quoted in Narazaki (p. 326). The colophon of the book, published after Hokusai's visit to Osaka in 1818, lists three Osaka artists as "copyist-pupils": Senkakutei Hokuyō, Sekkatei Hokushū, and Shun'yōsai Hokkei, and also lists the Osaka engraver Yamazaki Shōkurō.

VI

Jukōdō Yoshikuni

寿好堂よし国

Untitled color woodblock print, c. 1822.

A surimono-style *ōban* portrait of the actor Hyakumura Hyakutarō; an impression is located in the Museum of Fine Arts, Boston. The following poets, most of them also print designers, are mentioned as members of the Jukōdō Circle: Jukōdō Yoshikuni, Kishikuni, Hashikuni, Chikakuni, Yoshinao, Harukuni, Mitsukuni, Yoshiyuki, Masakuni, Umekuni, Hatsukuni, Tamakuni.

VII

Shunkōsai Hokushū

春好斎北洲

Untitled color woodblock print, 3/1824.

A large surimono-style double *ōban* showing Nakamura Matsue as Otaka, Ichikawa Ebijūrō I as Mokuemon, and Ichikawa Danzō V as Yashichi; an impression is located in the Museum of Fine Arts, Boston. The print bears seven poems signed by the following artists, engravers, printers, etc.: Umekuni *aratame* Kensan (?), Tessai, Suri To, Kasuke, Horikō Kasuke, Umetaka, Kunihiro.

VIII

Jukōdō Yoshikuni

寿好堂よし国

Untitled color woodblock print, c. 1827.

An *ōban* portrait of Nakamura Shikan II as Miyamoto Musashi (?); an impression is located in Ikeda Library, Ikeda. The print bears five poems signed by members of the Jukōdō Circle: Umekuni, Masakuni, Fujikuni, Toshikuni, Yorikuni.

IX

Toyokuni Sensei Eihitsu no Kihi

豊国先生瘞筆之記碑

1828.

A stone memorial erected for Utagawa Toyokuni I at Myōkendō, Yanagishima, Honjo, Edo; quoted in Yoshida, *Ukiyoe Jiten,* vol. 2 (pp. 271-72). The following Osaka print designers are named among the many Utagawa school artists who are listed on the monument as contributors: Kunikage (pupils of Toyokuni I); Kuniharu, Kunitsuru, Kunishige (pupils of Toyokuni II); Sadafusa, Sadanobu, Naniwa Sadahiro (pupils of Kunisada); Yoshinobu (pupils of Kuniyoshi).

X

Shunkōsai Hokuei

春江斎北英

Untitled color woodblock print, 9/1831.

An *ōban* diptych showing Arashi Rikan II as Karahashi Sakujūrō and an actor of the Asao family as Daidōji Gakutarō; an impression is located in the Museum of Fine Arts, Boston. The following Osaka engravers, printers, and geisha are mentioned on pilgrim's tags pasted on the walls and posts of the *Enmadō,* where the actors are battling: Naniwa Hori Kasuke, Naniwa Hori Man, Hori Hangi Ichi, Edo Hangi Ichi, Naniwa Suri Iida, Matsu Suri Toku, Edo Suri Tomo, Suri Toyo, Naniwa Matsui, Murakawa, Geiko Yae, Oren.

XI

Naniwa Shoryū Gajin Meika Annai

浪華諸流画人名家案内

c. 1831.

An anonymous single-sheet printed broadside listing Osaka actor portraitists and "block-copyists"; original is in the Deguchi collection, Wakayama (Deguchi catalogue no. 244); quoted in Kuroda, *Kamigatae Ichiran* (pp. 175-76). An invaluable matched list of Osaka ukiyoe artists divided into two categories:

Those chiefly doing actor portraits [*yakusha nigaoe o omo to su*]

Shunkōsai Hokushū of Ishiyabashi East
Gigadō Ashiyuki of Doshōmachi, Goryōsuji
Ganjōsai Kunihiro, one block north of Ebisubashi
Tōryūsai Shunshi of Futatsuido
Saikōtei Shibakuni of Ryōgokubashi
Shunshōdō Tamakuni of Imabashi
Shunchōsai Hokushō of Bakuromachi
Shunkōsai Hokuei of Itachibori 1-chōme
Shunyōdō Toshikuni of Karamonomachi
Yanagawa Nobumasa of Senba
Shunpusai Hokumyō of Dōjima
Kōjōdō Ashimaru of Bakuromachi
Ashinuki of north of Shinsaibashi

Those chiefly doing block copies [*hanshita o omo to su*]

Ryūsai Shigeharu of Mitsuderamachi
Akatsuki no Kanenari of Shinsaibashi, Bakuromachi
Tanseidō Hokuyō of Shiomachi, Shinsaibashi
Miki Genzō of South Kyūtarōmachi, Sankyūbashi
Hishikawa Kiyoharu of Uemachi
Tomooka (Yūkō [?]) of Uemachi
Hikei of Uemachi
Ukiyo Utayoshi of Mitsuderamachi
Edo Kunikage of Edobori

Those doing both actor portraits and block copies

Ryūsai Shigeharu of Mitsuderamachi
Yūrakusai Nagahide of Kyoto

XII

Mumeiō Zuihitsu (also known as *Zoku Ukiyoe Ruikō.*)
Compiled by Keisai Eisen

无名翁随筆（続浮世絵類考） 渓斎英泉

1833.

A manuscript of biographies of ukiyoe artists; reprinted in *Enseki Jisshu,* vol. 2; quoted in Kuroda, *Kamigatae Ichiran* (p. 170). Eisen, an ukiyoe artist in his own right, says the following about his great contemporary Katsushika Hokusai (pp. 224-26):

Hearing of Hokusai's fame, many people in Kyoto and Osaka became his pupils. So he traveled to Nagoya, then to the Kyoto-Osaka area, but no artist there approached his skill. . . . Everyone in Kyoto and Osaka imitated Hokusai's style and became his pupil, though without necessarily changing name. Even in the provinces artists became his pupils and studied his art.

XIII

Naniwa Zasshi Chimata no Uwasa (also known as *Machi no Uwasa*), by Heitei Ginkei

浪華雑誌街能噂（街能噂） 平亭銀鶏

1835.

A printed book illustrated by Utagawa Sadahiro giving the newly arrived Edo author's opinions of Osaka in a series of imaginary conversations with the local citizenry. In the third volume the discussion turns to the subject of ukiyoe and the following slangy episode is perhaps the only contemporary critical discussion of Osaka prints that has survived. Reprinted in *Naniwa Sōsho,* vol. 14, (p. 282):

"Say, Osaka prints have gotten pretty good lately. Some of them are just about like Edo ones."

"Yeah, there are some real master-hands at ukiyoe here these days."

"Who do you think are the best in Osaka?"

"Well, there's Utagawa Sadamasu. He does good actor portraits, especially of the seventh Danjūrō. Ryūsai Shigeharu has been here a long time from Nagasaki, and he's good at everything; his erotic prints are overwhelming. Then you've got Shunbaisai Hokuei, Kikukawa Chikukei, and Temmaya Kunihiro. There are lots of them. There's Utagawa Sadahiro, too—the guy who did the frontispieces for Ginkei's book *Chimata no Uwasa.* He's just in his twenties, but he's awfully good. You'll be hearing more about him. Take a look at his pictures when they get engraved."

"Sure, I've heard of Sadahiro. He lives in Hoteimachi doesn't he?"

"You've got it."

"By the way, isn't Utagawa Kunitsuru here in Osaka, too—the guy who lived at Yamashita up in Edo?"

"Yes, and he's awfully good, too."

"People certainly thought well of him in Edo."

XIV

Shunbaisai Hokuei

春梅斎北英

Untitled color woodblock print, spring, 1837.

A surimono-style *ōban* portrait of Nakamura Utaemon IV as the wrestler Inagawa, a role he performed in 1836, which was published as a posthumous memorial to the artist with an inscription by the publisher saying: "We publish this picture, the last work of the late Hokuei, designed on his sickbed, in hopes of adding a small tribute to his memory." Three memorial poems, including one by the actor Utaemon IV, are couched in imagery of early spring. An impression of the print is located in the Victoria and Albert Museum; another is reproduced in Kuroda, *Kamigatae Ichiran* (plate 72).

XV

Ōsaka Shōkō Meika Shū

大坂商工銘家集

1846.

A printed directory of Osaka; original is in the Osaka Prefectural Library; quoted in Kuroda, *Kamigatae Ichiran* (pp. 222, 225, and 237). The anonymous compiler mentions the following three men as designers of color woodblock prints in the year before the government ban on actor portraiture was successfully challenged: Utagawa Kunimasu of Nōninbashi Matsuyamachi; Hasegawa Sadanobu of Andōjimachi Naniwabashi; and Gorakutei Sadahiro of Tatamiyamachi Mitsuderasuji.

XVI

Denki Sakusho (also known as *Kyōgen Sakusho*), by Nishizawa Ippō

伝奇作書（言狂作書） 西沢一鳳

1843.

A manuscript account of the history and practice of kabuki by one of the leading playwrights of the nineteenth century; reprinted in *Shin Gunsho Ruijū,* vol. 1. Ippō has the following remarks to make on the history of actor portraiture in Osaka (pp. 95-96):

Shōkōsai Hanbei was a well-known ukiyoe artist who did actor portraits and died in the Bunka period (1804–17). He was devoted to the theater and wrote and illustrated the two-volume *Gakuya Zue,* which, on the model of early geographical guides, begins with Okuni of Izumo and ends with the Nishinomiya puppeteers, with backstage views and pictures of billboards.

Originally, there were no so-called ukiyoe artists in the Kyoto-Osaka area. Omitting Iwasa Matabei, the *Ōtsue* artist whom I have discussed earlier, the first person who made actor portraits and called himself an ukiyoe artist must be Ryūkōsai (Shiken, the fan painter, was his elder brother [*sic*]). Ryūkōsai's actor prints were always triptychs. His style was restrained, compared to modern work, but connoisseurs have always admired his skill in rendering likenesses. Shōkōsai, his pupil, had a different style and did several books of portraits.

Concerning theater billboard painting: Mokubei, Kyūemon, and others were at work in the heyday, but after Gako died, actor portraitists were hired to paint the billboards and the whole style changed. After Shōkōsai, the actor portraitists included Ashikuni, Shunkō (who never made it his real profession), Ashiyuki, Yoshikuni, Shigeharu, Hokuei, and others. But we do not see their pictures today, and perhaps they are no longer active.

XVII

Keisetsu Gesakusha Kō, by Kimura Mokuō (Uyūsanjin)
京摂戯作者考　木村黙翁（烏有山人）
Mid-1840s.

A manuscript giving brief and often inaccurate biographies of popular authors and artists in the Kyoto-Osaka area; reprinted in *Zoku Enseki Jisshu,* vol. 1 (pp. 258-83). Kimura mentions the following Osaka print designers:

SHŌKŌSAI. Osaka. Commonly called Hanbei. Lived at Shimizumachi, Shimanouchi. Skilled in ukiyoe and actor portraiture. Author of *Gakuya Meisho Zue, Gakuya Meisho Shūi, Yakusha Masukagami,* etc. Active 1790s–1800s.

SHŌRAKUSAI. Osaka. Contemporary of Shōkōsai. Personal name: Itoku. *Gō*: Shōju. Did actor portraits.

RYŪKŌSAI. Osaka. Ukiyoe artist, skilled in actor portraiture. Personal name: Jokei. Common name unknown. Lived at Kameibashi, Horie.

RYŪSAI (Shigeharu). Originally from Nagasaki. Lived at Mitsuderamachi, Shimanouchi. Skilled in ukiyoe and actor portraiture. All of the many ukiyoe artists in Osaka at this time had other professions and painted pictures on the side. Only Ryūsai made his living solely from ukiyoe, which shows that he was better than the rest. N.B. Ryūsai was originally from Nagasaki, but moved to Osaka with his family where his pictures were very popular. He died in 1853. His daughter, Yonejo, followed his profession and is a competent painter. Foreigners like her paintings of beauties and take them abroad with them. It is a credit to her art that they seem to appreciate them greatly.

Kiyōtei KUNISHIGE. Same as Ryūsai.

Seiyōsai Hishikawa KIYOHARU. Kyoto. Son of a Doctor Mura-someone. Childhood name: Kunijirō, later Kunisuke. Pupil of Ueda Kōchō. Now in Wakayama, Kii Province. New *gō:* Ono Hirotaka.

Asayama ASHIKUNI. Osaka. *Gō*: Kyōgadō. Common name: Nunoya Chūzaburō. Known as Ran'eisai of the Ranrinsai School. Later took the *gō* Kyōgadō. Died 5/9/1820 [*sic*], over forty years old. Posthumous name: Shaku Junsei. Tomb at Yūkōji, Shimoderamachi.

Utagawa SADAMASU. Osaka. Lived near Nōninbashi. Common name: Kaneya Wasaburō. A master-hand, second only to Ryūtei [*sic*].

Utagawa SADAHIRO. Osaka. Lived in Nanba Shinchi. Common name: Kyōmaruya Seijirō.

Utagawa SADAYOSHI. Osaka. Lived in Shimanouchi Shinsaibashi. Common name: Higoya Teishichirō.

Hasegawa SADANOBU. Osaka. Lived in Andōjimachi Naniwabashi. Common name: Naraya Tokubei.

Other artists cited with biographies are: Nishikawa Sukenobu, Tsukioka Tange, Urakawa Issen, Ippōsai Baen, Nichōsai, Nagayama Kōin, Kintarō Shujin, Shunsuirō Shujin, Yasukawa Harusada, Takeuchi Kakusai, Matsukawa Hanzan.

Artists cited without biographies are: Katsushika Hokusen, Ishida Gyokutei, Ichiyōsai Masanobu, Menharō Kunikage, Ryūsensai Kunishige, Ishida Gyokuhō, Ippyōsai Utagawa Toyohide, Hokudō Bokuzan, Sōyūtei Koyū, Rosai Setchū, Hokutei Hokusen, Tōnansai Hokuun, Yūshūsai Rantei, Gōsenkan Minwa, Ōishi Shinko.

XVIII

Kyakushoku Yoroku, by Nishizawa Ippō
脚色餘録　西沢一鳳
1851.

A manuscript miscellany on theatrical matters by a nineteenth-century playwright; reprinted in *Shin Gunsho Ruijū,* vol. 2. In the first section of volume 2 of his manuscript, Ippō discusses "Books on the Theater" (p. 36):

> Shōkōsai's *Gakuya Zue* described the theater in pictures. . . . Books of actor portraits started with Ryūkōsai and continued on to Shōkō, Ashikuni, and Shunkō (in Edo the descent was from Katsukawa Shunshō to Toyokuni). They portrayed the actors of their day with close resemblance.

XIX

Naniwa Meika Boshoshū. Compiled by Kimura Kenkadō and Akatsuki no Kanenari
浪華名家墓所集　木村兼葭堂・暁鐘成
c. early 1850s.

A manuscript grave register of famous Osaka citizens of the seventeenth to nineteenth century with some brief biographies, by an important mid-nineteenth-century Osaka author. The original manuscript has been lost; the following excerpts are from a late nineteenth century copy now in the Kanō

Library, Tōhoku University, of a manuscript, perhaps the original, owned by the painter Tomioka Tessai.

Asayama ASHIKUNI. Died 5/5/1820 [*sic*]. Buried at Enjōin Yūkōji. Osaka. Common name: Nunoya Chūzaburō. Studied painting with Suga Ranrinsai, and used the name Asayama Ran'eisai, later Kyōgadō Ashikuni. Earned a reputation by specializing in ukiyoe. Over forty at his death.

SHŌKŌSAI. Osaka. Common name: Hanbei. Lived in Shimizumachi, Shimanouchi. Ukiyoe artist, especially skilled in portraying actors. Also an author of many books. Truly an eminent man of recent years.

Ryūsai SHIGEHARU. Nagasaki. Common name: Yamaguchi Jinjirō. Ukiyoe artist, skilled in actor portraiture. An eminent personage of recent years.

RYŪKŌSAI. Osaka. Ukiyoe artist, skilled in actor portraiture. Personal name: Jokei. Common name unknown. Lived in Horie, Kameibashi; later said to have moved to Kyōbashimachi, Nanba Shinchi.

Taga SHIKEN. Son of Ryūkōsai. A skillful painter who unfortunately died in the prime of life. *Gō*: Bokusen.

Other artists mentioned include: Nagasawa Rosetsu, Okada Beisanjin, Ōoka Shunsen, Tachibana Morikuni, Shitomi Kangetsu, Suga Ranrinsai, Hamamatsu Utakuni, Tsukioka Settei, Nichōsai, Katsura Munenobu, Kagayama Kōin, Niwa Tōkei, Ippōsai Baen, Satō Gyotai (Gyodai), Tanaka Shūtei.

XX

Mimeguri Inari Shanai Kuniyoshi Shachū Himen

三圍稲荷社内国芳社中碑面

1873.

A memorial monument for the artist Utagawa Kuniyoshi erected at Mimeguri Shrine, Tokyo; quoted in Kuroda, *Kamigatae Ichiran* (pp. 159-60). The following Osaka print designers are mentioned on the memorial: Naniwa Yoshiume, Yoshiharu (pupils of Kuniyoshi); Yoshiyuki, Yoshitoyo, Yoshinobu (deceased pupils of Kuniyoshi); Umeyuki, Yoshimine, Yoshihide, Umeharu, Yoshitaki (pupils of Yoshiume); Yoshimitsu, Yoshikuni (pupils of Yoshitaki [?]).

XXI

Saitō Gesshin. *Zōtei Bukō Nenpyō*. With addenda by Kitamura Intei, Sekine Shisei, and Asakura Musei

斎藤月岑（北村筠亭・関根只誠・朝倉無声増訂） 増訂武江年表

1912.

A revised edition of *Bukō Nenpyō*, a chronological history of Edo from the founding of the Tokugawa shogunate in 1593, by the historian Gesshin (1804–1878), which was originally published in 1850. Intei's entry for the Kyōwa period (1801–1803) is reprinted in *Zōtei Bukō Nenpyō*, Tōyō Bunko, 1963, vol. 2 (pp. 26-27):

During this period many illustrated novelettes recently written and published in the Kyoto-Osaka area came to Edo. . . . The authors were Risshintei Kiran, Togetsu, Yūyūkan, Ryūrō, Fumimaro, and others. The artists were Ishida Gyokuzan, Seiyōsai Ashikuni, Ippōsai Baen, Niwa Tōkei, Aikawa Minwa, Shōkōsai Hanbei, Utagawa Toyohide, Hayami Shungyōsai, and many others. Shungyōsai was an author as well, and wrote many novelettes himself.

In the Bunka period (1804–17), Edo novelettes were often dramatized on the Kyoto-Osaka stage.

XXII

Ōsaka Hōhiroku. Compiled by Keijirō Kimura

大阪訪碑録　木村敬二郎

1929.

A grave register with photographs of tomb inscriptions and brief biographies of distinguished Osaka citizens; compiled for and printed in *Naniwa Sōsho*, vol. 10. The following print designers are mentioned:

Asayama ASHIKUNI. Burial temple: Yūkōji at Shimoderamachi. Pupil of Ranrinsai. *Gō:* Asayama Ran'eisai, later Kyōgadō Ashikuni. Posthumous name: Shaku Junsei. Date on tomb: 5/9/1818.

Hasegawa SADANOBU: Date on tomb: 28/3/1879.

Hasegawa KONOBU: Date on tomb: 16/7/1886.

XXIII

Kawasaki Kyosen (Ningyodō). "Nishikie ni naru made" *Kinsei Insatsu Bunkashi Kō*

川崎巨泉（人魚洞） 錦絵になるまで 近世印刷文化史考

1938, pp. 46-48.

An invaluable reminiscence titled "How Color Prints are Made," comprising the only firsthand account of the designing and production of Osaka actor prints, written by the son of the most prolific late nineteenth century actor portraitist, Yoshitaki.

Theater prints depict actors made up for the stage in various attire, and all of them are drawn as actors' portraits. The following took place in the early years of the Meiji period.

When the titles for the summer performances,

New Year's performances, and the like had been decided on at the theaters, we would pick the scenes from the hit plays that looked like they would be popular and would make interesting pictures (a chilling murder scene from a ghost play, for example), and these would be published.

In those days, certain Osaka publishers set out to the theaters on opening day with the artists who drew actors' likenesses. The dividers were removed from four or five boxes right in the middle of the floor section of the theater and spread with rugs. Tables were set up with brushes and paper, and all was made ready to sketch the happenings on stage. The artist sat in the middle, with the proprietor of the publishing house and his clerks alongside. Besides them, some first-class female entertainers managed the food and drink, so things were quite lively. This was a form of promotion, as much as to say that actor prints were being designed for this performance.

Customers would think to themselves that "so-and-so is an actor-print artist, and pretty soon some good prints of his are going to be on sale," and they would wait for them to appear. Prints for summer and New Year's performances were issued in quarter-block format (about 7 x 10″) as diptychs, triptychs, even five- and seven-sheet sets. No matter how well theater prints were designed, if the faces of the figures were not exact likenesses of the actors they would not sell at all, and the publisher took a terrific loss. So the publisher went to pains to obtain the services of the very best portrait artists, and sent them presents to encourage them to finish his commission even the least bit sooner than others. My father Yoshitaki and others were usually besieged for their actor portraits by several publishers.

Going to the theater and sketching scenes and actors live was nothing but a formality. We had drawn the same scenes so many times that there was really no need to see them over again, but the publishers had to show off their enthusiasm and put on their own little show. Once the cover was off the new plays, a publisher wanted to put his prints on sale a day, a half-day, even an hour earlier than his competitors, and he kept after the artists to finish the "block-copies" [*hanshita*] quickly. An artist with orders from two or three publishers would keep them all satisfied by passing out panels of triptychs one at a time to each of them in rotation, enabling them to get started on the engraving as soon as possible.

The block-copies were nothing more than an outline drawn on thin Mino paper with no color at all. The designs and detail were not subject to the publisher's approval, but left completely to the artist's discretion and the artist sent them directly to the engraver without the publisher so much as seeing them.

The engraver pasted the block-copy face down on a piece of cherry wood. The face, arms, and legs were left to a skilled specialist (the "head engraver") and the rest was done quickly by a regular craftsman (the "body engraver"). When the key block was finished the engraver sent it to the printer who printed up a set of fourteen, fifteen, or sometimes twenty impressions in black on thin Mino paper, which he sent back to the artist with a request for color indications [*irozashi*]. Using one sheet for each color, the artist indicated the colored areas in vermilion, and labeled each sheet with the proper color: red, yellow, blue, brown, etc. Once finished, the set was returned to the engraver who pasted them on both sides of cherry blocks, engraved and re-labeled them, and returned them to the printer. The printer arranged the black key block [*omoban*] and color blocks [*iroita*] and printed two or three trial proofs [*kyōgōzuri*], which he once again sent to the artist with a request for comments on color balance.

The work had to be finished within two or three days at the most, and slips were occasionally made in the hastily-carved colored areas. The artist would point this out and order the engraver to repair the flaw by inlaying a bit of wood and recarving it. He would also suggest that the sky should be a darker blue, the brown blacker, the red shaded at bottom, etc. When these changes were carried out, the editioning would begin.

The first printing was called "block-letting" [*ita oroshi*] and consisted of a "stack" [*ippai*] of two hundred impressions. Additional impressions [*oizuri*] were printed to demand in groups of two hundred. It was customary to give two or three impressions of the original edition to the artist.

Since everything from sketch to finished print was left up to the artist, the publisher had no idea of what to expect as a result. But he was used to this. When a fine print came out he was delighted and set it out for sale in the front of the shop where customers were already waiting. The first edition would sell out in no time at all and edition would follow edition, to his great gain. This is what happened when the portraits were well received. But the opposite could happen too, and sometimes not a single impression would sell, to the publisher's loss, and an entire edition would never see the light of day.

Most portraits lacked the actors' names and people recognized them from their faces and crests [*mon*] so it was essential to work the crest pattern somewhere into their costumes. Fans of the various actors would compete with one another to buy prints, and would mount them in albums to preserve them.

Prints of large format were called *ōnishiki* (about 15 x 10″). These were more deluxe than the quarter-block prints and were issued from time to time in special sets: "Seven Changes" [*Shichi henge*], "Six Poets" [*Rokkasen*], "Vying in Artistry [*Jutsu karube*], sets of ten for dance plays, etc. When an actor died, memorial portraits [*shini-e*] were published with his farewell poem and posthumous name.

The above is a general account of how theater prints were made. They were not at all like today's color prints, which imitate the effects of painting, but rested close to the artist's heart and showed the qualities of true woodblock prints.

(We omit the final paragraphs of the article, which describe a few technical terms and explain Kawasaki's dislike of "modern" prints.)

Bibliography

Asterisks indicate items not personally examined by the authors. The order of Japanese names follows current usage.

Brown, Louise Norton. *Block-Printing and Book Illustration in Japan*. London and New York, 1924.

A still useful, but frequently unreliable study with lists of illustrated books by some Osaka artists.

Dainihon Shoga Meika Taikan. Compiled by Tadashi Araki
大日本書画名家大鑑　荒木矩
4 vols. Tokyo, 1934.

A useful general reference for artists' biographies. Two volumes of biography, one of facsimile signatures and seals, one of index.

Dōmoto, Kansei. *Kamigata Engekishi*
堂本寒星　上方演劇史
Tokyo, 1928.

Disorganized and occasionally inaccurate, but valuable as one of the few books dealing with kabuki in the Kyoto-Osaka area.

Engeki Gedai Yōran. Edited by Nihon Hōsō Kyōkai
演劇外題要覧 日本放送協会
Tokyo, 1937. Reprinted 1954.

A dictionary of correct pronunciations of kabuki plays compiled for announcers of the national radio network.

Engeki Hyakka Daijiten
演劇百科大辞典
6 vols. Tokyo, 1960.

An invaluable encyclopedia of the theater with articles ranging from primitive ritual to contemporary ballet, edited by the staff of the Waseda Theatrical Museum. The choice of articles is sometimes patchy, but they are detailed and generally reliable. The sections on kabuki are particularly good and include bibliographies.

Enomoto, Yūsai. "Ryūkōsaiha no Kenkyū: Nagasawa Ingyō no Hakken." *Ukiyoe Geijutsu*
榎本雄斎 流光斎派の研究・長沢印暁の発見　浮世絵芸術
(*Ukiyoe Art*) 8 (December 1964), pp. 36-39 (English summary pp. 24-25).

A circumstantial account of the discovery of an album of drawings copied from an illustrated book by Ryūkōsai, with a note on Ryūkōsai's son, Shiken.

Enseki Jisshu
燕石十種
3 vols. Tokyo, 1927.

Originally published from 1857 to 1861, including:
Vol. 1: *Chirizuka Dan*, by Ogawa Kendō
塵塚談　小川顕道
1814.
With a note on the origin of actor portraiture, p. 254.
Vol. 2: *Mumeiō Zuihitsu* (*Zoku Ukiyoe Ruikō*) by Ikeda Yoshinobu (Keisai Eisen)
无名翁随筆（続浮世絵類考）　池田義信（渓斎英泉）
1833.
See Appendix XII.

Ernst, Earle. *The Kabuki Theater*. London, 1956.

Fujikake, Shizuya. "Edo igai no shochi ni bokkōseru ukiyoe." *Ukiyoe no Kenkyū* 3
藤懸静也　江戸以外の諸地に勃興せる浮世絵　浮世絵の研究
pp. 57-65. Tokyo, 1944.

A short, cavalier account of printmaking in Osaka and Kyoto.

Gunji, Masakatsu. *Kabuki*. Rutland, Vt., and Tokyo, 1970.

An excellent short essay dealing with many aspects of kabuki omitted in books by Western authors. Ably translated by John Bester and copiously illustrated.

Hajek, Lubor. *The Osaka Woodcuts*. London, 1960. Published in German as *Hirosada, Holzschnitte aus Kamigata* in 1959.

The only book in a Western language devoted to Osaka actor prints, with an essay, sixty-three illustrations (mostly in color) of prints in Czech collections, a spotty list of artists, and a short glossary of technical terms. The author's thesis, that Osaka culture was impersonal compared to Edo, and that Osaka prints are depictions of roles, not actors, is untenable, and the preponderance of prints of the late 1840s and early 1850s among the illustrations gives an unbalanced picture of the school, but the author deserves praise for presenting and appreciating what was then a thoroughly neglected form of Japanese printmaking.

Halford, Giovanni M., and Audrey S. *The Kabuki Handbook*. Rutland, Vt., and Tokyo, 1956.

Clear plot synopses of many currently performed kabuki plays, with a useful glossary.

*Haruyama, Takematsu. "Ōsaka no Ryūkōsai ni tsuite"
春山武松　大阪の流光斎に就いて　浮世絵芸術
Ukiyoe Geijutsu 4 (issue no. 8)

———. "Ryūkōsai to Shōkōsai: Naniwa Nishikie no Kenkyū." *Tōyō Bijutsu* 12
春山武松　流光斎と松好斎・難波錦絵の研究　東洋美術
(July 1931), pp. 1-42.

An admirable attempt to gather all surviving information about two important early Osaka print designers, with a list of their illustrated books, chiefly taken from earlier writers, and a necessarily confused list of prints and drawings attributed to both artists in the Isajirō Okada collection and the *Kyota Kyakushoku Jō*.

Hasegawa Konobu. *Anona*
長谷川小信　あのな
(September 1929), p. 22.

Untitled paragraph revealing Sadanobu's love for tea, written by his son.

*———. "Meiji jidai Ōsaka no hangakai." *Kinsei Insatsu Bunkashi Kō*
長谷川小信　明治時代大阪の版画界　近世印刷文化史考
Osaka, 1938.

Brief reminiscences of printmaking in the Meiji period.

*Hasegawa, Sadanobu II (Konobu). "Naniwa meisho no hensen." *Ōsakajin* 9
二代長谷川貞信　浪花名所の変遷　大阪人
(May 1930).

———. "Ōsaka Ezōshiten no Tsuioku." *Anona*
二代長谷川貞信　大阪絵草紙店の追憶　あのな
(October 1929), pp. 13-14.

A short, evocative account of print publishers and retailers in the Meiji period.

Hayashi, Yoshikazu. *Enpon Kenkyū: Shunshō*
林美一　艶本研究　春章
Tokyo, 1963.

A discussion of Shunshō's erotica, with a biographical section suggesting that Shunshō may have come from Osaka.

Hillier, Jack, and Jūzō Suzuki. "The Hokusai/Ryūkōsai *Hyōsui Kiga* and *Ehon Ryōhitsu*." *Ukiyo-e Art* 13 (December 1966), pp. 19-34, 40-47.

A thorough discussion of the transformation of a book of landscapes by the Osaka actor portraitist Ryūkōsai, which was altered by Katsushika Hokusai and republished several times, with a detailed description of the changes and several illustrations.

*Hirakata, Igoshichi. "Sadanobu-ō no Katsurakake." *Kinsei Insatsu Bunkashi Kō*
枚方一五七　貞信翁の桂歌計　近世印刷文化史考
Osaka, 1938.

Reminiscences of Hasegawa Sadanobu I.

Hirano, Chie. "The Training of Ukiyoe Artists, Carvers, and Printers, and the Technique of Making Prints." *Kiyonaga, A Study of His Life and Works*, pp. 29-41. Boston, 1939.

Largely based on Ishii's *Nishikie no hori to suri*, and still the most readable, detailed, and reliable account in English of the materials and processes of eighteenth-century Japanese printmaking.

Ihara, Seiseien (Toshirō). "Ōsaka ni okeru yakushae: eiri nehon to sono gaka." *Nishikie* 20
伊原青々園(敏郎)　大阪に於る役者絵ー絵入根本と其の画家　錦絵
(November 1918).

A discussion of illustrated theater books in Osaka and their artists.

Ihara, Toshirō, ed. *Kabuki Nenpyō*.
伊原敏郎　歌舞伎年表
8 vols. Tokyo, 1956–63.

The *vade mecum* of all students of kabuki and actor prints. During a lifetime of theatrical research Ihara gathered material for a completely documented chronology of kabuki performances from the seventeenth to the late nineteenth century. His notes were disorganized and unpublished when he died. In their present form, ably edited by Teruji Yoshida and Shigetoshi Kawatake, they are a rich, fragmentary, inconsistent, and often maddeningly inaccurate patchwork of documentation. All in all, the *Nenpyō* solves at least as many problems as it raises, and Ihara and the editors warmly deserve our gratitude.

———. *Kinsei Nihon Engekishi*
伊原敏郎　近世日本演劇史
Tokyo, 1913.

A sequel to *Nihon Engekishi* below, covering the period between the 1790s and mid-nineteenth century.

———. *Meiji Engekishi*
伊原敏郎　明治演劇史
Tokyo, 1933.

A second sequel to *Nihon Engekishi*, dealing with the late nineteenth century.

———. *Nihon Engekishi*
伊原敏郎　日本演劇史
Tokyo, 1904.

A still unsurpassed history of kabuki through the 1780s told through biographies that include very convenient, if occasionally incomplete and inaccurate, résumés with roles, plays, and theaters of each important actor's career.

Iijima, Kyoshin. *Katsushika Hokusai Den*
飯島虚心　葛飾北斎伝
2 vols. Tokyo, 1893.

The standard biography of Hokusai, with comments on his illustrated books.

Iizuka, Tomoichirō. *Kabuki Saiken*
飯塚友一郎　歌舞伎細見
Tokyo, 1926.

A valuable study of the transformations of plot in kabuki plays, arranged by category with a remarkably incomplete index of roles and titles. The author generously assumes that the reader is thoroughly familiar with the basic plots of most plays he deals with and has seen most of them staged.

Inoue, Kazuo, ed.; revised by Sakamoto Sōshi. *Zōtei Keichō Irai Shoka Shūran*
井上和雄・坂本宗子　増訂慶長以来書賈集覧
Osaka, 1970.

A list of book publishers in Edo, Kyoto, and Osaka during the Edo period with dates and addresses. An enlargement of the original edition of 1916.

Inoue, Kazuo, and Watanabe Shōzaburō, eds. *Ukiyoeshi Den*
井上和雄・渡辺庄三郎　浮世絵師伝
Tokyo, 1931.

A biographical dictionary of mainstream, sideline, and background ukiyoe artists, including painters, book illustrators, and print designers, regarded to be the most comprehensive of its kind. Much of the material was reprinted with occasional typographical errors in Yoshida's *Ukiyoe Jiten*.

Ishii, Kendō. *Nishikie no Kaiin no Kōshō: Ichimei Nishikie no Hakkō Nendai Suiteihō*
石井研堂　錦絵の改印の考證ー一名錦絵の発行年代推定法
Tokyo, 1920.

An important study of censor's seals and their use in dating Japanese prints, with many dated facsimiles, and a good account of censorship following the Tenpō Reforms of 1842.

———. *Nishikie no Hori to Suri*
石井研堂　錦絵の彫と摺
Kyoto, 1929.

The fullest account of the traditional techniques of printing and engraving Japanese prints, based on conversations with craftsmen who had been trained during the Meiji period.

*Ishiwari, Matsutarō. "Bakujinsha Manpitsu: Haiyū to egokoro: Ukiyoe no shodai Tomijūrō." *Daimai Geijutsu* 13
石割松太郎　貘人舎漫筆ー俳優と絵ごころ（浮世絵の初代富十郎）　大毎芸術

A discussion of the actor Nakamura Tomijūrō I as an ukiyoe artist.

———. "Kamigatae; Ryūkōsai no ikkei ni tsuite." *Ukiyoe Geijutsu* 4 (issue no. 12)
石割松太郎　上方絵ー流光斎の一系について　浮世絵芸術
(August 1932), pp. 45-46.

A discovery that Ryūkōsai was a pupil of Tsukioka Settei's son, Kangetsu, with illustrations of his prints and those of Shōkōsai.

———. "Ryūkōsai Jokei to haikai." *Beizandō Geppō* 5
石割松太郎　流光斎如圭と俳諧　米山堂月報
(August 1933), pp. 1-4.

A discovery that Ryūkōsai was a *haiku* poet, with samples of his verse.

Kabuki Kyōgen Hyakka
歌舞伎狂言百科
5 vols. Tokyo, 1957–60.

A handbook of still-performed kabuki plays published by the monthly kabuki magazine *Engekikai* with photographs, plot synopses, and highlights.

Kabuki Nenpyō. See Ihara.

Kabukie Taisei: Kanseiki. Edited by Kyōjirō Taguchi
歌舞伎大成寛政期　田口鏡次郎
Tokyo, 1930.

Reproductions of prints and paintings by Ryūkōsai and Shōkōsai, with comments by Teruji Yoshida.

Kamigata
上方
151 issues. Osaka, 1931–44.

A periodical dealing with various topics on the culture of the Kyoto-Osaka area, containing much informative background material.

Kamuroji, Yūshō. "Tōkyo, Hokusai gassaku no *Miyako Hyakkei.*" *Kyoto* 5
禿氏祐祥　東居，北水合作の都百景　京都
(May 1933).

An account of a set of one hundred views of Kyoto published in Osaka in the late nineteenth century.

Kawasaki, Kyosen. "Nakai Yoshitaki Sensei Ryakuden." *Ukiyoeshi* 31
川崎巨泉　中井芳瀧先生略伝　浮世絵志
(July 1931), pp. 6-7.

A biography of Yoshitaki, the author's father.

———. (Ningyodō). "Nishikie ni naru made." *Kinsei Insatsu Bunkashi Kō*
川崎巨泉（人魚洞）錦絵になるまで　近世印刷文化史考
1938, pp. 46-48. *See* Appendix XXIII.

Kawatake, Shigetoshi. *Kabuki Meiyū Den*
河竹繁俊　歌舞伎名優伝
Tokyo, 1956.

Short biographies of fifty major kabuki actors from Izumo no Okuni to the present.

———. *Kabuki Sakusha no Kenkyū*
河竹繁俊　歌舞伎作者の研究
Tokyo, 1940.

Extended biographies of kabuki playwrights, with description of training and professional practices.

Keyes, Roger S. "Japanese Fan Prints." (15 April–3 May 1969). San Francisco, 1969.

A catalogue of an exhibition of Japanese fan prints offered for sale by R. E. Lewis, Inc., including seven octagonal fans with bust portraits of actors by Nagahide, six of them reproduced.

Kimura, Kinka. *Sankaku no Yuki*
木村錦花　三角の雪
Tokyo, 1937.

Engaging recollections of kabuki and the actor's life offstage, with an especially useful chapter describing the annual events of the theater world of Edo and the Kyoto-Osaka area.

Kitagawa Morisada. "Zōgeki 1,2." *Kinsei Fūzokushi (Morisada Mankō)* 31/32
喜多川守貞　雑劇　上下　近世風俗史（守貞漫稿）
pp. 491-596. Tokyo, 1964.

A series of essays comparing Edo and the Kyoto-Osaka area begun in 1837 and left unfinished in 1853. First published in 1908.

Kōda, Naritomo. *Edo to Ōsaka*
幸田成友　江戸と大阪
Tokyo, 1934.

A comparative study, chiefly economic, of the two cities.

Kōjien. Compiled by Izuru Shinmura
広辞苑　新村出
Tokyo, 1966.

An incomparably well-edited, useful dictionary and encyclopedia.

Kokusho Sōmokuroku
国書総目録
8 vols. Tokyo, 1963–72.

A National Index of pre-Meiji manuscripts and printed books in major public and private collections. Entries alphabetical by title, giving author, date, type of book, and location of copies, occasionally listing artists and distinguishing editions. Since the entries are transcripts of library cards, their quality varies from pellucid to incoherent. Still, for all its shortcomings, a treasure trove.

Konohana. Edited by Gaikotsu Miyatake
此花　宮武外骨
(Osaka edition). 22 vols. Osaka, 1910–12.

A periodical devoted to ukiyoe with articles and extracts by the editor on Osaka prints and print artists. Volume 17 includes "Nichōsai to Ryūkōsai," an essay on two late eighteenth century Osaka artists, with valuable quotations from original sources, which have been requoted by all subsequent writers.

Kubota, Seon. "Keihan ni okeru ukiyoeshi." *Nishikie* 25
久保田世音　京阪に於ける浮世絵師　錦絵
(May 1919).

An essay on ukiyoe artists in the Kyoto-Osaka area.

———. "Keihan no Nishikie." *Nishikie* 5
久保田世音　京阪の錦絵　錦絵
(August 1917).

———. "Nōto no naka yori: chihōdeki no nishikie." *Nishikie* 31
久保田世音　ノートの中より－地方出来の錦絵　錦絵
(November 1922).

Notes on provincial print production.

Kuroda, Genji. "Kamigatae Hanmoto Ichiran." *Ukiyoe no Kenkyū* 3 (issue no. 3)
黒田源次　上方絵版本一覧　浮世絵之研究
(October 1924). pp. 11-19.

An incomplete, undated list of Osaka and Kyoto publishers, reproducing a few of their marks and citing prints on which they were found.

———. *Kamigatae Ichiran*
黒田源次　上方絵一覧
Kyoto, 1929.

A thorough, well-illustrated, painstakingly researched account of printmaking in the Kyoto-Osaka area, with sections on stencil prints, Osaka actor prints, and Western-influenced copper-plate intaglio prints. The book was based on a study of the Isajirō Okada collection and over half of it is a catalogue of prints arranged by artist, listing signatures and publishers, actors and roles, dated whenever possible. In spite of omissions and occasional mistakes, this is still the standard and indispensable work on the subject.

Kyōgen Sakusho. *See Shin Gunsho Ruijū.*

Kyōka Jinmei Jisho. Compiled by Kaian Kanō
狂歌人名辞書　狩野快庵
Tokyo, 1928.

A dictionary of brief biographies mainly of Edo *kyōka* poets.

Kyota Kyakushoku Jō
許多脚色帳
42 vols. Osaka.

An annotated scrapbook of prints, drawings, programs, and other theatrical documents dating from the late seventeenth or early eighteenth century and continuing through the mid-nineteenth century, arranged chronologically by performance and particularly rich in documents related to Nakamura Utaemon III, a personal friend of the supposed compilers, Yoshino Goun V and Hamamatsu Utakuni. Still unpublished, and often exasperatingly inaccurate, but the most important single source for the history of Osaka kabuki. The scrapbooks are owned by the Waseda Theatrical Museum, which allows interested students access to photographs of the collection.

Lane, Richard. "Some Japanese Bans on Art and Literature." *Felix Tikotin—zum Siebsigsten Geburtstag.* Basel, 1963.

A short essay with translations of government edicts earlier in date than the period of Osaka prints, but conveying the tone of official censorship.

Lewis, R. E., Inc. "Osaka Prints of the Nineteenth Century" (1–27 January 1962). San Francisco, 1962.

Announcement of the first exhibition of Osaka prints to be held outside Japan, with a foldout reproduction of a Hirosada *chūban* triptych depicting Nakamura Utaemon IV and Nakayama Nanshi as the Six Immortal Poets.

Machi no Uwasa. See *Naniwa Sōsho,* vol. 14.

Makita, Tōjō. *Keihan Shosekishōshi*
蒔田稲城　京阪書籍商史
Tokyo, 1928.

An account of book publication in the Kyoto-Osaka area during the Edo period, with transcriptions of documents and some mention of print publishing.

Matsudaira, Susumu. "Shunkōsai Hokushū: Kamigata no yakushae 1." *Baika Joshi Daigaku Bungakubu Kiyō* 4
松平進　春好斎北洲ー上方の役者絵（一）
梅花女子大学文学部紀要
pp. 65-112. Osaka, 1967.

———. "Gigadō Ashiyuki: Kamigata no yakushae 2." *Kokubungaku* 43
松平進　戯画堂芦ゆきー上方の役者絵（二）国文学
pp. 29-44. Suita, 1968.

———. "Shunbaisai Hokuei: Kamigata no yakushae 3." *Baika Joshi Daigaku Bungakubu Kiyō* 5
松平進　春梅斎北英ー上方の役者絵（三）
梅花女子大学文学部紀要
pp. 63-106. Osaka, 1968.

———. "Ganjōsai Kunihiro: Kamigata no yakushae 4." *Ōsaka no Kenkyū* 5
松平進　丸丈斎国広ー上方の役者絵（四）大阪の研究
pp. 333-69. Osaka, 1970. Reprint.

———. "Jukōdō Yoshikuni: Kamigata no yakushae 5." *Baika Joshi Daigaku Kiyō* 7
松平進　寿好堂よし国ー上方の役者絵（五）
pp. 1-31. Osaka, 1970.

The first serious studies of Osaka actor prints since Kuroda's monograph was published in 1929. Each article gives a clear résumé of the known facts of each artist's career, followed by a catalogue of the artist's actor prints arranged chronologically by performance with information on actor, role, play, date, theater, publisher, signature, engraver, and seals. The catalogues are lists of prints the author examined in Japan, chiefly in the Ikeda Library collection, and those published by Kuroda and others, and are necessarily incomplete. Some of the role identifications and dating are controversial and a lack of photographs makes them occasionally difficult to use, but these are still the most useful contribution to the study of Osaka actor prints yet published. An article on Ryūsai Shigeharu is to be published shortly.

Misumi, Sadakichi. "Okada Isaji-san o shinobu 1-3." *Nihon Bijutsu Kōgei*
三隅貞吉　岡田伊三次さんを偲ぶ　日本美術工芸
(December 1958, February and April 1959).

Recollections of Isajirō Okada, a great collector of Japanese art, whose collection of Osaka prints formed the basis of Kuroda's monograph, written by a dealer who knew him intimately.

———. "Sharaku no Shinkenkyū." *Nihon Bijutsu Kōgei* 59
三隅貞吉 写楽の新研究 日本美術工芸
(March 1948).
An essay suggesting stylistic similarities between portraits by Sharaku and Ryūkōsai.

Mizutani, Yumihiko. *Kohan Shōsetsu Sashieshi*
水谷弓彦 古版小説挿絵史
Tokyo, 1935.
One of the few books ever written on the subject of Japanese illustrated books with virtually nothing on Osaka books of the nineteenth century.

Nakada, Katsunosuke. *Ehon no Kenkyū*
仲田勝之助 絵本の研究
Tokyo, 1950.
Another of the rare studies of Japanese illustrated books, with passing reference to a few publications by Osaka artists.

*———. "Ōsaka no nishikie ni tsuite." *Nichi Futsu Geijutsu* 10
仲田勝之助 大阪の錦絵について 日仏芸術
An essay on color prints in Osaka.

Naniwa Meika Boshoshū. Compiled by Kimura Kenkadō and Akatsuki no Kanenari
浪華名家墓所集 木村兼葭堂・暁鐘成
c. early 1850s. *See* Appendix XIX.

Naniwa Sōsho
浪速叢書
16 vols. plus supplement. Osaka, 1926–30.
Including:

Vols. 1-6: *Setsuyō Kikan*, by Hamamatsu Utakuni and others.
摂陽奇観 浜松歌国
Transcription of a 60-volume manuscript completed in 1833 dealing with local Osaka customs and history, with a detailed but incomplete biography of Hamamatsu Utakuni by Seiichirō Funakoshi.

Vols. 7-8: *Settsu Meisho Zue Taisei*, by Akatsuki no Kanenari
摂陽名所図会大成 暁鐘成
Transcription of an illustrated, unpublished manuscript gazetteer of Osaka completed in the late 1850s, with a biography of Akatsuki no Kanenari by Matsutarō Ishiwari.

Vol. 10: *Ōsaka Hōhiroku*, by Keijirō Kimura
大阪訪碑録 木村敬二郎
1929.
A compilation of burial records and tombstones in Osaka. *See* Appendix XXII.

Vol. 12: *Kyōka Ehon Naniwa no Ume*. Edited by Hakuensai Baikō
狂歌絵本浪花のむめ 白縁斎梅好
(pp. 499-612).
A reprint of a 5-volume poetry anthology with illustrations by Gyokuensai Jukō, published in 1800.

Vol. 13: *Tenpōzan Meisho Zue*, by Akatsuki no Kanenari
天保山名所図会 暁鐘成
(pp. 479-567).
A reprint of a 2-volume account of the construction of Tenpōzan, published in 1855.

Vol. 14:
Naniwa Zasshi Chimata no Uwasa (also known as *Machi no Uwasa*), by Heitei Ginkei
浪花雑誌街能噂 平亭銀鶏
(pp. 1-124).
A reprint of a 4-volume novel in dialogue with illustrations by Utagawa Sadahiro, written in 1835. *See* Appendix XIII.

Kyojitsu Satonamari, by Kōguya Sensei Rodō
虚実柳巷方言 香具屋先生魯堂
(pp. 125-222).
A reprint of a 3-volume guidebook account of life in the gay quarters of Osaka, published in 1794. *See* Appendix II.

Naniwa Jūnikagetsu Gafu, by Kyōgendō Harunoya Sengetsu
浪花十二月画譜 狂言堂春のや繊月
(pp. 569-615).
A reprint of a 2-volume account of annual events in Osaka with humorous illustrations, published in 1849.

Vol. 15:
Shibai Gayuka Zue and *Gayuka Zue Shūi*, by Shōkōsai Hanbei
戯場楽屋図会 楽屋図会拾遺 松好斎半兵衛
(pp. 59-285).
An invaluable account of the contemporary Osaka kabuki and puppet theaters, written and illustrated by an Osaka actor portraitist. The first two volumes were published in 1800 and the sequel in 1802.

Ōkabuki Gedai Nenkan
大歌舞伎外題年鑑
(pp. 286-607).

A transcript of a 5-volume manuscript listing performances at the three chief Osaka kabuki theaters between 1716 and 1854. Largely incorporated in Ihara's *Kabuki Nenpyō*.

Nanki, Yoshitarō. "Ōsaka ni hattatsuseru kabuki nishikie ni tsuite." *Kinsei Insatsu Bunkashi Kō*
南木芳太郎 大阪に発達せる歌舞伎錦絵について
近世印刷文化史考
Osaka, 1938.
A general article on Osaka actor prints.

Narazaki, Muneshige. *Hokusai Ron*
楢崎宗重 北斎論
Tokyo, 1944.
The most complete and scholarly study of Hokusai's career to date.

Nihon Bungaku Daijiten. Compiled by Tsukuru Fujimura
日本文学大辞典 藤村作
Tokyo, 1950-52.
A standard reference work on Japanese literature with biographies of authors and plot summaries.

Nihon Gikyoku Zenshū: Kabuki hen. Edited by Seitarō Atsumi
日本戯曲全集 歌舞伎篇 渥美清太郎
50 vols. Tokyo, 1928–35.
A collection of 389 scripts of kabuki plays, some fragmentary, from the late seventeenth to the late nineteenth century, arranged by category with short introductions.

Nihon Hanga Bijutsu Zenshū III: *Ukiyoe* 2, *Shunshō-Kiyonaga*. Edited by Teruji Yoshida
日本版画美術全集第三巻 浮世絵（二）春章ー清長 吉田暎二
Tokyo, 1961.
Several reproductions of Osaka prints, most previously published, with a note by the editor encouraging further study of Osaka prints.

Ōkabuki Gedai Nenkan. See *Naniwa Sōsho*, vol. 15.

Ōmagari, Kuson. "Hasegawa Sadanobu." *Ukiyoeshi* 28
大曲駒村 長谷川貞信 浮世絵志
(May 1931).
Biographical notes on Hasegawa Sadanobu I.

———. "Nisei Sadanobu, Konobu, sonota." *Ukiyoeshi* 29
大曲駒村 二世貞信，小信，その他 浮世絵志
(June 1931).
Sequel to "Hasegawa Sadanobu" above; notes on Sadanobu II, Konobu, and others.

———. "Utagawa Kunitsuru to dō Kunimatsu I." *Ukiyoeshi* 30
大曲駒村 歌川国鶴と同国松（上）浮世絵志
(July 1931).
Biographical notes on two Edo artists, one of whom worked in Osaka.

Ōsaka Bunkashi. Edited by Ōsaka Mainichi Shinbun
大阪文化史 大阪毎日新聞
Osaka, 1925.
A collection of scholarly essays on various aspects of Osaka culture.

Ōsaka Furitsu Toshokanzō Shibai Banzuke Mokuroku
大阪府立図書館蔵芝居番附目録
Osaka, 1968.
A catalogue of theatrical *banzuke* owned by the Prefectural Library in Osaka. A valuable index of holdings, mainly for nineteenth-century kabuki performances in Osaka, but of limited use, as actors and roles are not listed.

Ōsaka Kikuyamachi Shūshi Ninbetsu Chō
大阪菊屋町宗旨人別帳
1639–1869. 145 vols.
The city register of the Kikuyamachi district of Osaka, the only extant record of its type. Nineteenth-century entries list the publisher Tenmaya Kihei with annual reports on the membership of his household. A printed edition of the register will be published soon.

Saitō Gesshin. *Zōho Ukiyoe Ruikō*. *Onchi Sōsho* 4
斎藤月岑 増補浮世絵類考 温知叢書
Tokyo, 1891.
One of the last of several revisions of a manuscript of biographies of ukiyoe artists begun by Ōta Shokusanjin in the late eighteenth century and revised by Shikitei Sanba and others. Gesshin was a trained historian and was able to include new material like the *Mumeiō Zuihitsu*. His manuscript was completed in 1844.

———. *Zōtei Bukō Nenpyō*. With addenda by Kitamura Intei, Sekine Shisei, and Asakura Musei
斎藤月岑（北村筠亭·関根志誠·朝倉無声）増訂武江年表
1912. *See* Appendix XXI.

Sako, Keiji, ed. *Kohan Ōsaka Chizu Shūsei*
佐古慶二 古板大坂地図集成
Osaka, 1970.
A collection of five facsimiles of old maps of Osaka with a printed commentary.

Scott, A. C. *The Kabuki Theater of Japan*. London, 1955.

*Shichinohe, Kichizō. "Utagawa Kunitsuru o kataru." *Ukiyoe-kai* 3 (issue no. 7)
七戸吉三　歌川国鶴を語る　浮世絵界
Notes on an Edo print designer who visited Osaka.

Shimaya, Seiichi. *Nihon Hanga Hensenshi*
島屋政一　日本版画変遷史
Osaka, 1939.
A history of ukiyoe with notes on the Osaka school and short biographical comments.

Shin Enseki Jisshu
新燕石十種
5 vols. Tokyo, 1927.
Including:
Vol. 1:
Hanashi no Nae by Akatsuki no Kanenari
噺の苗　暁鐘成
(pp. 78-125).
Transcription of a 6-volume manuscript written in 1814 listing events in Osaka from 1801 in chronological order.

Naniwa Hyakuji Dan
浪華百事談
(pp. 337-535).
Transcription of an anonymous 9-volume Osaka miscellany, c. 1892.

Vol. 5:
Shūkaku Zuihitsu, by Nakamura Nakazō I
秀鶴随筆　初代中村仲蔵
(pp. 244-79).
Transcription of the actor's diary of a visit to Osaka in 1787 mentioning woodblock prints.

Setsuyō Ochiboshū and *Setsuyō Kenbun Fudebyōshi,* by Hamamatsu Utakuni
摂陽落穂集　摂陽見聞筆拍子　浜松歌国
(pp. 337-495).
Transcription of two 10-volume manuscript miscellanies by the Osaka playwright, the first dated 1808, dealing with local history, geography, customs, and legends.

Shin Gunsho Ruijū
新群書類従
10 vols. Tokyo, 1906–1908.
Including:
Vol. 1:
Denki Sakusho (also known as *Kyōgen Sakusho*), by Nishizawa Ippō
伝奇作書(言狂作書)　西沢一鳳
(pp. 1-474).
Transcription of the first fifteen volumes of an 18-volume manuscript of notes on actors, plays, and other aspects of the Osaka kabuki theater, completed around 1850. Ippō was a playwright himself, and intimately acquainted with the theater. He was generous in his dislikes and seldom objective, but his manuscript is one of the most important sources of information on nineteenth-century Osaka kabuki. *See* Appendix XVI.

Kōto Gosui, by Nishizawa Ippō
皇都午睡　西沢一鳳
(pp. 479-752).
Transcription of a 9-volume manuscript miscellany on the author's experiences in everyday life and the world of kabuki, said to have been written between 1847 and 1850 on a visit to Edo.

Vol. 2:
Kyakushoku Yoroku, by Nishizawa Ippō
脚色餘録　西沢一鳳
(pp. 1-175).
Transcription of a 9-volume supplement to *Denki Sakusho,* finished around 1852, with extensive notes on plots and dramatization of plays. *See* Appendix XVIII.

Sanbutsujō, by Nishizawa Ippō
讃仏乗　西沢一鳳
(pp. 273-441).
Transcription of an undated 6-volume manuscript miscellany, including a copy of Ichikawa Danjūrō VII's sentence of exile from Edo.

Nansui Manyū, by Hamamatsu Utakuni
南水漫遊　浜松歌国
(pp. 471-669).
Transcription of a 15-volume miscellany on kabuki and *jōruri* in Osaka, written in the mid-1800s. Hamamatsu Utakuni was a kabuki playwright and this collection is an invaluable source for Osaka theatrical history.

Vol. 3:
Namiki Shōzō Ichidai Banashi, by Namiki Gohei
並木正三一代咄　並木五瓶
(pp. 174-85).

An anecdotal biography of the playwright Namiki Shōzō.

Denki Sakusho, by Nishizawa Ippō
伝奇作書　西沢一鳳
(pp. 286-334).
Transcription of the final three volumes of this work.

"Shodai Hasegawa Sadanobu gojūnenki kinen sakuhin tenran mokuroku." *Anona*
初代長谷川貞信五十年忌記念作品展覧目録　あのな
(May 1928).

A catalogue of works by Sadanobu I in a memorial exhibition for the 50th anniversary of his death.

Shuzui, Kenji. *Kabuki Josetsu*
守随憲治　歌舞伎序説
Tokyo, 1943.

An often superficial, but extremely useful companion to kabuki studies with chapters on architecture, music, actors, actor prints, programs, and contemporary criticism, a catalogue of *hyōbanki,* and good short biographies of playwrights, actors, and print designers in Edo and Osaka.

Shuzui, Kenji, and Yoshimi Akiba, eds. *Kabuki Zusetsu*
守随憲治・秋葉芳美　歌舞伎図説
Tokyo, 1943.

A pictorial history of kabuki with 709 annotated illustrations of prints, theater programs and illustrated books, a historical survey, and biographies of artists.

Siebold, Philipp Franz von. *Edo Sanpu Kikō.* Translated by S. Saitō
江戸参府紀行
Toyo Būnkō 87. Tokyo, 1970.

A translation into Japanese of sections of *Nippon (Archiv zur Beschreibung von Japan . . .),* the young German doctor's diary of a trip from Nagasaki to Edo and back in 1826 with an audience with the shogun and a visit to a kabuki performance in Osaka (pp. 242-45).

Sorimachi, Shigeo. *Nihon Eiribon oyobi Ehon Mokuroku*
反町茂雄　日本絵入本及び絵本目録
[Catalogue of Japanese Illustrated Books and Manuscripts in the Spencer Collection of the New York Public Library]. Tokyo, 1968.

A checklist in Japanese of Japanese illustrated books in the New York Public Library, with some illustrations, published by the author for private distribution.

Speiser, Werner, and W. Netto. *Die Osaka-Meister: Japanische Farbholzschnitte. Ein Geschenk an das Kunstmuseum Düsseldorf (Austellung 15 Mai–26 Juni 1966).* Düsseldorf, 1966.

A catalogue of the first major European exhibition of Osaka prints with 85 reproductions, most previously unpublished. The full descriptions of each print are courageous, but usually inaccurate.

Strange, Edward F. *Japanese Illustration.* London, 1897.

The half-chapter devoted to the Osaka school is the first mention of these prints in a Western language. The dashing generalizations are tempered by a few interesting illustrations.

———. "The Osaka Group." *Japanese Colour Prints,* pp. 72-79. London, 1904.

With all its shortcomings, this chapter has been the direct or indirect source of most Western opinions on Osaka prints through the present day. Strange based his essay on the large but not brilliant collection of Osaka prints in the Victoria and Albert Museum. His book is still valuable for the many facsimiles of signatures of Osaka artists included in an appendix.

Suzuki, Jūzō. *Nihon Hanga Benran*
鈴木重三　日本版画便覧
Tokyo, 1962.

A supplement to *Nihon Hanga Bijutsu Zenshū,* with a technical vocabulary of Japanese prints, biographies of artists, bibliography, and new material on nineteenth-century Edo publishers and engravers.

Suzuki, Jūzō, Shōkichi Harigaya, and Osamu Ueda. *Ukiyoe Bunken Mokuroku*
鈴木重・針ケ谷鐘吉・上田収二　浮世絵文献目録
Tokyo, 1962. Revised edition published 1972.

The most extensive bibliography of publications on ukiyoe yet published, including books and articles in Western languages.

Suzuki, Jūzō, and Jack Hiller. "*Hyōsui Kiga* (Hokusai Ryūkōsai gappitsu) to *Shibai Gashi* (Ryūkōsai ga) to no kanren." *Ukiyoe Geijutsu*
鈴木重三　萍水奇画（北斎，流光斎合筆）と戯場画史（流光斎）との関連　浮世絵芸術
Ukiyoe Art 13 (December 1966), pp. 40-47.

A discussion in Japanese of Ryūkōsai's illustrated book *Shibai Gashi,* which was republished in Nagoya with changes by Hokusai.

*Takeuchi, Umematsu. "Shunkōsai Hokushū ni tsuite." *Geijutsu* 1 (issue no. 4)
竹内梅松　春好斎北洲に就いて　芸術

An article on the Osaka print designer Hokushū.

Toda, Kenji. *Descriptive Catalogue of Japanese and Chinese Illustrated Books in the Ryerson Library of the Art Institute of Chicago*. Chicago, 1931.

Thorough, accurate descriptions, including a few books illustrated by Osaka artists, and several by Edo artists published in Osaka.

Toita, Yasuji. *Chūshingura*
戸板康二 忠臣蔵
Tokyo, 1957.

A documented account of the historical and theatrical versions of the story of the forty-seven *Rōnin* with a scene-by-scene description of the play *Kanadehon Chūshingura* and some photographs.

Tokuno, T. "Japanese Wood-cutting and Wood-cut Printing." *Report of the U.S. National Museum for 1892*, pp. 221-44. Reprinted by the Government Printing Office, Washington, D.C., 1894.

An excellent technical discussion of the traditional methods of Japanese printmaking by a highly skilled practicing craftsman.

Tōkyō Kokuritsu Hakubutsukan Zuban Mokuroku: Ukiyoe Hanga hen 3
東京国立博物館図版目録 浮世絵版画篇（下）
[Illustrated catalogues of the Tokyo National Museum. Ukiyoe Prints 3]. Tokyo, 1963.

The final volume of the Museum's official catalogue, with postage-stamp reproductions of a few Osaka prints. A catalogue in Japanese and English lists artist's name and format, and occasionally identifies an actor.

Tsubouchi, Shōyō. *Shōnenjidai ni mita Kabuki no Tsuioku*
坪内逍遙 少年時代に観た歌舞伎の追憶
Tokyo, 1920.

The first serious study of the Osaka actor print designers with a brief survey of the origins of the style, biographies of a few artists, and an often repeated, rather uncritical list of illustrated kabuki scenarios (*eiri nehon*) the author had personally examined. Tsubouchi was a novelist and playwright, the first literary translator of Shakespeare into Japanese, and a passionate student of actor prints. His book of Toyokuni I and the Utagawa school is still unsurpassed, and his interest in Osaka prints laid the foundations for future work.

Ukiyoe Ruikō. Edited by Katsunosuke Nakada
浮世絵類考 仲田勝之助
Iwanami Bunko 2785-86. Tokyo, 1941.

A variorum edition of the chief source of biographies of Edo ukiyoe artists, with certain later additions and revisions clearly marked. (Additional data under Saito Gesshin.)

Ukiyoe Taika Shūsei 19: *Kamigatae, Ōtsue, Nagasakie*. Edited by Rinpū Sasagawa
浮世絵大家集成第十九巻 上方絵, 大津絵, 長崎絵 笹川臨風
Tokyo, 1932.

Twenty-six illustrations of Osaka actor prints, nine in color, with brief explanatory text.

Ukiyoe Taisei 11. Edited by Teruji Yoshida
浮世絵大成第十一巻 吉田暎二
Tokyo, 1931.

Over 120 small illustrations of actor prints by Osaka artists, many by extremely rare and otherwise unrecorded artists, with artists', actors', and often role names given in captions, but no dates. Published two years after Kuroda's monograph, and including many artists Kuroda did not know.

Ukiyoe Zenshū 5: *Yakushae*. Edited by Teruji Yoshida
浮世絵全集第五巻 役者絵 吉田暎二
Tokyo, 1963.

A few reproductions of Osaka actor prints with full information, occasionally mistaken, on actors, roles, theaters, plays, and performances.

Volker, T. "Ukiyoe Quartet." *Mededelingen van het Rijksmuseum voor Volkenkunde, Leiden*, no. 5. Leiden, 1949.

A sympathetic discussion of the teamwork required to produce Japanese prints, focusing on the publisher as the coordinator of the efforts of designer, engraver, and printer.

Yoshida, Hiroshi. *Japanese Wood-block Printing*, Tokyo, 1939.

A good account by a practicing artist of the methods and problems involved in traditional color woodblock printing.

Yoshida, Teruji. *Kabukie no Kenkyū*
吉田暎二 歌舞伎絵の研究
Tokyo, 1965.

One volume of Yoshida's collected works with reprints of several articles dealing with Osaka prints, including:

"Edo to Ōsaka no Yakushae"
江戸と大阪の役者絵
A comparison of Edo and Osaka actor-print style.

"Ōsakae Kenkyū Danpen"
大阪絵研究断片
A review of Kuroda's monograph with additions to his list of artists.

"Kamigatae no Rinkaku"
上方絵の輪郭
A general survey of prints of the Osaka-Kyoto area, with charts of artists' genealogies.

———. "Shōkōsai Hanbei hitsu Rokkasen zu." *Ukiyoe* 9
吉田暎二 松好斎半兵衛筆六歌仙図 浮世絵
(May 1964), pp. 36-39.
A brief article introducing, but not dating, an actor painting by Shōkōsai.

———. "Suifutei Gigafu no sonzai." *Ukiyoe* 39
吉田暎二 翠釜亭戯画譜の存在 浮世絵
(Winter 1969), pp. 120-29.
An extended, but inconclusive, discussion of the enigmatic album of actor portraits published in the Osaka area in 1782, with reproductions of all text and illustrations.

———. *Ukiyoe Jiten*
吉田暎二 浮世絵事典
3 vols. Tokyo, 1965–71.
The life work of a fine ukiyoe scholar. Yoshida began his career as a print collector and editor of a kabuki magazine and was, until his recent untimely death, probably the greatest living authority on Japanese actor prints. Organized as a dictionary and arranged in alphabetical order, these three volumes are a compilation of Yoshida's own researches and the published studies of his predecessors, friends, and associates over the last fifty years, and constitute a vast summation of what is presently known about ukiyoe. In spite of errors, lack of cited sources, casual organization, and vestigial proofreading, an invaluable work.

Yoshida, Toshi, and Rei Yuki. *Japanese Print Making: A Handbook of Traditional and Modern Techniques.* Rutland, Vt., and New York, 1966.
A clear, well-illustrated presentation by two practicing printmakers.

Zōtei Bukō Nenpyō. See Saitō Gesshin.

Zoku Enseki Jisshu
続燕石十種
3 vols. Tokyo, 1909. Reprinted 1927.
Including:
Vol. 1:
Keisetsu Gesakusha Kō, by Kimura Mokuō (Uyūsanjin)
京攝戯作者考 木村默翁（烏有山人）
(pp. 258-83).
Transcription of an undated manuscript giving brief biographies of Osaka and Kyoto writers and illustrators of the seventeenth to nineteenth century. *See* Appendix XVII.

Kezai Roku. Attributed to Namiki Gohei
戯財録 並木五瓶
(pp. 414–36).
Transcription of a manuscript essay dated 1801 on the writing of kabuki plays, with a cryptic section on differences between audiences in Edo, Osaka, and Kyoto and how to write for each. Traditionally, but not firmly, attributed to the playwright Namiki Gohei.

Glossary

aiban: paper format; roughly 9 x 13″

aratame in: censorship seal used in Edo from the early 1840s to the early 1870s

atari: stage success

atozuri: late impression

bakufu: military dictatorship

banzuke: program

beni-e: eighteenth-century hand-colored print

benizuri-e: mid-eighteenth-century two-color print, usually printed in pink and green

bijinga: figure print

bokashi: graded color printing

bugaku: court dance

Bunraku: puppet theater

chirimen-e: creped print

chō: *sculpsit,* engraved by; also pronounced *hori*

chūban: paper format, in the nineteenth century, roughly 7 x 5″

daisen: title slip

dōsa: solution of glue and alum, used for sizing, stopping colors, and sparkle

Dōtonbori: Osaka theater district

e: picture; often, in compound words, woodblock print

ebanzuke: illustrated program

Edo: modern Tokyo

Edo-e: "Edo picture"; often used of woodblock print

egoyomi: calendar print

ehon: illustrated book

ehon banzuke: illustrated theater program

eiri kyōgenbon: early illustrated scenario

ekyōdai: picture of *mitate* subject with an inset analogue

fūkeiga: landscape print

fukibokashi: shading by graded application of pigment to woodblock

fukusei: facsimile, reproduction

ga: *pinxit,* drawn by; in compound words, picture

gasan: drawn and inscribed by

geisha: female entertainer

gō: pseudonym, *nom de plume*

gofun: opaque white pigment mixed with other pigments or overprinted for special effects

haigō: name for signing poetry

hama shibai: small Osaka kabuki theater, usually off-Dōtonbori

han: *excudit,* published by

hanga: woodblock print

hangi: woodblock

hangishi: "block master"; engraver

hanji-e: print based on rebuses or visual puns

hanmoto: publisher

hanshita-e: block-copy; a finished design on thin paper ready for engraving

harugoma: "spring pony"; a New Year's dance

hashira-e: "pillar print"; a narrow upright format, roughly 26½ x 5″

hengemono: dance based on a series of changes in costume and mood

hikkō: copyist; a professional who made fair copy for engraving of an author's draft

hikkō monjin: young artist who assisted major book illustrators as collaborator, finisher, reviser, block-copyist, or none of these

hitsu: *delineavit,* drawn by

hori: *sculpsit,* engraved by

horikō: engraver

horishi: carver, engraver

hosoban: paper format, usually vertical; after the 1760s, roughly 13 x 6″

hyōbanki: annual critique with ratings of kabuki actors and prostitutes in Osaka, Kyoto, Edo, and elsewhere

ichimai-e: single-sheet print

ichimonji: narrow horizontal band of color, a printing effect

inkoku: engraving in reserve

ippai: edition; often the number of impressions printed in one day

iro: color

iro ita: color block

isse ichidai: retirement performance

itame mokuhan: printing with woodgrain

jihon toiya: wholesale book publisher

jōruri: chanted narration for the puppet and kabuki theaters

kabuki-e: theater print, actor portrait

kabusebori: facsimile engraving using print as *hanshita-e*

kachō-e: bird-and-flower print

kakemono-e: vertical *ōban* diptych

kakihan: paraph; often used in place of signature or seal

kamigata: Kyoto-Osaka area

kamigata-e: woodblock print of the Kyoto-Osaka area

kamuro: child attendant to a courtesan

kana: Japanese syllabary

kaomise: eleventh-month performance introducing actors and beginning the theater year

kappazuri: stencil printing

karakuri: mechanical toy, automated device

karazuri: embossing, gauffrage

kashihon'ya: lending library

kashirabori: skilled cutting of the most important details by the senior engraver

keisei: courtesan

kentō: register mark

kinpirabon: vigorous seventeenth-century illustrated book about the hero Sakata Kinpira

kirazuri: "mica-ground" impression; printing with crushed mother-of-pearl

kiri: finale

kiwame in: censorship seal used in Edo from about 1790 to 1842

koban: woodblock format; imprecisely used for various small sizes

koma-e: print with illustrated cartouche

komusō: mendicant priest, often concealed in deep hat

koshimoto: lady-in-waiting

kouri: retailer

kudari: travel away from the Kyoto-Osaka area, usually to Edo

kurogo: stagehand

kyōgenbon: illustrated theatrical chapbook

kyōgōzuri: proof impression

kyōka: thirty-one-syllable verse, often humorous or unconventional

mameban: "bean" size; twelfth-to-twentieth-block miniature format

manzai: New Year's street entertainer

megane-e: pictures designed in reverse for use in optical viewers

Meiji: 1868–1912, the reign of the Meiji Emperor

mitate: portrayal of subjects in art and literature that may involve modernization of classical themes, fictitious representations, ingenious comparisons, allusion, or parody

miyaji shibai: shrine theater

moji-e: image made of distorted syllables and written characters

mokumezuri: printing a pattern of woodgrain

mon: crest, worn on clothing and useful in identification of actors

monjin: student

mudabori: pattern cut in the key block as guide for color-block engraving and later removed

nagaban: paper format; roughly 27 x 5½″

nehon: scenario

nigao-e: actor's likeness

ni no kawari: "second change-of-program"; New Year's performance

nishiki-e: "brocade picture"; full-color woodblock print

nishiki-e shinbun: late nineteenth century color print of current events

niwaka: geisha festival

nobori: travel to Kyoto-Osaka area

nunomezuri: printing with cloth texture

ōatari: great stage success

ōban: standard paper format; roughly 15 x 10″

obi: sash

ōkubi-e: bust portrait

onagori kyōgen: farewell performance

Ōsaka-e: Osaka print

oshidori: mandarin duck

oshi-e: cloth patchwork picture, often of actors; an early Kyoto-Osaka word for full-color woodblock prints

otokodate: chivalrous man-about-town

Ōtsu-e: folk painting produced in Ōtsu

rōnin: samurai without a lord

saihan: "reprint"; facsimile

sairei banzuke: festival program

sanmaitsuzuki: triptych

sha: delineavit, drawn by; occasionally copied by

shibai-e: actor portrait

Shijō: school of painting that began in Kyoto in the late eighteenth century

shini-e: memorial portrait

shinzō: attendant to a courtesan

shirabyōshi: dancer

shirozake: rice wine

shōgun: military dictator

shohan: first edition

shōmenzuri: applying a pattern by surface polishing

shozuri: early impression

shunga: erotic print

soroimono: series, set

sōsaku hanga: modern creative print movement

sumizuri-e: black-and-white print

sumō-e: wrestler print

suri: impressit, printed by

surimono: privately commissioned print, often elaborately printed

surishi: printer

tairō: senior government official

tan-e: early print hand-colored with red lead and yellow

tayū: highly-ranked courtesan

tengu: long-nosed demon

tenjōmaku: long horizontal strip of cloth hung over the stage, sometimes painted with actors' portraits

Tenpō kaikaku: governmental reforms (1841–1843)

toiya: wholesaler, also pronounced *ton'ya*

ton'ya: see *toiya*

tsuzuki-e: continuous composition on more than one panel

uchiwa-e: fan print

uki-e: perspective print

ukiyo-e: "picture of the floating world"; a general term for Japanese woodblock prints

urushi-e: eighteenth-century print, hand-colored with lacquer

yagō: actor's nickname, always ending in "ya"

yakko: servant of a samurai

yakusha-e: actor print

yakusha hyōbanki: actor critique

yatsugiri: paper format; roughly 3¾ x 5″

yomihon: genre of illustrated fiction

yotsugiri: paper format; roughly 5 x 7½″